THE DARK HORSE

A CONDENSATION OF THE BOOK

RUMER GODD

ILLUSTRATED BY **KEITH RICHEN**
PUBLISHED BY MACMILLAN

Dark Invader looked the picture of a thoroughbred racehorse. But his record on the turf was as dark as his colour: a win the first time out, followed by a series of bewildering failures. Only his diminutive stable lad, Ted Mullins, still believed in him. Somehow, Ted knew, the animal's will to win had been broken. Patient training and the right jockey just might bring it back. Once Ted, too, had lost his will to win—and then the Invader had entered his life. Now, suddenly, they were bound for faraway Calcutta, and who knew what would be next in store for them?

But Ted had not reckoned with the Invader's new owner, Mr. Leventine, an outsider, too, in Calcutta—and a solid judge of horses and men. Nor with John Quillan, a trainer with a passion for excellence. Their goal for the dark horse: the crown of Calcutta's racing season—the gleaming gold Viceroy's Cup.

And *no* one had reckoned with Mother Morag, an extraordinary nun who was to show them that, through prayer and ingenuity, there is more than one way to the winner's circle.

PROLOGUE

He was born in Ireland in the early 1930s, a big foal, longer-legged than usual, legs that were slender but strong, already showing incipient power. His eyes, as with all foals, looked over-large in his narrow fine-boned face; his nostrils were large, too. At birth he was black, except for one white off-hind fetlock, with the usual lighter ridge of mane and flock of tail. His dam was Black Tulip, he was sired by Bold Crusader and so was registered as Dark Invader, but for two days of his life he was to be known as Beauty.

As a yearling, Dark Invader was seen and bought by the rich and spoiled young racehorse owner, Captain the Honourable Peter Hay, on the advice of his trainer, Michael Traherne. He paid a hefty price, but it was a well-bred colt and, "Having gone to Dublin, Peter was going to buy something anyhow," Michael told his wife, Annette, "and this seemed a likely one."

The big youngster was shipped to the Traherne stables at Dilbury on the Berkshire Downs where, lucky horse, he came under the care of that gnome of a stable lad, Ted Mullins. At the end of their career it was difficult to think of one without the other.

11

CHAPTER I

Early every morning of each racing season Mother Morag, Reverend Mother of the Sisters of Our Lady of Poverty, saw the string of horses go by; brown, bay, chestnut—worst of all colours in the heat; now and again a roan, or a grey, dappled or flea-bitten.

Mother Morag not only saw them, she deliberately came up to her cell to watch them—her window overlooked the road—but this was not Dilbury or England, not the mists and freshness of the downs. There, the first sound was the bird chorus, especially larks; here, the first sound was the cawing of crows. In the cold weather there was mist, but it swirled above arid dust, because this was Calcutta in India and the string was not Michael Traherne's— Michael, friend of royalty and other famous owners—it was John Quillan's, he who had defiantly chosen to drop out.

When Mother Morag had first seen his horses in 1923, there were just seven; now, ten years later, there were nearer forty. Yes, John Quillan has made his way, thought Mother Morag, simply because he's so good.

Racing news was relayed to her by the convent's Gurkha gate-keeper, Dil Bahadur—Valiant Heart. "He has earned that name," Mother Morag often said. "Dil Bahadur has been through the war, fought in France and on the frontier. Have you seen his scars and medals?" Dil Bahadur shared Mother Morag's passion for horses. It was he who told her John Quillan's name. "John Quillan sahib—was captain sahib, but not now," said Dil Bahadur.

Mother Morag had picked John Quillan out long before that. He always led his cavalcade down to the racecourse riding the stable "steady", a bay mare that she guessed was his own. Mother Morag had noticed the grace with which the long lean trainer sat in the saddle, the quietness of his hands and voice—she never heard him shout at horse or groom or riding boy. She knew the old felt hat he wore where everyone else had topees; the, she discovered after-wards, deliberate shabbiness of his clothes; she even noted the signet ring on his little finger. A splendid pair of Great Danes,

12

amber-coloured, loped on each side of him. They struck terror into people but looked neither to right nor left and always sat by the side of the road until he gave the whistle to cross.

"I wish I had your authority," Mother Morag was eventually to tell him. And she told him how she watched his string and added, "You're so good."

"Good? Perhaps a little less disastrous than the other shockers." Then the shutter, as she was to call it, came down over his face. "Most of the trainers here, though, are ex-jockeys. I'm not and in this city that counts against me."

"Why?" Mother Morag's "whys?" were always direct.

"People know where they are with them; with me they don't, which is awkward for them."

"And for you?"

"For me?" He shrugged. "I'm as thick-skinned as a rhinoceros and I have ceased to care."

"I don't believe you. In fact, I think you care about your work as much as we care about ours."

"Touché," and, for a moment, he smiled. Then, with sudden seriousness, he had said, "We can't compare. I just play with rich men's toys unfortunately—or fortunately"—a mocking tone had come into his voice—"Nabobs don't mind what they spend on their toys. The only rub is they're boxwallahs and they want a sure return. Horses can't be made to fit a ledger." A boxwallah is a businessman, and Mother Morag felt sure that if she had not been there he would have said, "Bloody boxwallahs."

Not all John's owners were boxwallahs. He had the nawab of Barasol's horses and three of Lady Mehta's, wife of Sir Prakash Mehta, the Parsi millionaire from Bombay who was always called Sir Readymoney Mehta because he let his exquisite Meena buy where and what she liked. "Unhappily," said John. She had given him many a headache. But it was true that most of his owners were businessmen.

Calcutta has been a city of traders since the first small trading posts were set up on the swampy banks of the Hooghly, that great river up which, from the Bay of Bengal, first sailing clippers, then liners, paddle steamers from inland tributaries, barges and the age-old native country boats would come to deliver and load the cargoes that made those merchants so fabulously rich.

It was for those nabobs—the men who so astutely dealt in jute or tea—once upon a time in opium, or in hides, shellac, coal, jewels—that Indian landlords built ornate Palladian-style mansions. A row of these great houses edged the L made by the Esplanade and Chowringhee, Calcutta's widest street; they fronted the Maidan, the central area of open green. Some spread into the streets that ran back from Chowringhee; others were built along the shaded roads that led to the rich suburbs of Alipore and Ballygunj, and it was in one of the latter mansions left to them by a long-ago plutocratic patron, that the Sisters of Our Lady of Poverty had their convent and old people's home.

"What a waste," most people said. Mother Morag had first met John Quillan when he, like others, had come to see her about the convent's site.

It was certainly a favoured site, among the most pleasant in that arid crowded city. The Maidan was wide with trees, grass, above all, space. It held the old British fort, the Football Club, hockey fields, two polo grounds and, divided from them by a road, the Victoria Memorial with its white marble domes and paved gardens where Calcutta's more prosperous citizens liked to walk in the cool of the evening. The Maidan had great pools, refreshing to sit by; several of them, yet there was still room to hold enormous political or religious meetings, and room for goats and the lean sinewy cattle to graze, for children to play, for beggars or pilgrims to camp; at night their twinkling fires shone far across its darkness. It had room still for riders and, most importantly, there was the racecourse with its stands, two courses and an inner circuit for work. On its far side the Maidan was bounded by the river, so that if there was any breeze, it was fresh.

"Such an expensive site," said the lawyers who were continually sent by their clients, most of them racehorse trainers, to see Reverend Mother Morag. The convent was not four hundred yards up Lower Circular Road, which led up to Ballygunj, and abutted on

14

Circular Road proper, which ran past the racecourse. "The horses would only have to cross the road!" and it was not only the position; the convent had many outbuildings which could be converted to stables, and there was a garden. "Think what you could sell it for!" the lawyers told her. Mother Morag was unmoved, but they persisted in "pestering", she said.

John Quillan had only asked her once, though for him it would have been even more ideal than for the others; his own stables were just up the road and he badly needed to expand. The plan seemed sensible to him on both sides. "You could move farther out," he told her. "Move where land is cheaper so you could build just what you want," and he had asked, "Does it really matter where your sisters live?"

"Of course it matters. Think." That took him aback.

"You'll have to mind your p's and q's," Bhijai, the young maharajah of Malwa had told John. Oddly enough that unreliable but charming playboy was a friend of Mother Morag's, as he was of John's, one of his few friends. "My father, the late maharajah, knew her father," Bunny told him. Bhijai, like other young Indian fashionables, had adopted an English nickname. "When she came out here, her father asked my father to look after her. He died and so it fell to me, but in fact, Mother Morag looks after me. I often ask her advice," said Bunny. "I love her, but she awes me."

"Which takes a bit of doing," John had teased him, but face to face with her he understood the awe. Mother Morag, though she seemed young to be a Reverend Mother, had surprising dignity. She was tall, almost as tall as he, though far too thin. He liked her poise, the clear bones of her face and the hazel eyes set off by the close white coif she wore. Her habit was white, too, and immaculately clean, though it was patched. There was another surprise; her eyes lit almost with mischief when he mentioned Bunny and John saw why the two of them were cronies, but now she looked directly, almost sternly, at him.

"Not matter where we live? Think."

John knew, in part, what she meant. For most foreigners Calcutta was a city of sojourn, where they made their pile, or did their

15

service, then went home. "But not for us," Mother Morag said. "We are usually here for life. Of course it's by our own choice, but remember nuns have no holidays, no leaves and so, to keep ourselves healthy—and sane"—she gave him a quick smile—"we need our haven."

She did not tell him that they shared the haven with some two hundred others; it was reward enough to know that these old men and women, after their hardworking or starved, neglected lives, could end their days in what seemed to them incomparable comfort and beauty, and Mother Morag smiled again as her eyes rested on the convent trees, *gol-mohrs*—peacock trees—and acacias, mangoes and jacarandas that in spring and summer brought a wealth of flowers and fruit, and where bright green red-beaked parakeets flew and played. "Also, has it occurred to you," she asked John, "that here we are near our work?"

That was true. The sisters did not stay in their haven—they were to be found in the narrow lanes of the slums that made a congested and evil web close behind Calcutta's elegant façade. If any flowering or fruit trees had been planted in those gutter streets, goats and bulls would immediately have eaten them; the bulls—plump, with hides like velvet, their humps capped with beaded coverings—ate what they chose, because to the Hindus they were sacred. The goats ate because they were hungry, but not as hungry as the swarm of men, women and children.

In an Indian village, though people go hungry, they seldom starve; it is a virtue to feed the poor, but in a city that virtue is quickly lost.

"There are just too many of them," said Mother Morag. "We feed perhaps a thousand a day, but it's a drop in the ocean. Still, it's a drop."

"I don't know how you manage it," said John.

"Nor do we, but we have our lifelines."

ONE LIFELINE of the Sisters of Poverty was their beloved horse, Solomon—bright bay cob with white points and as solid as if he were stuffed. "Which he is," said Mother Morag. "All those tidbits."

16

Gulab, his old Hindu syce, or groom, brushed him until the coarse coat almost shone, and polished the brass and leather of his harness so that no one could have guessed how old it was; but it was not only his looks or that Solomon worked so hard in the cause of charity that made everyone love him; it was his gentle manner—the way he would let even the dirtiest gutter child pat him—and, though he was slow, his dignified gait; he still moved with the arched neck and high-flung forefeet that showed he had been well trained to a carriage, "though I could never have believed a pair of hoofs could stay in the air so long without being brought down by the law of gravity," said Mother Morag.

The convent had two conveyances—they could not be called carriages; one was a high shuttered box on four wheels, the same as the Indian tikka gharries—carriages for hire. It went out every afternoon, sometimes taking the sisters in pairs to the business houses to gather in the donations, or alms, that were the sole support of their convent and old people's home. For this Mother Morag sent young nuns, Sister Bridget, plump and jolly, and Sister Joanna, the English nun whose brown eyes could glow with indignation or be tender or laughing. The sisters usually caught the men at their desks and, "It's hardly fair," said Sister Joanna. "Particularly the young ones, poor lambs. They don't know how to say no to a nun."

"They know how to say no to their tailor's and bootmaker's bills." Old Sister Ignatius, the subprioress and Mother Morag's right hand, was as tart as she was faithful.

On other afternoons Solomon would drive to the Newmarket, Calcutta's great covered bazaar, where the sisters would pick up sacks of unsold vegetables from particular stalls. Sometimes flowers for the chapel would be given them, too, and while Solomon stood waiting in the forecourt, boys and girls would come to pet him and give him what Sister Bridget called "goodies".

"Yes. He too feeds from alms," said Gulab with pride—to Indian thinking it is the receiver who has the merit, not the giver. At the side of the cart was a brass-bound collection box with a cross carved on it and a slit through which brown hands—and sometimes white

17

ones—put annas, the smallest silver coin, and copper pice and even smaller coins. "You would be amazed how much we get," said Sister Emmanuel, the cellarer. "I think we often live on poor people's pennies." Solomon's real work though was the night round of the city's restaurants just as they were closing, to haul in the convent's big battered containers the leftovers from dishes served to customers. For this he drew a cart like a bullock cart, heavy, with wooden wheels not properly tyred, so that it shook and rattled. Its canvas hood made it seem like a covered wagon and its wooden seats were hard.

It was the night round that took the heaviest toll of Solomon,. Gulab and the sisters. When Mother Morag watched John Quillan's horses go by at first light, she had already been up and dressed since one o'clock because, as Superior, she made it her task to meet Solomon and his cart and the two sisters who went with it. To the nuns the leftovers seemed the height of riches. "Some hardly touched," they marvelled. "To order such expensive food and then not eat it!"

"The height of gluttony!" Sister Ignatius was sharp-tongued. "It should be brought home to them."

"Then we shouldn't have the food." That was Sister Joanna with the remorseless logic of the young.

"Yes, see how out of sin comes good." Sister Mary Fanny, the pretty little Eurasian, was given to what Mother Morag called "cuckoo words", or platitudes. But in this case they were true. "How else would we feed our old people?" asked Sister Joanna.

"We, the Sisters of Poverty, have always had a curious form of bookkeeping," Mother Morag was to tell John Quillan. "First we take in the needy and helpless, then we find the means to keep them."

"Sounds crackpot to me," said John. "How can you help people when you haven't the means?"

"Because when the need is there, the means come. They always have if you trust. Almost a hundred years ago our foundress, Thérèse Hubert, who had no idea she was a foundress, used to go round the houses of Bruges collecting scraps for the two old people

18

she had taken into her tiny home. She got not only food but clothes, furniture, fuel."

"There were just two!" John objected. "Now?"

"At the last count our Order cares for more than fifty thousand old people. We have houses all over the world, but in poor countries like India, it is more difficult. They don't want more beggars"— Mother Morag smiled—"and we are, of course, beggars."

"Then what happens?"

"It still works. We believe we bring Providence by our very 'collecting', as we call it. It wakes people up, but don't think it's easy to beg." Mother Morag spoke seriously. "You need to be very humble, Mr. Quillan, to hold out your hand, to smile and say, 'God bless you,' when doors are slammed in your face, when you are patronized or derided as nuisances—which, of course, we are." The smile had come back. "I sympathize because we're a continual reminder of what people don't want to know—but it's wonderful the way things do come. In her later years Thérèse Hubert told how, in one of the houses, when the old men and women had been fed, there was nothing left for the sisters, but they still gathered round the empty table as is the Rule, and said Grace. There was a knock at the door; someone unknown had sent round an entire dinner."

"Just then?" John's face was half amused, half full of pity.

"Just then," Mother Morag said firmly. "It's usually very prompt. It wouldn't be much use if it wasn't, would it?"

THE NIGHT ROUND was hard, not only on the sisters but on Solomon and Gulab. Solomon often had to stand for half an hour—some restaurants seemed to take pleasure in keeping the sisters waiting— and in the cold-weather months Solomon and Gulab shivered. The sisters, too, often met with contempt. They had to wait in the outer kitchens, among squalid washing up, shouting, horseplay. Sometimes waiters or cooks were drunk. Mother Morag could never send young nuns for this chore. She sent Sister Timothea of the sharp elbows, Eurasian and, since childhood, used to fending for herself; Sister Jane, a truly plain Jane; or the French Sister Ursule, who had warts on her nose and hairs on her chin. "No one is going to pester me," she said.

Some places, though, were kind. The Italian headwaiter at Firpo's always had a cup of coffee for the sisters, and many of the Indians had an innate respect for the religious; but seldom was the food properly separated in the canisters the sisters carefully labelled "meat" "fish" "vegetables" "curry" "rice". Sometimes it was thrown in so mixed that even the sisters could not eat it.

When at last the cart came in, no matter how late or tired they were, the sisters always gave Solomon the slice of bread and salt Sister Barbara, the caterer, had left ready; often, too, he had pieces of sugarcane Gulab bought out of his own money. Then Solomon was walked away to be rubbed down, rugged in his old blanket and fed. Mother Morag sent the sisters to bed, and the heaviest work of the night began as another two nuns began to carry the canisters in and sort the, by now, greasy food. It was all carefully stored, and when that was done the canisters had to be scrubbed with disinfectant, then scalded. Often, seeing the sisters tottering—they had usually worked all day as well—Mother Morag sent them to bed and finished alone. When, at last, she took off her apron and the "sleeves" that protected her habit, she went upstairs to wash her face and hands. Though it was an hour or so before the caller came around to wake the Community for the thirty-five minutes of meditation they had before Mass, and it would have been sensible to have at least taken off her shoes and coif and lain down to rest, she found it strangely more refreshing to sit at her window waiting till the string came by.

SHE COULD HEAR THEM before she saw them—a light drumming on the track, an occasional clinking of a bit, muttered words. Then they came, each beautiful animal swathed in rugs in the maroon of the stable colours; each led by its own two syces, or grooms, the men's heads swathed, too, in their chadors—small cotton shawls, one end of which was usually wound over their mouths and noses. They wore long coats of good cloth, braided with maroon, good shoes in keeping with the high rank of their charges. "I wish we could give Gulab a coat

20

like that," the nun in Mother Morag could not help wishing, and then she forgot the nun in the sheer joy of watching the horses. Some moved steadily; some, curvetting and trying to shy, had a riding boy atop as well. All were led by John Quillan on his mare, Matilda, and on each side of him were the Great Danes, Gog and Magog. Mother Morag had learned their names.

AT MICHAEL TRAHERNE'S stables in Dilbury, Dark Invader was two years old; far removed from the long-legged foal and the clumsy promising yearling. His coat now was a dark brown with a dapple in it. The proud curve of his neck was not yet showing the crest of his sex, but his majestic shoulders, the great breadth and leverage of his hocks, and his feet, well-shaped and firmly placed, made him a handsome individual.

The day was celebrated by some extra carrots and half a pound of lump sugar. Ted Mullins, his stable lad, would allow no more. "Never met such a greedy guts." No one could have guessed from Ted's brisk strictness that Dark Invader was the glory of his heart. "Never had one quite like this, sir," he told Michael, and the trainer admitted he had seldom had a youngster that looked better.

Michael was cautious, but Peter Hay, Dark Invader's owner, was "like a peacock with two tails," Michael told his wife, Annette.

"We'll run Darkie at Lingfield," said Peter, "and get Tom Bacon—'Streaky'—to ride him."

"If we can," said Michael.

"*I* can," which was true; Peter could buy almost anything, and on his next visit he said, "Bacon will do it. He'll probably come down here. Should be a formidable combination, Darkie and Streaky." He rubbed his hands. "What do you think, Ted?"

Peter always tried to get on with the lads; the young ones admired his clothes and cars, but when it came to horses, "Not up to much," was the verdict, and he never got as much as a ghost of a smile from Ted.

Ted Mullins was truly a gnome of a man, dried, weatherbeaten, with a tuft of hair part white, part childishly fair. He looked far older than his forty-nine years, but his watery eyes, blue as larkspurs,

21

were continually alert for an order or the well-being of his horse.

"What's that chap's story?" Peter had asked Michael.

"Ted? I've known him for years, my father had him as a fifteen-year-old, went on to be a jockey—pre-war. Enlisted in the war, demobilized to find his wife, Ella, dead of the flu, his racing contacts lost and a lot of up-and-coming youngsters competing for the few available rides. Found a job with a small trainer in the north who got warned off, and Ted lost his licence. Then he didn't seem to care any more. Whisky didn't help either. In fact, I think he was killing himself with drink, then he remembered my father. The old man had thought a lot of him."

"And so do you," said Peter.

"Best stable lad I ever had," said Michael warmly. "Still has an occasional bout, but keeps it and himself to himself. Rides work beautifully and has uncommonly good hands. Look what he has done with Darkie."

"I grant you that," and now Peter tried the little man again. "What d'you think about Lingfield, Ted?" hoping at least for recognition, but Ted's face was like a mask. "It's not for me to say, sir."

A few minutes later Peter roared off in his bright red latest Bugatti, and Michael asked, "What *do* you think, Ted, about Bacon and Darkie?"

"Well, I s'pose it's a compliment, sir." Ted would say no more, but after the trial gallop with Bacon he took the uncommon liberty of following Michael into the office.

"No, sir. Never," he said.

"No? I thought it was a success."

"Have you looked at the hoss?"

"Yes. Seems all right."

"Wasn't. Should have seen him when he come in and this was only a gallop. It's going to be a *race*, sir." Ted usually had few words, but now he burst out, "Some hosses come on normal like, some too fast for their own good, as you well know, sir, but some is slow. The Invader"—Ted never called his charge Darkie—"the Invader's one of those. It's not that he's green ezackly, he's too

22

smart for that. P'raps it's because he's so big, intelligent-like, and he wants time to look and think."

"Come off it, Ted. Horses don't think."

"Most hosses. If 'twas *my* choice . . ."

"Are you being a bit of an old hen, Ted? Bacon's report was good. Darkie's in first-class condition. Right time. Right age."

"I said, if it was my choice."

Michael hesitated. "Captain Hay is set on it."

"Him." Ted's croak, harsh from years of wind, rain, sun—and whisky—was scornful. "Hosses, cars, boats, all alike to him."

Michael had to agree and sighed. "Ted, horses have to have owners," he said, "or there wouldn't be any racing."

"Owners have to have horses or there wouldn't be any racing," answered Ted.

JOHN QUILLAN came to see Mother Morag again. He brought Gog and Magog but left them at the gates like two mammoth ornaments, greatly reinforcing Dil Bahadur's prestige. The portress showed John into Mother Morag's office, where she was working with Sister Ignatius.

"I haven't come to pester you," said John and came straight to his business. "You have only one horse, so I thought you might have stabling to spare. I have a new client, a Mr. Leventine."

"Leventine!" Bunny had expostulated. "Why to heaven are you taking on an outsider like that?"

"His horses," John had said simply.

No one could deny that Mr. Leventine had an extraordinary flair for horses, but his ebullience, his plump glossiness, his overdressing, the perpetual pink rose in his buttonhole—"Pink is for happiness," he often said, beaming—his curly auburn hair that, with his slightly dusky skin, looked strange to Western eyes, and his over-emphatic sibilants, "are a bit off-putting," admitted John.

"Johnny, how do you keep so lean?" Mr. Leventine had lamented. John gritted his teeth whenever anyone called him Johnny.

"Sweat," said John, "and I don't lunch at the Bengal Club." The

Bengal Club had the best food east of Suez and a renowned wine cellar. Mr. Leventine did not lunch there either—anyone thinking of inviting him would have been quietly persuaded not to by the secretary, "as they would with me," John could have said, "for a different reason." But his voice betrayed no feeling as he said to Mother Morag, "Mr. Leventine is importing horses from England and France. I am pressed for room and I wondered if you would rent us a few stalls."

There was an embarrassed silence. Then Mother Morag said, "We have to put people in ours."

"And they don't have electric fans and are not fed five times a day." Sister Ignatius could not restrain herself. "They are only people, not racehorses."

"I see, and I beg your pardon." John turned to go and was almost at the door when Mother Morag called him back. "Mr. Quillan, I understand your wife is a Catholic."

"Yes." He was ready to be defensive.

"We were wondering," said Mother Morag, "as Saint Thomas's is quite far, whether she would care to come here, to our chapel, for Mass. We are so close."

The silence was so long she thought she had offended him, then John said, "Thank you. This is the first time in this city of upstarts that anyone has called Dahlia my wife, or asked her to come anywhere."

"The children, too, of course."

The shutter came down at once. "That wouldn't do." John had a tribe of children who were a byword in Calcutta. Dahlia, sweet and warm, loved babies but had no control over children. Their children were as good-looking as John, or as pretty and peach-skinned as Dahlia with her great dark eyes and silky lashes, but they were untamed, went barefoot and wore and did what they liked. They could talk good English when they wanted—oddly enough they followed John's unconscious perfection, not Dahlia's chi-chi—but preferred to chatter in Hindi or Bengali. They ran away from every school they were sent to. "Sensible children," was all John said. He seemed curiously helpless over them.

"Well, remember they are tainted with the Eurasian," said Sister Ignatius. In the thirties that was a real taint—even the most indigent Indian, the poorest white, kept himself apart—and Mother Morag thought that John's habitual bitterness, his mordant humour and defensiveness were not for himself, nor for Dahlia—he had too much tenderness for her—but for his children whom he called the *bandar-log*—the monkey people.

"Why wouldn't it do?"

"Dahlia tried to take them to Mass, but they wouldn't dress properly."

Mother Morag could guess how shamed Dahlia would have been—many of her own people went to Saint Thomas's. It was a church parade, but, "We don't mind how people dress," said Mother Morag. "Bring them."

He looked so startled and—was it softened? that she wondered if, perhaps, this was the first time he had thought of his *bandars* as people. She did not know, but every month thereafter John Quillan sent his own farrier to shoe Solomon without charge.

"I REALLY MUST GO and thank Mr. Quillan," said Mother Morag to Sister Ignatius. "This is the third set of shoes." And taking a sun umbrella to shade her, she walked up the road.

John lived in what had once been the country home of some eighteenth-century nabob, a graciously built house named Scatter-gold Hall. The town had caught up with it and now, like the convent, it was surrounded by slums. Most of its once vast garden was taken up by the stables, but there was still a tumble of flowers and creepers, bougainvilleas, tacomas, roses, jasmine; still massed flowery shrubs, lofty trees; still fountains, though broken, and empty pools.

The house was of stucco with shuttered windows. Pillars supported its wide verandas and the porch had the height and width to take an elephant and howdah; broken brick had replaced the gravel on the paths, and geese, ducks and disreputable cocks and hens scratched in a sea of red powder. There were rabbit hutches, and pens for guinea pigs.

25

"Papa gave us five and we have forty-two now," one of the *bandars* told Mother Morag.

The Reverend Mother found John on the drive with Gog and Magog. She thanked him for Solomon's shoeing. "And as I am here," she said, "may I call on Mrs. Quillan?"

"Mrs. Quillan?" The name seemed to give him almost a shock. Then, "Of course. Dahlia will be delighted," and he took her into the house. "I don't suppose," Captain Mack, the veterinary surgeon, told Mother Morag afterwards, "that an English lady had ever been in that house before."

"I'm not exactly an English lady," said Mother Morag. "I'm a sister," and that was how Dahlia, in her simplicity, welcomed her now.

She wore heelless embroidered slippers and a loose wrapper that gave a plentiful view of her warm peach and brown skin; her hair was loose on her shoulders.

The house itself smelled of cooking, particularly curry. Dahlia was no housekeeper; toys, saucers of food for animals, bowls of sweets and nuts, snaffle bits, whips, children's shoes littered the rooms which Dahlia had furnished with comfortable chairs and chintz-covered sofas, brass-topped tables, dhurries or Indian cotton carpets, "that can come to no harm," she said, which at least was sensible, with babies and animals everywhere. There were lamps with shades, fringed and tasselled; vases of paper flowers obviously prized far more than the pots of violets, lilies or chrysanthemums the gardeners set along the veranda. But for all the chaos Scattergold Hall was a joyful place, and many more people would have been glad to come if John had let them in, for Dahlia's sole ambition was to make every creature who came into her orbit happy and comfortable, from the John she adored, through children, horses, pet lambs, cats, mynah birds, Gog and Magog, of course, but, just as much, the pariah bitch who at that moment was having puppies under the veranda table.

"This iss verree nice," Dahlia said to Mother Morag. A chi-chi accent is usually shrill, hers was soft. "And here, too, just in time, is our good friend, dear Captain Mack."

26

The bitch under the veranda table was being helped, or hindered, by four of the *bandar-log* squatting down beside her. They were worried. "Mumma, it's hurting her."

"She'll soon be better. See, Sandy has come m'n." Dahlia soothed them and, to Mother Morag, "Captain Mack is a good friend to us."

"And to us," said Mother Morag.

The big, red-haired, freckled Scotsman was the official veterinarian for the Turf Club, but he would turn out for a suffering pariah bitch as he would for one of the Quillan blood horses, "and as he does for us," said Mother Morag.

Now he hid his surprise at seeing Mother Morag and only said, "Out of the way, scamps, and let me have a look."

John showed Mother Morag around the stables, but first the children propelled her by the elbows to come and see their ponies, their own and others. The *bandar-log* were useful in schooling ponies, "belonging to other and better children," John said severely.

"We can't ride and ruin their animals." The eldest *bandar* boy spoke so exactly like his father that Mother Morag could not help laughing, but she could see that this was serious; Quillans were always serious about horses, and the children all rode, "like angels— or devils," said John. It was the first time she had heard pride in his voice.

In contrast with the untidy house the stables were impeccable; the stalls, shaded by a veranda, ran around three sides of a square. Mr. Leventine had lent John the money to build the concrete block that filled the fourth side, a row of twenty up-to-date loose boxes with verandas and fans and roofed with tiles from outbuildings that had fallen down.

The old stalls and verandas were floored with brick; each, too, had an electric fan and, over the open fronts, guarded by wooden rails, hung rolled-up khuskhus, thick grass matting blinds that were let down in hot weather and sprayed with water for added coolness. Each horse had its halter hung beside the stall, its name above it. Mother Morag read them as she walked along: Ace of Spades, Rigoletto, Flaming Star, Flashlight. "Those last two are Lady

Mehta's," said John. Ontario Queen, Belisarius, The Gangster. "He's the nawab's newest buy."

The bedding had been put down for the night, and across the front of each stall the grooms had made a thick plait of straw to prevent wisps coming out. The horses were tied outside ready for the evening grooming.

A tan track ran around the square's central lawn, which was green and smooth; Mother Morag could guess it was watered every day. There were white painted benches and chairs under the trees, because it was here the owners gathered to watch the evening parade when the horses, groomed to perfection, were exercised around and around.

Now the Quillan headman, the jemadar, attended John and Mother Morag as they went from horse to horse and handed her, as the guest, appropriate tidbits for each, and heads came around and necks strained to catch them.

One or two horses laid back their ears, but John saw Mother Morag was not afraid. "There are always one or two bad seeds," she said; besides, the groom was always standing by to give a sharp slap of reproof. "Ari bap! Shaitan!" John's mare, Matilda, started whickering at the sound of his footsteps. "Give her a banana," said John. "She'll peel it herself."

"What a beauty!" Mother Morag patted the satin neck. "Mr. Quillan, she's outstanding."

"Was. I had her in the regiment." Warmed by her delight, he unguardedly gave that fact away. "Not for racing, of course, for polo; but she's fourteen now. He ran his hand across her neck in a caress and again she saw the signet ring on his little finger, its worn crest. "Yes, we could do with some of your quality, couldn't we, old girl?" John said to Matilda. "Makes the rest look work-a-day squibs."

"Squibs! You have splendid horses here, but I'm intrigued," said Mother Morag. "Polo, then training racehorses. There's such a difference. How did you come to know . . . ?" She stopped. "I'm sorry. One shouldn't be curious, but horses run away with you in more senses than one."

John Quillan was one of the few men she had met who could look down on her, and now he looked almost with fellowship. "How did I come to know? I can't remember a time when I didn't. My grandfather, when he retired from the army, did a little breeding and training at Mulcahy, our home in Ireland."

Mulcahy! He is one of those Quillans. Of course! I ought to have guessed, thought Mother Morag. "My father did the same," John continued, "only more so, and my brother decided to do it in a big way. Then . . ." The easiness went and he said abruptly, "came a time when I had to do something—rather quickly; couldn't—didn't," he corrected himself, "go home. There was a trainer here, an old Englishman called Findlay with a small stable. I had a horse with him, just for fun. When it wasn't fun—the old man was past it and needed a manager. He took me on, for a pittance, but I was fond of him. He died the following year and, well, I inherited and built it up more or less."

"More or less! Bunny says you have win after win."

"Not the big ones."

"Why not?"

"The owners still won't give me the cream. So—no golden pots." He shrugged, but Mother Morag knew how much they meant: the Wellesley Plate, King Emperor's Cup, the Cooch Behar Cup and, crown of the season, the Viceroy's Cup. She laid her hand on John Quillan's sleeve. It was her left hand, and on its third finger was her own ring, the plain golden band, the sign of her wedding to Christ and the Church.

"There will be, one day," she said.

MOTHER MORAG seldom felt as tired as she had that evening. The containers had seemed unusually heavy, greasier than ever, more smelly; also she could not get John Quillan out of her mind. "There will be, one day," she had prophesied.

Now, at her window, resting her tired arms on the sill, suddenly she seemed to smell broom in flower, wet grass and horses sweating, to hear larks shrilling. Mother Morag was far from Calcutta; she had fallen asleep and what she had said was not, "There will be, one day," but, "One day there will be one."

30

CHAPTER II

That smell of broom and wet grass filled the air as Michael Traherne rode with Peter Hay on the Berkshire Downs, and they heard the larks. Work was finished for the morning, and far down the rough track they could see the lads putting the blankets back on the horses for the two-mile walk back to the stables.

Michael was on his new young mare, a brilliant chestnut and still as nervous as a dancer on her first night. Peter had settled for the stable cob. "I like them better when I'm off than on them," he had confessed.

On the crest of a hill they halted without speaking. Michael broke the silence.

"I have an offer for Dark Invader," he said.

"Have you? Who, and how much?"

"Two thousand. A man called Leventine from Calcutta. I met him when he was over here two years ago."

"Calcutta! Poor old Darkie."

"Not necessarily. Racehorses out there are treated like princes," but Peter was not listening.

"Leventine. Middle East, do you think?"

"Could be anything. His given name is Casimir Alaric Bruce. Immensely rich. Grandfather is said to have made a million."

"Jewels? Hides? Tea? I know," said Peter. "His grandfather was the man who first imported umbrellas into India."

"In that case Leventine would be a multimillionaire. May be for all I know. He doesn't give anything away. The Bruce suggests some Scots in him which probably makes him cautious, yet he's a simple soul—somehow wistful. I think horses are his dream and, though he's something of an outsider in Calcutta, he's coming up to be one of the most important owners in India. He's a member of the Turf Club and will be a steward before he's finished. Mr. Leventine knows exactly what he wants."

"And now he wants our horse. I wonder why."

"I imagine he's after what people there call the classics, the open races of a mile and upward. He's ignoring Darkie's form and going by his breeding."

"And that, of course, puts the horse at the top of any class. But what has the brute done?" Peter's tone was suddenly wrathful. "Nothing. Nothing since that win at Lingfield."

Lingfield. They were both quiet for a moment. Michael was thinking of the big dark two-year-old, left flat-footed at the start, then taken to the front by his long stride, collared just inside the distance by his better-knit contemporaries, then fighting up again to win by a neck.

"Superb riding by Streaky Bacon," said Peter.

"At least we thought it was superb," and Michael's puzzlement showed as he said, "It's not as if Darkie had been cut to pieces."

"You said he hadn't a mark on him."

"Nor had he, but Bacon doesn't need to do that. Remember that second race at Doncaster?"

"I was away. Ascot."

Michael went on, "Darkie put Bacon over his head and bolted for the stables."

"Was Streaky hurt?"

"Not he. Indestructible, but he didn't like it. Of course, two-year-olds dump their jockeys on occasion, but this was different, as neat and determined a performance as I have ever seen. In fact, I'm beginning to agree with Ted," and Ted's voice echoed in Michael's mind. " 'Tisn't the Invader, sir. There's nothing wrong with the hoss. It's that Streaky."

"Ted!" Peter was contemptuous. "That little runt! Still soaking it up?"

"Actually not," said Michael. "Ted hasn't had a spree since you bought Dark Invader. When Ted has a purpose . . ."

"Some purpose!"

But Michael was steady. "I believe Ted's right. Streaky can do something to a horse. Darkie wouldn't eat properly for a week after that first race and you know what a glutton he is."

"I think you believe," said Peter, "that Darkie has it in for Bacon personally. It wasn't just racecourse nerves?"

32

"No doubt about it. It showed again here at home. Streaky came down to try a gallop, and the horse wouldn't let him get near."

"What did Streaky do?"

"Just laughed. Still, he didn't like it. That laugh wasn't pleasant. I've had no time for the man since, but what it adds up to is that Darkie reckons if he goes to the front, he gets some almighty punishment, physical or mental, so he wisely stays behind."

"Which is no good to me," said Peter. "Two thousand is a good price for a dog of a horse, and that is what I am afraid he has turned out to be."

"We could run him over hurdles," Michael suggested. "That sometimes does the trick. If he responded, he might go back to the flat in handicaps, or you could send him over fences. He's big enough."

Peter was silent, then, "To be frank, I don't feel like spending any more on him."

Michael did not answer; instead, "Look, here they come," he said, his gaze concentrated on his charges. They were all walking well except the fillies Tarantella and Bagatelle, jiggling as usual. After they had passed, Dark Invader came into sight.

Michael turned to Peter. "Here's our problem child. He walks so fast on the way home that he sets all the others jogging, so we've taken to sending him separately. That only goes for the return journey. Going out you can hardly kick him along."

"Idle devil! But he certainly can walk when he wants to. Look at him now."

To a few horses is given a gift of movement that is a joy to watch. Dark Invader, blissfully ignorant that his fate was in the balance, strode in glorious rhythm, his great shoulders rolling, muscles rippling under the satin skin, his simple mind concentrated on one thought—breakfast.

"Here a minute, Ted." Ted swung the tall horse off the track and halted.

"Well, Ted, how's he going?" asked Peter.

"First class, sir." Ted said it stiffly.

"Keen?"

"Keen enough. Galloped a treat. And such a gentleman with it."
Ted spoke defiantly. "He's a bloody lovely hoss, sir."

"Ted's not far wrong at that, you know, Peter," said Michael. "Just look at him."

Resigned to the interruption of his journey, Dark Invader was standing quite still, interesting himself in the sights and sounds of the awakening countryside. His ears were a little long for a thoroughbred, and loosely set. They would lop sideways in moments of rest, contentment or embarrassment. Now they were pricked, eager and active, moving to catch the distant sounds and the voices around him and he seemed the portrait of his breed.

"He certainly fills the eye," said Peter, and Ted burst out as he had once to Michael, "There's nothing wrong with the Invader, sir. It was that Streaky. Streaky as they come. He—"

"Happens to be one of Britain's top jockeys," Peter said icily. "If he can't manage Dark Invader, no one can."

Sitting on the big horse, Ted was able to look down at Peter. If Peter's tone was icy, so was the look on Ted's face. "Will that be all, sir?" he asked Michael.

"Thank you, Ted," and Ted wheeled the Invader around and rode off.

Peter was slightly disconcerted, then quickly recovered himself. "The trouble is, Michael, conformation's no good without guts. We have to face it. Darkie is a great big beautiful washout."

BACK IN THE YARD, they dismounted. The horses were led away. All the lads' eyes were on Peter's car, a new black Sunbeam 3 litre, with the cycle-type front wings and slightly backswept radiator of the marque.

"Well, what do you want me to do?" Michael asked abruptly. "I must give Leventine an answer."

"I don't think that sending the horse over fences is the answer," said Peter. "And money's a bit tight. Besides, I have decided to winter abroad, so . . ."

"So?"

"Sell him. No good getting married to the brutes." Peter swung

34

his legs over the side of the car's low open body, ignoring the vestigial door. "So long." He raised his hand in salute.

The lane resounded with the crescendo of his going. Michael listened for the last triumphant gear change at the turning into the main road. Then he walked heavily into his office.

THE VOICE speaking to Michael on the telephone was harsh and imperious, like the quacking of an angry duck. Yes, Mr. Leventine was still a buyer (quack). It was a deal? (Quack?) Subject to vet's examination (quack). Some horses for other owners were being shipped in three weeks' time, and there was a box to spare. Michael could expect his veterinary surgeon next day. Mr. Leventine's cheque would follow as soon as the certificate was in his hands. Short credits long friendships—laugh—(quack, quack), silence.

"YOU'LL HAVE to tell Ted," said Annette.

Breakfast with his wife in the warm dining room was for Michael the best part of the day; he was cold and hungry after the dawn start and three strenuous hours' work, so a plateful of porridge and cream, then bacon and eggs, hot toast and marmalade and coffee usually seemed like heaven. But this morning he had left the yard without a glance at the end stall where Dark Invader was craning his neck for attention and a few of the lumps of sugar Michael kept in his pockets.

A sale is a sale, all in the day's work, he told himself; but he seemed to see Darkie's future with a horrible certainty: the horse hated racing; he would be a total failure and would finish flogged to death in the shafts of some ramshackle carriage for hire or even a cart. Michael pushed his plate away.

"Have some more coffee," said wise Annette. When he had the steaming cup in his hands, she said gently, "Tell Ted before he hears it from anyone else."

"As a matter of fact," said Michael, "Ted's part of the deal. He's to take Darkie out."

"Ted! To Calcutta!"

"If he will. It's one of Leventine's conditions. He seems to have been thorough in his inquiries," and Michael quoted, " 'As the horse is temperamental, I should be glad if you would allow his own lad to make the voyage with him.' "

"This Mr. Leventine—he will do that for the sake of the horse?" said Annette. "I think I like Mr. Leventine."

"But will Ted go?" asked Michael.

"IN'JA!" said Ted. "You mean you're sending the Invader all that way? 'Mong all them heathens?"

"They're not heathen, Ted, but yes, India, and not only him— you."

"Me." Ted's voice was shrill.

"Mr. Leventine has asked that, to give Darkie the best possible chance, his own lad should take him out. Which means you."

"Strewth!" said Ted. "To Calcutta?"

"To Calcutta."

There was a silence. Then, "You mean this gentleman will pay my ticket there and back?"

"There and back, and pay you."

"Just so as the Invader's not upset?"

"That's it."

"I'll go," said Ted.

CHAPTER III

The sun was already hot that October morning. Papers in hand, John Quillan waited with his Indian grooms on the dock quay while crates swung the horses ashore. Other trainers were waiting, too, but after the first greeting they kept apart.

"One mitigating thing about Darkie," Michael had told Annette; "he's going to John Quillan. He's Leventine's trainer."

"John? A trainer in Calcutta! John! But isn't he in the Queen's Own?" Annette was startled.

"Was. Should have had his majority by now."

"John has left the regiment?" Annette, a colonel's daughter, could

36

not believe it; not the John Quillan she had danced with in her twenties, watched play polo. "Why?" she demanded.

"There was some blow-up. Pity. I believe that when it happened John was aide-de-camp to the governor of Bengal. Could have been one of the chosen ones, silly idiot, until . . ."

JOHN QUILLAN still remembered the day the governor's military secretary, Colonel Maxwell, had sent for him.

"His Excellency"—the colonel did not say H.E., which showed the formality of the occasion. "His Excellency has decided that you should go on immediate leave. *Home* leave." The colonel emphasized that point. "And on your return you will rejoin your regiment. I don't have to tell you why," he added.

John had met Dahlia at a party, a B party. "In this salubrious city," Robert Kerr, a fellow ADC had said to John, then a newcomer to Calcutta, "there are A and B girls, the latter for the hot weather only. Naturally most of ours go home then."

"I see," said John. "What happens at the party?"

"Usual thing. They behave very well and we behave very badly and then they behave worse."

Dahlia, then eighteen, had been brought by her cousin, cajoled into it—"They need more girls"—and had sat terrified in a corner in her bright cheap net dress, a little fish out of water; indeed, her eyes were like a sea anemone's that drop their fringes against the next wave they see coming.

John had taken pity on her. "You're not enjoying this."

"Oh yess. Yess," but he knew she meant, "No, no."

"Let me take you home."

A gasp. Dahlia had been warned about those five little words. "You mean—my home?"

"I mean your home," and she had trusted him.

As John later told Mother Morag, he had even then been disgusted by "the hypocrisy and callousness of this hateful city, the endless protocol and snobbishness of Government House, come to think of it, of my own regiment," and he had defiantly made friends with Dahlia's father, an Irish Eurasian mechanic on the railway who had married an Indian woman. John had liked Patrick McGinty and his big calm wife and was soon openly calling for Dahlia and protecting her at the parties to which he still went—"from monsoon boredom, I suspect."

Dahlia had also been wonderfully pretty, with a dew of innocence that touched John's heart and often, in his car, they escaped into the night where, between deluges of rain, the drenched spaces of the Maidan were dense and dark as velvet and there was no one to see them, except when the clouds parted, stars big as sequins of Indian gold. Nestling in his arms, Dahlia was sweet and, unlike other Calcutta women, absolutely without guile. "How many people are that?" John asked Mother Morag.

He had been warned by the young and more experienced Robert, "Don't get too enchanted, John. It can be expensive, you know."

"Expensive?"

"If you have to buy them off—for a reason," said Robert.

John had been warned off, too, surprisingly, by Dahlia's father. "We would please ask you, Captain Quillan, not to take our daughter out any more."

"Why not?" John had been furious, but Mr. McGinty was undaunted.

"Dahlia is our only child. We think she is beginning to love you and we know, and you know, what happens to girls like Dahlia."

"You don't know anything," John had said, "about this."

"Don't we? You are Captain Quillan of a famous regiment. Also you are ADC at Government House. As soon as your superiors hear, conveniently you will be sent back to England. In our world we are used to broken promises and broken hearts, but please not for Dahlia."

Mr. McGinty was not angry, only sad.

John was silent, then he asked, "Do you play chess, Mr. McGinty?"

"Chess?"

"Yes. In chess there are kings, bishops and knights—I'm not any of those—and pawns that serve the whim of the player. I am not a pawn, Mr. McGinty."

"WE HAVE BOOKED you a sleeper on the Blue Train tonight," said Colonel Maxwell. "*Tonight*, John. You sail on the *Orion* next Tuesday. His Excellency has written to your colonel."

"He could have saved himself the trouble," said John. "I have written to him myself. Sent in my papers. You see, I married Miss McGinty this morning."

"You *what?*" and then, as Max took it in, "You young fool!"

"Exactly the congratulation I thought I should get."

"HE WAS a bloody fool," Michael told Annette. "No doubt about it; he could have paid the girl compensation if he felt he had to, as dozens of others have done. Think, Annette, his father, grandfather, great-grandfather were all in the regiment, but John was always uncommonly quixotic."

"Or uncommonly honourable," said Annette. "I think he was the kindest young man I knew."

DARK INVADER and Ted had been shipped with a dozen other racehorses by the *City of London* from Birkenhead. It had been a cold, dark, drizzling day and now, a month later, the ship was moored in warmth and sunlight to discharge horses and grooms at the docks of a broad river. Earlier, leaning over the rail with the other grooms, Ted had seen the domes of a great building in dazzling white marble, brooding over a wide expanse of grass and trees.

"Thought it would be dry and brown," Ted had said. "Look, there's flowers," and there were white people, cars and in the distance an English-looking church with a spire and the familiar white rails of a big racecourse. "Doesn't seem such an outlandish place as I thought," he had commented.

On the quay the horses were stepping gingerly out of their crates. Seven of the newcomers were for John Quillan. Two were Lady Mehta's, five for Mr. Leventine. With Lady Mehta, John could not guess what he would get; spending every summer in France, she bought as she fancied. Now John saw a mare—light bay, silky mane, lustrous eyes, a lovely appealing thing, but "Back at the knees,"

39

groaned John. "Narrow-bodied as a board on edge." He flipped over the papers to find the vet's certificate. "Sound," written aggressively in green ink. "You may be now, but you won't be in a year." John tried to keep the pity out of his voice as he patted the silken head. The next was better, a dark bay with the broad, well-muscled quarters of a sprinter. "Thank God we can do something with you." But John's real interest was in Mr. Leventine's five, his first experience of what that enigma would buy.

Two mares, a gelding and a colt, sharp little horses good for races of six furlongs to a mile. Sound legs and good feet, bright-coloured coats, even after a long voyage and little or no grooming. The stuff to turn out week after week in the winter handicaps, to stand the stifling heat and the Monsoon Meetings. No-nonsense types, thought John. His respect for Mr. Leventine increased.

Last out of his box, overtopping the others by a hand, was Dark Invader. John looked at his papers. Leventine couldn't have bought this one, surely? But there it was: "Brown colt, off-hind fetlock partly white." Seventeen hands at least, thought John, too big for the course. John looked at the paper again; unplaced since a win first time out eighteen months ago. He frowned. He wouldn't have thought Mr. Leventine would have thrown money away.

"Good morning, sir," said a hoarse voice, and John found himself looking down at a little man whose blue eyes were appraising him from head to toe. The polite "Good morning, sir," was quite unlike the "Hy-ah" or "Hullo there" of the other travelling grooms, who relinquished their charges sometimes without a backward glance as they went off with the trainers to collect their pay and blow it during their few days in Calcutta.

In contrast to their sloppiness, this little man was spruce in a clean shirt with a celluloid collar such as John had not seen for years, a waistcoat with a silk watch chain, cord breeches, boxcloth leggings and worn but brilliantly polished boots; those boots sent John back on a wave of nostalgia to his father's stable yard and the standards he knew he had lost.

There was even the inevitable cloth cap, touched respectfully by a finger. "The name is Mullins, sir. Ted Mullins."

40

"And I'm John Quillan. I train for Mr. Leventine."

"Yes, sir, and this is Dark Invader."

If Ted had expected eulogies, he did not get them. John Quillan walked slowly around Dark Invader, appraising the horse as closely as Ted had appraised him.

"Certainly fills the eye," was all John said, exactly like Peter Hay. That was too much for Ted. "He's a bloody lovely hoss, sir, and such a gentleman with it."

The horse was not the only gentleman. "Would it be in order with you, sir, if I walked the Invader home?"

John noted the use of the word "home"; evidently Ted's appraisal had ended in approval, but John had to hesitate. "It's a longish walk, all of three miles."

"Good. After tramping round them decks, the Invader'll feel a bit strange. He's used to me."

"Of course, but . . . would you just walk with him?"

Ted flushed. "You mean out here an Englishman shouldn't be seen leading a hoss?"

"It's a question of prestige, yes, but not yours," said John. "I'm thinking of Sadiq and Ali, who will be Dark Invader's grooms—we call them syces out here. Sadiq is waiting to take charge and if he doesn't, well, there would be a loss of face."

"I see, sir. Would he—Mr.—is it Saddick, sir? Would he mind if I walked along?" asked Ted.

TED NEVER FORGOT that first walk in Calcutta.

Sadiq was a head taller than Ted, the turban he wore making him seem even taller. He was burly—dark with a fierce upturned moustache and prominent brown eyes with curiously yellowed whites that reminded Ted of snail shells; already they were looking at Dark Invader with the pride of a mother in her firstborn son, and Ted had to swallow and turn his head away.

"You'll need a hat," John Quillan was saying. "That cap's no good in this sun. I expect I have a topee in the car."

A second groom had joined Sadiq on the offside. Dark Invader led the way, the other Quillan horses coming behind, but even with the stiffness that came from the weeks of being boxed, his great stride soon outpaced them. "Him fast," Sadiq said.

"*Ji-han!*" The other groom panted as he tried to keep up. Ted was glad to see neither of them jerked on the reins. He put a restraining hand on Dark Invader's bridle. "Steady, boy, steady."

"S-steady. S-steady." The s's hissed through Sadiq's teeth.

Their way led, at first, through streets lined with ramshackle houses, most of them hung with notices in Hindi and English— MALIK AMRIT LAL PATNEY, ADVOCATE, GOODWILL ELECTRIC COMPANY, HAPPINESS COFFEE AND TEA HOUSE—alternating with shacks and open-fronted shops. The streets seethed with traffic— streetcars, buses, carts drawn by white bullocks or massive black water buffalo. Ted shuddered at the sight of the sores on the animals' necks and as he saw how the drivers cruelly twisted their tails. Queer high box carriages clattered past, and again he was sickened by the horses that drew them, some no more than ponies. Though they wore strings of blue beads around their necks and some had feathers in their browbands, their ribs and hipbones stood out.

The trucks had tassels, too, as did some of the cars and taxis, with turbanned black-bearded drivers who never stopped sounding their horns. Now and again a shining car slid through with perhaps one person in it and a smart-capped chauffeur, but each taxi seemed to hold a dozen passengers and there were laden rickshaws pulled by skinny little men, glistening with sweat, running between the shafts. And around and among them on the pavements and in the gutters and in the road itself was a river of brown-skinned people.

Some of the men wore only a loincloth, balancing loads on yokes across their shoulders, or on their heads, as did sari-clad women, with a poise Ted could not help admiring. A few men were dressed in immaculate flowing white, a loose shirt, draped muslin instead of trousers, slipper shoes, and carried umbrellas and briefcases—but babies were naked except for a charm string; they crawled on the pavements.

It seemed people lived in the streets. A man, squatting on the pavement, was having his head shaved. Another was dictating a letter; the letter writer had a desk, without legs, on the ground. Men relieved themselves in the gutter, and Ted, astounded, saw women slapping cakes of dung—yes, manure!—to dry on walls. It was only afterwards he learned dung was used as fuel.

Pigeons picked grain from the grain shops, pai dogs nosed rubbish and everywhere was a hubbub of voices, creaking wheels and motor horns mingling with a smell of sweat and urine, woodsmoke and a pungent smell that later he was to learn came from cooking in hot mustard oil. Occasionally there was a waft of heavy sweetness as a flower seller passed, or now from a woman in a flowing sari, with flowers around the knot of her hair. Ted saw that her midriff was bare. What would Ella say? he thought, shocked to the depths of his Methodist soul—this is a dreadful place—yet, at the same time he was so fascinated that he almost forgot Dark Invader.

Dark Invader, though, passed unruffled; he did not know it, but this was his first encounter with his public.

TED WAS GLAD when they left the streets and the hordes of people, to strike off across the green turf he had glimpsed from the ship. "Maidan," said Sadiq, and here again was the racecourse with its well-kept lawns and paddocks.

They passed mounted policemen, Englishmen in white uniforms and Indians in khaki. Then Sadiq turned right, crossed a wide busy road into a quieter one and turned in through two open gates. Dark Invader went still faster as if he knew he was coming to what Ted had called it—home.

"GOOD LORD," said Ted. It was the first time he had seen Indian syces grooming.

He had seen Dark Invader into a roomy stall, seen what a good feed was waiting, not in a manger as in England but in a heavy galvanized tub, seen the crows, big black and grey birds with strong beaks and darting pirate eyes, fly down to perch on the rails, waiting for droppings of corn. They were, John Quillan told him, every horse's constant companions. Then Ted had gone with John to the

43

Eden boardinghouse, where, after lunch, exhausted by the heat and strangeness, Ted had slept until John had come to fetch him. "Thought you might like to see my string."

Ted had blinked at the sight of the *bandar-log* outside Scattergold Hall. Two were fighting over a large pet ram which, in its turn, was fighting them; one, a girl, was swinging like a monkey on a branch of a tree. An older boy was earnestly schooling a pony, while two, almost babies, were making mud pies on the edge of the drive, pouring red dust and water on each other's heads. Dahlia sat peacefully in a rocking chair on the veranda, wearing her usual loose wrapper and fanning herself with a palmleaf fan.

"My wife and children," John had said absently. But he did not introduce Ted; instead he led him to the stable square and Ted blinked again. He had never seen anything like it.

The horses were tethered outside their stalls to rings set in the wall, the syces, two to a horse, ranging themselves one each side. As Dark Invader was so big, Sadiq and the second groom, Ali, stood on boxes set far back so that they could throw their weight on their hands, then laid into him with what John told Ted was the classic hand rubbing—*hart-molesh* in Hindi—of Indian horse care. "You mean they groom with their *hands?*" asked Ted.

"Every part of their hands—fingers, thumb, the heel of the hand and right up to the forearm. Watch."

Now and again Sadiq or Ali turned to rinse hands and forearms in a bucket of cold water to wash off the dead hair, then sweating and panting, back again, while Dark Invader grunted with ecstasy and nipped playfully at Sadiq's plump bottom. "Ari! Shaitan!" Sadiq cursed him happily and Ted saw, with another pang, that already they understood one another perfectly.

At a call from the jemadar, the Quillan headman, imposing in his maroon turban, well-cut coat and small cane, the hand rubbing stopped and each man put on leather pads like boxing gloves and began using them in a rhythm that resounded through the square: right pad, left pad hard on the horse, then both pads hit together in the air to free dust and sweat; *thump, thump—thrump*, over and over again for fifteen minutes. Then came the final polishing with soft brushes and cloths; manes and tails were brushed out, tails bandaged into shape, hoofs cleaned and oiled. Finally the men stood by their horses as the jemadar walked around to inspect them.

Afterwards John approved each animal and the horses were led out to walk around the tan track for an hour's gentle exercise. This was the time when, in the cool of the evening, the owners and sometimes jockeys and riding boys gathered to watch. Meanwhile the undergrooms prepared the feed, filled buckets of water, hung rugs and surcingles ready and made the bedding for the night, carefully edging it with the plait of straw Mother Morag had seen. Then they laid out the bedroll of their particular senior syce on his charpoy—a wooden-framed string bed—set on the veranda. "They *sleep* with their horses?" asked Ted.

"They pull their charpoys right across the stall," said John. "A good groom like Sadiq hardly lets his horse out of his sight."

To Ted it was a different world. It was not only the torrid air, the pale glare of the sky; not only the strange smells and sounds, the brilliant colours in the garden of the boardinghouse—a whole hedge of poinsettias, crimson hibiscus, beds of flaming cannas—and here, in the Quillan garden, the tumbled masses of bougainvillea, the gorgeous blue of morning glory, paler blue of plumbago. It was not the surprise of the stables either, nor of Dahlia and the *bandar-log*. Ted felt as though barriers that had penned him all his life had fallen down.

After that sleep, when he had come out of the boardinghouse with John, a travelling bearer had approached him. Bearer, he gathered, meant valet. "I look after you, sahib. Save you much trouble."

"I look after meself," Ted had said gruffly, but the man had called him "sahib", him, Ted, who, except for a few short seasons and the three years of the war, had always been a "lad". And with John Quillan, though they had only exchanged a few words, Ted felt freer and more equal than he had ever done with Michael Traherne, for all their mutual affection and respect.

As Ted had stood with John, watching Sadiq and Ali at work, he had felt happier than he had thought he ever would again. Then he

45

watched more closely. It seemed to him that now and again, when the strapping approached the Invader's neck, a muscle twitched and he flinched. At once Sadiq's hand discarded the leather pad to smooth and gentle the place, and Dark Invader grunted with pleasure again. "Might be," said Ted as he watched, and as he saw it repeated, "Might be—might do the trick." He had said it under his breath, but John's sharp ears had heard.

NEXT DAY a big, sandy-haired, soft-voiced man in breeches and Newmarket boots appeared with a sheaf of papers. This time John did introduce Ted. "Ted Mullins, Captain Mack, our Turf Club official vet. He's here to identify Dark Invader as the horse of that name and breeding entered in the stud book."

"What did he make of him, sir?" Ted asked John when the captain had gone.

"Mack doesn't say much unless he's making a diagnosis. He said Dark Invader looked very like a horse."

Ted was disappointed, but it was not all Captain Mack said. That night he called at Scattergold Hall for a drink, and when the *bandar-log* had got tired of their exuberant welcome and gone to their own occupations and Dahlia was singing the current baby to sleep, the two men sat comfortably drinking their whisky. Dahlia's slow lullaby punctuated their talk, the ayah's song that had lulled generations of foreign babies to sleep:

> "*Nini, baba, nini,*
> *Roti, mackan cheeni.*
> *Sleep, baby, sleep,*
> *Bread, butter and sugar.*"

"How I remember that," said Captain Mack. "I was out here as a child, you know," and his big body relaxed into peace. It was not long, though, before he brought up Dark Invader.

"Leventine's new importation—that's some horse, John."

"Maybe, but he also has some record." John held out a paper. "Read this note Mullins gave me from Michael Traherne."

46

Dear John,

I send you in the care of his lad, Ted Mullins, one of the nicest horses I have come across, which is saying a good deal.

From the viewpoint of our profession he is a problem. As you will see from his record, a win first time out in good company, nothing since; in fact, the highlight of his three-year-old season was fifth in a field of washouts at Folkestone.

What the record does not show, though, is his form on the home gallops; at a mile and a half or upward he is pretty nearly unbeatable—but *not* in public.

I had hoped to find the solution, but his owner has lost patience, so . . . Now he's all yours and good luck to you.

"What do you make of that?" asked John.

Captain Mack pondered. "I don't like it," he said. "It doesn't sound like a physical thing, or it would be there all the time, home gallops or race. If we could find something, we could probably cure it, but . . ."

"You mean," said John, "a sound horse that won't try under pressure is usually one that has been whipped at the finish of a race and has learned his lesson that if he takes the lead he will be punished."

"Exactly. 'The shadow of remembered pain.' " Sandy Mack was given to quotation. "It's in the mind, John. Besides, it's the leadership instinct; you don't need me to tell you, even in thorough-breds, it's a rare and frail thing—crush it and it has gone for ever. No, John. I doubt if this hope of Leventine's will win any race this side of doomsday."

"Any race! He's aiming at the Cup."

Captain Mack laughed. "What! The Viceroy's? I'm not a betting man, but if Dark Invader gets anywhere near winning that race, I'll eat my hat."

"H'mmm," was all John said, but next evening, as he and Ted were watching the grooming, "What did you mean, Mullins," he asked, "when you said this"—he gestured at the working grooms—"might do the trick?"

"You heard?" Ted was amazed.

"I heard. What did you mean?" John looked down at Ted, who was silent. Some inward struggle was going on. John tried to help.

"Dark Invader was thoroughly examined and pronounced sound before he was bought, by Mr. Leventine's veterinarian."

"He certainly was."

"But, in spite of that, and Captain Mack's opinion, you still think there's something wrong. What?"

"Ar!" Ted drew a breath of satisfaction. "Soon's I saw you, I knew one day you would be asking me that. I believe it's his muscles, sir, high on the shoulder."

"Yet they didn't find anything?"

"Couldn't," said Ted. "Not looking at him like that. Can't see nothing, nor feel it. Pass your hand firm and there's nothing, but with pressure . . . muscles have two ends, sir, and it's deep. Did you see when Mr. Saddick was strapping, the hoss flinched." Then Ted burst out, "It was that Bacon what began it. His infernal bowlegs. Nutcrackers squeezing a hoss in a place God never meant a man's legs to be—he rides so short, see, and the Invader, he were nothing but a great sprawling baby, and it were his first race. But that Captain Hay was set on a win, no matter what."

"Which he got," said John.

"Yes." Ted's face was grim. "Will you watch, sir? Just watch when Mr. Saddick lays it on hard."

John watched, and as Sadiq came up the shoulder, he saw the Invader flinch.

"You're right," he told Ted. "There is a tender spot. We'll get Captain Mack to have a look."

CAPTAIN MACK stood, like John had, close beside the horse, but his scepticism showed as he let Sadiq guide his fingers slowly up the Invader's shoulder, pressing all the way. Suddenly the horse grew restive. Captain Mack pressed harder—scepticism giving way to intentness. There came a definite flinch and Dark Invader threw up his head, almost jerking Sadiq off his feet.

"Get me something to stand on," ordered Captain Mack. "You great brute!" He patted Dark Invader affectionately as he got up on

48

a bench. His fingers reached steadily on; a moment later he was looking with interest, not where Sadiq had shown him the tenderness but above it, where the hairs of the mane came to an end.

"John," he said, "look here." John joined him on the bench. "See? There's a small scar under those hairs."

"But . . . it's miniscule."

"On the surface, yes. Mullins, hop up. Have you ever noticed that scar before?"

"Course," said Ted. "Them's the only other white hairs he's got. Had them when he come from Ireland. I reckon when he were a baby running loose he maybe caught a bit of barbed wire, or cut hisself—but that was long before, so it couldn't be the trouble . . . or could it?" Ted had seen Captain Mack's satisfaction. "*Could* it?"

"It could. Probably did happen when he was a foal, but not on wire. He was rolling in the grass more like and met a bit of broken bottle or a sharp stone—anything—which made a small cut that healed on the surface but left damage. Maybe a bit of gravel or a chip of glass got in and caused infection deeper down. The muscles lost flexibility, fibrous—left a scar in the muscle if you like—nothing to see on the outside, but any pressure on there would cause pain. When the horse was overstretched, tired as well—remember how young he was . . ."

"It must have hurt terribly," said John, "and I can guess that Streaky Bacon's grip just caught it, which could account for everything. Sandy, you clever old devil."

"Don't thank me, thank Ted and Sadiq." Captain Mack got down from the bench. "But you're not out of the wood yet. Sadiq's *hart-molesh* is the best possible treatment, but there's more to this than that. Everything to do with the finish of a race, other horses challenging, the noise, the excitement, tells Darkie, Stop before it hurts. That's it, isn't it, old fellow?" He pulled one of the dark ears.

"So we still have our problem."

"You do indeed. John, face it. You know that a spoiled horse never comes back."

49

"MULLINS," said John when Captain Mack had gone. "Why didn't you tell Mr. Traherne what you thought about the horse?"

Ted hesitated. "The Invader was never no trouble with me, sir, and there was nothing I could be sure of. Anyway, it wouldn't have mattered to Captain Hay. I thought with Mr. Leven . . ."

"Leventine."

"Yes. You see, sir, two of them travelling lads would have done to bring out all his hosses to In'ja, but for the Invader he brought me out special and so I thought with him . . ."

"Dark Invader might have a chance?"

"Yes, sir, but has he? Couldn't follow all that talk," said Ted, "but I guess what Captain Mack meant was, if the Invader was to meet Streaky again, even now, he would remember."

"Possibly, but he won't see Streaky. We'll see to that."

"Then you think he has a chance spite of Captain Mack?"

As always when John Quillan met opposition he was obstinate. "He's going to have a chance," he said. "I don't know how—yet—but somehow. We must see to it. I'm glad you came, Ted."

"So am I," said Ted.

AFTER DINNER, when the last *bandar* had hushed, the last baby been fed, when Dahlia had gone to bed and the last round of the stables been done, John liked to light a cigar—he allowed himself one every evening—and stroll in his tumbledown garden to think over the problems of the day. Tonight his thoughts turned to Dark Invader.

John could visualize that first race at Lingfield. Dark Invader well away—Michael Traherne had assured him the horse was a willing starter—but when the field caught up with him, forced to quicken his stride by an almighty squeeze in an unexpected place, and John saw the typical Bacon finish, the furiously urgent figure, the rhythmically swinging whip, shown but not striking, the horse desperately extended, those knees gripping vicelike above the saddle. "It must have hurt hideously—a stab from a knife," Mack had said. Poor old Darkie, thought John. That's probably what you were trying to tell us stupid humans. Well, we're there at last, but what to do about it? I don't know. With which dispiriting thought he threw away the butt of his cigar, called to Gog and Magog and turned to go to bed.

On the veranda he paused; a phrase came back to him. "I never had no trouble with him . . ." "I wonder," said John to Gog and Magog. "I wonder."

"TED," SAID JOHN next morning, "I've been doing some thinking. I should like you to show me how you ride Dark Invader."

It was Dark Invader's fourth day in India, and during early work John had had him walked quietly down to the racecourse and onto the exercise track.

Like most trainers, John Quillan retained his own jockey, a young quarter-English, three-quarters-Chinese called Ching. Ted had already met him, slim, eager, with alert black eyes. John had picked him out from a set of young jockeys from Singapore and had slowly trained him. "Will Mr. Ching mind?" asked Ted. "It's the Invader's first ride here."

"No. No. I maybe learn." Ching stood with John, watching as Ted mounted.

Dark Invader had acknowledged Ted's arrival in the saddle with a backward slant of an ear. Nothing else. "Not much awkwardness about him after a month at sea," said John.

"Didn't expect it, sir. Easiest horse alive," and Ted told Dark Invader, "Walk on, boy. *That's* the fella! Just a little trot now. Gently does it," and Dark Invader trotted around the circuit soberly, as he was told. There were new things to look at: a fat little sheep, three geese, a vulture picking at some small dead animal. Dark Invader examined them all with prick-eared attention, without faltering in his steady trotting. Then Ted brought the big horse back to where Sadiq was waiting, dismounted and patted the handsome neck, while Dark Invader nosed impatiently at his pockets.

"Thanks, Ted." John came up. "Just what was wanted." Then, "Ted, would you ride a bit of work for me? Would you take Snowball, that old grey there, and do the whole circuit with the riding boy on that bay mare? She's to race in a fortnight. Snowball's not in the same class, but he has been racing in the Monsoon Meeting so he's that much fitter. Take them to the four-furlong mark and come home as fast as you like."

"Fast! On Snowball!" said Ching.

"Exactly. The mare should lose him fairly quickly," said John.

Snowball was Australian bred, a gelding, now twelve years old; his coat, once grey, had whitened; years of slogging around the same racing and practice course had hardened his mouth and soured his temper. "I hate ride him," said Ching.

John watched closely as Ted began by taking the old horse around them, and saw how Snowball tried to get his bit into its usual position against his back teeth—and failed. "Hands!" said John to Ching. "Watch Mullins's hands." They saw Snowball begin to chase the bit with his tongue with a flicker of interest. Then John heard Ted's voice, "Cheer up, old cuddy. 'Tisn't such a bad world," and saw him run a finger up the hogged mane and pull one of the stiff ears in what seemed one continuous movement. Snowball shook himself and gave a little hoist to his quarters. "Good boy," said Ted. "Come on, let's show them what we old 'uns can do," as they set off to join the mare and riding boy.

At the four-furlong mark John pressed his stopwatch and waited for the mare to draw away from Snowball. After a furlong she led by a half a length but could not shake him off, and Snowball finished galloping stride for stride with his head level with her girth. The stopwatch showed a satisfactory time for the mare, a surprising one for Snowball.

"Well, well," said John. "The old English long rein finish. I never thought to see it in this city."

Ching was dumbfounded. "Is English style?" he asked.

"Was," said John. He walked over to the riders as they dismounted. "Thank you. Ted, you certainly sweetened that old plug and kept him going. He didn't even do his usual ducking-out towards the rubbing-down sheds."

"No, I told him different." Ted said it as if it were nothing unusual. "I think I often know what's in a hoss's mind before he knows hisself. Comes from being with them."

52

"I guess that's true. Ridden with the best in your day, haven't you?"

"I did quite a lot," Ted admitted. "Pre-war Derby, four times. Never in the frame, though. Come to think of it, I was third in the Oaks once, and fifth twice."

"And what are you doing now when not seeing the world free of charge?" They were walking towards the stands. "Still riding?"

"No . . . retired from all that."

Lost his ticket, John thought. I wonder why.

"Didn't do much after the war," Ted went on. "It didn't seem to matter. You see, I lost my wife in the flu epidemic of—'18 that was."

"I'm sorry."

"Her name was Ella." John did not know it, but this was a rare confidence; Ted had not spoken Ella's name in all these years. "Wouldn't swop my Ted for the King of England," Ella had often said. She had made Ted feel like the King of England, too. Ella, a heap of clay with his flowers beaten into the soil by the rain, and yet it seemed to Ted now as if Ella were suddenly with him again. Egging me on to talk, thought Ted. "Mr. Michael, he took me on 'cos of his father, I think," he continued. "A man on his own doesn't need much. Must admit there was a bit of whisky—more'n a bit. Then the Invader came. After that it was just him. Somehow I never got round to thinking he would be sold. Now . . ." and Ted looked away over the Maidan, then quickly recollected himself. "You were saying, sir?"

"I was interested in your finish, the long rein," said John. "Seems a lost art. The boys nowadays can't drive a horse without climbing up its neck and chewing its ears off. Interesting, too, that you don't ride as short as most."

"Not surprising. When I were a boy, it was all straight legs, toes down. Soon we was all taught different, but I never took to the very short style, like Streaky's—stirrups buckled high, legs doubled up like a frog."

"Yes. I should guess you ride four to six holes longer," and John was thoughtful.

TED HAD a fortnight before his ship sailed for England. "You should see something of India," John told him. "Darjeeling, Everest."

"They are lovelee," said Dahlia. She and Ted had become fast friends.

"Delhi, Agra and the Taj Mahal," said John. "And you could go across and see the Ellora and Ajunta caves and sail from Bombay," but all of India Ted wanted to see was here in the Quillan stables—the track that led down to the racecourse, the racecourse itself and its circuits. "Well, what do you want to do?"

Ted cleared his throat. "If it's all right by you, sir, could I stay here a little longer? There's another boat in about three weeks, and I think Mr. Michael could spare me as he hasn't the Invader. I have a bit put by so could pay my way."

"No need for that," said John. "I was wishing you could give me a hand. Ching hasn't much experience. There's Dark Invader to acclimatize and"—he added as an afterthought—"Mr. Leventine."

BACK FROM EUROPE, Mr. Leventine came to watch the evening parade. Several owners were there, gossiping and visiting their horses, giving them sugarcane, carrots, even apples. "Apples! Think what they cost!" Sister Ignatius would have said.

Never at this time was there a sign of Dahlia or the *bandar-log*. Gog and Magog, sitting on each side of the veranda steps, kept guard. Ayahs were putting the babies to bed, the children were having their supper. Now and again a wail or the sound of a fight would float out over the lawn, but this was one rule that had to be kept because, "Out of sight, out of mind—almost," John said bitterly. It took time for Ted to understand.

Mr. Leventine arrived in a large blue Minerva with huge brass lamps and a bulb horn in the shape of a brass serpent. The chauffeur was in blue to match, with polished brass buttons. Mr. Leventine himself was in a pale grey suit, a carefully folded white silk handkerchief in the breast pocket, a pink rose in his buttonhole. Of the other owners, the men, mostly in jerseys, sports coats and flannels, looked shabby beside him and as he advanced with a strong

54

waft of cologne, a few said, "Good evening, Leventine," but most of them parted before him and became immersed in talk. Only Lady Mehta smiled and waved.

"Well, Johnny. How are you?" and Mr. Leventine laid a diamond-ringed hand on John's shoulder who was spared from responding, "And you, Cas?" as Mr. Leventine would have liked him to, because the excited voice went straight on. "Where is he?"

"Dark Invader?"

"Of course."

John presented Ted, who was given a curt nod. Ted could see nothing wrong with Mr. Leventine. "Dressed up," he would have conceded, "but that's natural. He's a foreigner and they have different ways. Can guess he's very rich, and talks loud 'cos he's interested." Ted followed as Mr. Leventine went along the stables—his horses had been kept in for his visit—discussing each with John. Then they came to Dark Invader, who whickered when he saw Ted.

"Ah!" said Mr. Leventine and stood still. Ted noticed that Sadiq's eyes gleamed at the sight of Mr. Leventine and he gave a deep salaam. "Ah!" and then, "You asked me why I bought him," said Mr. Leventine in a reverent tone. "Well, just look at him, Johnny." Mr. Leventine's voice was as loud as if he were addressing a stadium. "He's bred to the big open races." Then he lowered his voice. "I can guess what happened. His owner—this Captain Hay—is, by all accounts, a young man, ambitious for a big win. They tried Dark Invader, a certainty to win first time out as a two-year-old, got good odds on him and engaged the famous Tom Bacon to ride him. Colt was green; got left six lengths, but Bacon had his orders so he set about him and got him home. Colt hasn't tried a yard since. Why? He's bred right, looks right and moves right."

"But isn't right," John said calmly.

"Then find out why." Mr. Leventine dropped his voice still further. "Don't you see, now's our chance, Johnny. His record's so terrible he'll be put in class four with a lot of Australian washouts and English weeds, and so . . . slowly, slowly, if we handle him carefully, he need never have another hard race."

56

"Till he gets back to his own class."

Mr. Leventine gave his trainer a long, purposeful stare. "He's in a class by himself," he said with finality.

"That's what I say," Ted offered boldly, and Mr. Leventine turned. "Ted Mullins, sir."

"Ah! I remember. Dark Invader's stable lad." Mr. Leventine, Ted noted, did not call him Darkie. "I had you bring him out."

"That's right," said Ted, "and I thank you, sir."

The unexpectedly good manners struck Mr. Leventine. He gave Ted a long, hard look, then made what John called one of the swift Leventine decisions.

"Johnny," he said, "this man must stay with the horse. Right through."

"But he's working for Michael Traherne," began John.

"Traherne," and Michael was brushed away like a fly. "Settle terms, any terms they like," ordered Mr. Leventine, "but this man must stay."

AGAINST his usual custom—he detested getting up early—Mr. Leventine began to come down to the racecourse for the morning's work, wrapped in a camel-hair coat, his throat muffled in a cashmere scarf. A bearer in a crested turban stood behind him holding a shooting stick, a pair of binoculars, and a topee for when the sun grew warm. Mr. Leventine watched with John as Ching on chosen horses, the riding boys on others, and Ted on Dark Invader, took their turn.

The scene was always the same; each trainer had his "camp" with horses and syces moving around it, a heap of rugs and saddlery in the middle. The jemadar called the horses out to the group of waiting riders. After work, while the grooms and riding boys walked the horses home, most trainers and their owners and jockeys went over to the stands for coffee and chat. John usually avoided this, riding Matilda straight back to the stables, but with Mr. Leventine it was different; he demanded his full rights and the daily discussion was one of them.

Over coffee he asked John suddenly, "Why wasn't that little man riding for Traherne?" He had watched Ted minutely. "He's a jockey," he said firmly.

"Yes. He was quite well-known before the war."

"Then why?"

"Lost his licence."

"Not mixed up in any dirty work, I hope." The small brown eyes were sharp.

"Wouldn't have been with Traherne if he had," said John. "It was a doping case. Mullins obviously didn't know anything about it, but as you know, once the powers get working they'll warn off anything in sight, up to and including the stable cat, and ask questions afterwards. Poor Ted!"

"Humph!" said Mr. Leventine. He beckoned to his bearer and was gone.

IN THE EVENINGS Mr. Leventine liked to play billiards at the Turf Club. The Royal Calcutta Turf Club was the only club where he was an acceptable member; its criteria were not colour, race or class but a true interest in racing and absolute integrity, points on which no one could have faulted Casimir Alaric Bruce Leventine. He was proud of his membership, loving the club's flower-filled park, its airy rooms, its portraits of past senior stewards, and admiring its members with most of whom he could not have fraternized except through racing and games like billiards. On this particular evening he was playing in a tournament against one of the most eminent, the high court judge Sir Humphrey Hyde, who was also a steward.

The game was close and, though Mr. Leventine was good, he lost by a narrow margin. Sir Humphrey was amused by the ingenuity with which Mr. Leventine allowed the victory. "I wondered what the fellow wanted," he told a crony afterwards. "Favour from the Bench? Hardly, he's too shrewd and far too well-established. Racing? Probably. I suspect he wants to be a steward. Well, in a year or two, why not?" But that, for once, was not in Mr. Leventine's mind. "I have a new horse," he said.

"Several," commented the judge. "I've been looking at the new arrivals you just registered. One of them puzzled me. Dark

Invader—is that the one?" Mr. Leventine nodded. "More fashion-ably bred than we usually see here," added Sir Humphrey. "Indian stake money doesn't as a rule justify the price you must have paid."

"I got him cheaply," said Mr. Leventine. "Spoiled by a hard race as a two-year-old. I'm hoping he'll change his way."

"Rogues don't as a rule."

"Perhaps he won't, but he's not a rogue; besides, I don't like to see such beauty and breeding thrown on the scrap heap."

The judge looked at him with approval. For the first time, for anyone in that club, he gave Mr. Leventine a pat on the shoulder. "I wish you luck with him."

"Thank you, Sir Humphrey." Mr. Leventine spoke with just the right touch of deference. "I expect I'll need it."

TED FITTED QUICKLY and happily into the life of the Quillan stable and, to his surprise, into Scattergold Hall. John had suggested he move from the boardinghouse into a one-room annex of the Hall. Ted's scrupulous soul was satisfied when John let him pay his rent and board from the salary—to Ted enormous—that Mr. Leventine paid him.

Michael had agreed without demur to his staying, so there was no disloyalty. Ted liked his stone-floored room; its windows and doorways had shutters, no glass or door. The furniture was so plain that his scant possessions did not seem too cheap, yet there were things he had never had before—a bathroom of his own and a private veranda with cane chairs and a table. Along the veranda edge the gardeners put pots of violets and carnations. "I didn't think vi'lets grew in In'ja."

The bearer, Danyal, looked after Ted's clothes, made his bed and dusted his room, "But you mustn't ask him to touch any food," said John. "It's against his caste." It was Ahmed, a Muslim, who brought Ted his meals from the kitchen. Ahmed wanted to stand behind Ted's chair while he ate, and Ted begged John to tell him to leave the dishes and go away.

"You will have to get used to it," John said. "It's a sign of respect—not for us but from us."

"You mean we recognize their ways." That made Ted feel easier—he was used to giving respect, not to getting it—and soon he fell into the routine of the day. It began with the rise at dawn, a tray of tea and, extraordinary to Ted, buttered toast and bananas brought to him by Ahmed, who seemed to work all hours and never, Ted discovered, had a day off or a holiday. Then came the ride to the racecourse and the morning's work, carefully regulated by John to the demands of the Invader's big frame, with long periods of walking or trotting under Ted's expert hands. After that the slow walk back, when Ted had, perforce, to watch Sadiq and Ali do the rubbing down, grooming and the morning feed. "As Mr. Leventine's paying me, couldn't I, sir?"

"These are my stables and my syces," John reminded him.

"Sorry, sir."

"Besides, it's not the custom," John said more gently, "and in India we don't go against that."

After breakfast, an English breakfast, came the cleaning of the tack, saddles, bridles, reins, stirrup leathers; stirrups, bits and whips had to be laid out for inspection. This was the time, too, when Captain Mack came; he was called for the slightest cause. "We don't take chances with other people's horses," said John.

At two o'clock, when the midday feed was done and the men themselves had eaten, for horses and syces alike came peace—the syces asleep on their charpoys, the beasts in their stalls. Then the only sound in the stables was a human snore or the stamp of a hoof to keep the flies away—the horses wore light nets that even covered neck and heads. A crow might give a lazy caw, a goose or duck quack, hens scratch, but the cats were curled in the veranda chairs, the Great Danes stretched prone on the floor. John slept, too, as did Dahlia and the babies, even the children.

At first Ted had tried to keep awake. "Sleep in the afternoon!" But the general laziness caught him, too, or perhaps it was the after-effect of the curry and rice he was beginning to like, and that Dahlia ordered every day. It was only the rattle of china that woke him when Ahmed again brought tea, and Ted heard the jemadar's call in the stables, the horses' answering neighs, and it was time for more

60

work; sometimes back to the racecourse for an hour, sometimes schooling in the yard, then the evening ritual.

Dark Invader had taken to the country as though in some previous incarnation he had been an inhabitant. He made no objection to the crows that sidled along the bars of the open stall and robbed his food tub. He blew appreciatively on the huge ram that lived in the yard, and formed a kindly friendship with the *bandar-log* and accepted their offerings of stolen sugar and sweetmeats out of the bazaar: sticky sugar rings, coconut ice or *sandesh*—thick white toffee. Above all he liked the attention. His muscles began to harden, his coat to glow. His appetite was prodigious.

The fact that Dark Invader's food cost three times Sadiq's total pay, four times Ali's, did not worry either. By the standard of their trade they were well-off and had prestigious and steady work where each was given a blanket, a thick serge coat, a brown woollen sweater for the winter and two cotton shirts for summer. Sadiq lived and slept on the veranda in front of his horse's box. Twice a day he handed over for an hour to Ali while he went to cook and eat his food, and five times a day he turned towards Mecca and, as a good Muslim, made his prayers. Ali, when Sadiq came back, did the same.

Once a year Sadiq took a month's leave and travelled to Bihar to see his family. "That's a rum go," said Ted, trying to think of himself parted from Ella for eleven months of the year and, what was more, "I think this year I no go," said Sadiq.

"But you *must*. Your wife, children . . ." but, "Not go," said Sadiq and smoothed Dark Invader's mane. "I stay him."

The cooperation between the two—necessary, Ted had to admit—was complete; the horse's great handsome head would come down to be groomed, to have the halter put on, to accept the bridle. He had never been as confident and tractable. With Ted to ride him, Sadiq always near, and the wonderful *hart-molesh* that was beginning to disperse that spot of tenderness, pain and fear seemed to have vanished. "Come on a marvel," Ted wrote to Michael Traherne.

"But he hasn't raced yet," said John.

CHAPTER IV

During the four cold months of the winter, Bengal's cold weather is halcyon, "for those with warm clothes," said Sister Ignatius. As November turned to December, when the string went down in the morning, mists lay so thick over the Maidan that John had difficulty tracking the horses through his binoculars. By the time the horses had finished the evening parade, it was dusk—the brief Indian twilight called by the Bengalis "cow-dust time", because it was then that the cattle were driven home. Almost at once the light faded, it was night, and all along the stalls hand lanterns were lit; though there was electricity, the syces needed the lanterns to look at hoofs and deep into the food tubs to see how much of the feed had been eaten. The horses were warmly rugged, then bedded down for the night. John issued extra blankets for the men. He also sent a warm coat to the convent for Gulab and a rug for Solomon. "You needn't thank me. It's patched."

"Patched or not, it is a godsend," wrote Mother Morag. The sisters wore their long black cloaks and hoods made of sturdy French frieze when they went "collecting", and for early prayer and Mass. But Mother Morag knew only too well what little defence a cotton shirt or a thin muslin sari or a toddler's jacket that only came just past the navel was against the chill and, for the poorest of the poor, she wondered which was worst—the heat or the deluges and dankness of the monsoon, or the cold? But at least for most the sun was no longer an enemy; humans and beasts alike could bask in it at midday and in the afternoons.

It was a time of mixed flowers. In the gardens, with roses, petunias and pinks, the tropical flowers Ted had marvelled at still bloomed, and there were new ones: the pink and white sandwich creeper that festooned walls and gateways, and on the stable's lawn frangipani trees blossomed into their strange temple flowers that looked almost chiselled in the thickness of their petals, growing without leaves directly on bare, thickened branches. Ted had never smelled anything like their heady fragrance.

Unknown to him, Calcutta's "season" was in full swing. Though no longer the capital of India, it was still a city of importance with its own governor, the governor of Bengal, but in December and early January the viceroy came from Delhi and the old Palace of Belvedere, with all the splendour of its marble terraces, sweeps of steps, its state rooms and park, was opened.

It was now that the most important races were run, including the Viceroy's Cup on Boxing Day, the first weekday after Christmas. The All India Polo Tournament and the golf championships were held, and there were balls, both at Belvedere and Government House, and private balls, too.

It was a lively time. Wives and daughters arrived from England, the men's dress clothes were brought out from airtight tin boxes and hung in the sun. There were cocktail parties, dinners, and brunches on Sunday morning after riding.

Only the racing concerned John. He could not bring himself to watch the polo. "Watch! You should be playing," protested Bunny, the young maharajah of Malwa. "You're a six-handicap man, for heaven's sake!" John answered, "No, thank you, Bunny," and Bunny sighed.

Mother Morag was concerned because the canisters were filled to overflowing; in fact, the sisters had to take extra ones because restaurants and hotels were crowded. "It's welcome, of course, our people need it in colder weather," but she worried in case the extra load were too much for Solomon.

The season concerned Ted and Dark Invader not at all. They stayed in their own world of the stables, racecourse, and the track on the verge of Lower Circular Road that lay between them.

"WHAT HAS happened to the children?" Mother Morag asked John when, as had become a habit on Sunday mornings, he fetched them and Dahlia from Mass.

"A little Englishman called Ted Mullins," said John.

Mother Morag had picked out Dark Invader at once from her window and noticed he was ridden by a small white man, noted, too, his stillness in the saddle compared to the riding boys, and his quiet authority when the big horse cocked his ears in curiosity or tried to swerve or break out of his walk. Thinking of that, she said, "What works with animals, works with children, too."

Ted had been scandalized by the *bandar-log*. "I never did," he could not help saying to John.

"I know." John sounded helpless. "Nobody seems to be able to do anything with them. Mrs. Quillan's wonderful with babies, but . . ."

Ted cleared his throat. "Seeing how with Mr. Saddick and Mr. Ally I've so little to do for the hoss . . ."

"You would like to try your hand on my monkeys?"

"Well, sir, my wife was a schoolteacher—miles above me. She taught me lots. So, if you and Mrs. Quillan wouldn't mind."

"*Mind!* We would be infinitely obliged, but I doubt if you can even catch them."

Ted did not say he had caught them already.

They had been attracted first by Dark Invader. "We have never had a horse like that." Ted noticed the "we". Now and again he swung one of them up on the Invader's back, but that was a privilege and Ted knew how to bestow his privileges. Then came a mutual respect for each other's riding; they had come to echo their father's reverence for Ted, and Ted had watched them schooling their ponies. Certainly know their business, he thought, but off the ponies!

"Turned nine and ten and don't know your tables! Seven and you don't know your alphabet. Disgraceful!" he told them, and as with Dark Invader and countless other horses, the stricter he was with them, the more they adored him. "Now stand up and begin. Twice five are ten. Three fives are fifteen." "C A T; R A T; B A T . . . Go on. You can read that easy."

"You're sure they don't come for nuts and bananas?" said John.

"Nuts and bananas!" Ted said scornfully. "That's just about what they had, begging your pardon, sir," and, "Stand up. Keep still. This is a hanky, see. You blow your nose on *it*, not on your fingers. Disgusting!"

It had culminated on a Sunday morning when he had met Dahlia

64

on the drive, wearing a linen suit, stockings, high-heeled shoes and a hat; she was carrying a bag, parasol and gloves and was accompanied by the children dressed as their usual selves.

"Where are you going?"

"To church." Dahlia gave him her happy smile. "I am taking the children, m'n."

"Taking the children like *that!*" Long-ago memories of Sunday school came up in Ted; Sunday school—clean collars, being scrubbed even behind his ears, his nails inspected—and he was shocked. "To church like that!"

"I do try," wailed Dahlia. "Their clothes are all laid out. Clean shirts and shorts and frocks, but they won't . . ."

"Won't they!" To Ted, this was something far more important than the respect due to John and Dahlia as his superiors, to John's expertise as a trainer. "I'll give you ten minutes," he said to the *bandar-log*. "Wash faces and hands and knees, clean nails. Brush hair. Change into your clean clothes, be neat and tidy and come back ready, and I *mean* ready."

JOHN TOOK TED to the races; the Quillan stable had more than thirty runners that season, "So I'm here on business," said John. "Not as one of your groomed-up apes." Ted thought the grooming-up very pretty, "Like Ascot, it is," but it brought him another pang. When Dark Invader won here, and he surely would, it was Sadiq who would lead him around the paddock and Mr. Leventine who would lead him into the winner's circle. He, Ted, would have no part in it except to watch. John kept to the paddocks, the rubbing-down sheds and the reserved stand, which trainers and jockeys frequented. He accepted no invitations for iced coffee or tea. He had reason to be sour; Lady Mehta's Flashlight, running in the Viceroy's Cup, was not even placed.

"Never mind, Johnny," said Mr. Leventine. "She should never have bought Flashlight." Mr. Leventine seemed basking in some warm secret thoughts of his own. He was impeccable in his usual pale grey. "Like one of our state elephants," said Bunny. "He only needs some ornaments and tassels," but Mr. Leventine had no need of tassels; with his rose in his buttonhole he was perfectly contented.

Every morning, too, he braved the mist to join John at the course, his binoculars trained on the striding figure of Dark Invader and the dot on his back that was Ted.

MR. LEVENTINE had an appointment with Sir Humphrey Hyde in his chambers. Sir Humphrey was not surprised—"I had guessed he wanted something."

Now he leaned forward, his elbows on his desk, his fingertips joined, and said, "Well?"

The room with its littered table, bookcases filled with leather-bound books, its look, not of an office but of a study of a particularly learned style, subdued Mr. Leventine. "It's good of Your Honour to see me," he began.

"Not at all. I'm here to see people," and the judge said gently, "Sir Humphrey would be in order." Then, "I gather we are not on legal business."

"No . . . it's about racing. Matter of a jockey who is here, name of Mullins. As I understand it, he had ridden a lot in England but now he has no licence, and I wondered if it would be possible to find out, on the quiet, how he lost it—I have heard one side of the story and it seems he was blameless—and whether there would be any bar to his riding here?"

"I could do that easily," said Sir Humphrey. "One of the Jockey Club stipendiaries is an old friend. I could cable him, but tell me about this Mullins. What is so special about him?"

"You remember the new horse we spoke about in the club the other night? Mullins came out with the shipment. He tells me he was Dark Invader's groom at Lingfield and the other races."

"Ah! Dark Invader, the well-bred horse with the slightly questionable racing record."

"Mullins swears the horse is genuine at bottom. Only needs to be ridden in a style that doesn't frighten him."

There was a pause. Sir Humphrey was obviously searching the filing cabinets of his memory. Then, "I think I remember Mullins.

66

Ted Mullins, wasn't it?" He leaned back in his swivel chair. "If your Mullins and mine are the same, I owe him a good turn. I often had a bet on him when I was a young barrister and the nimble shilling was hard to come by."

Mr. Leventine smiled dutifully. He had no idea what a nimble shilling was, but it seemed Sir Humphrey was favourably inclined. He pressed the point. "The important thing, Your Honour, I mean, Sir Humphrey, is to find out if he can race here."

"That I have understood. I'll find out for you with pleasure."

MR. LEVENTINE had to wait ten days, and Sir Humphrey did not summon him to his chambers. They met, it seemed by chance, in the billiard room at the club, but it was Sir Humphrey who challenged Mr. Leventine to a game. It was not until they had finished that Sir Humphrey said, "By the way, Leventine, good news. Your man is all right. Nothing against him. Could have had his licence back long ago but didn't apply."

"So he could have a licence now?"

"Certainly. He has only to apply with the necessary backing."

"We shall, but of course we shan't be ready till the next cold weather."

"Well, don't go telling me any stable secrets." Sir Humphrey laughed. "And Ted Mullins *is* my man. Give him my compliments and tell him he used to carry my money twenty years ago."

Mr. Leventine drove off to Scattergold Hall immediately to see John Quillan.

TIME HAD SLIPPED past for Ted, immersed in his work with Dark Invader and the children.

The cold weather ended. February grew warm and Calcutta's glory of flowering trees heralded the hot weather, too hot for pampered racehorses, and Dark Invader was led by Sadiq and Ali over the bridge that spanned the Hooghly to Howrah Station. There he was loaded into a massive horse box with padded partitions, and the railway trundled him majestically to the Quillan stables in the cooler, low-lying hill town of Bangalore. His ex-shipmates stayed behind, already far enough forward in training to be entered among thinning fields for the last races of the season, but a few chosen ones went as well, including Flashlight, and a fidgety chestnut called Firefly that Lady Mehta had impetuously bought for fifteen thousand rupees after, by a fluke, it had won the King Edward Cup. "He won't again," predicted John.

With the horses went Ted—and Gog and Magog, a yearly ritual. "Big dogs can't survive Calcutta's hot weather," John explained.

Ted was in charge in Bangalore to continue the patient day-in, day-out training and supervision, and Ted took, too, the three eldest *bandar-log* to go to boarding school. Dahlia wept, but "Poor school," said Bunny. John himself hardly knew his two sons in grey flannel shorts, grey shirts and sweaters, or his daughter in a blue pleated skirt, blue blouse with a sailor collar and a straw hat.

"If you settle down and behaves proper," promised Ted, "I'll take you out every Saturday and give you a sausage tea." Sausages had only entered their lives with Ted; to the *bandar-log* they were delectable.

In late June, John went to see them, but, he had to admit, more importantly to see Dark Invader and to bring Ted some application forms to sign.

"You just sign here—and here," John said.

"You mean I can ride again?" asked Ted. He got up from his chair, swallowed, then walked to the office window and stood with his back to John for at least three minutes. "You mean I can really ride again?" He turned, his blue eyes wet.

"Not only ride. You will be up on Dark Invader."

"Dark Invader!" Ted sounded as if he were in a dream.

"Yes." John was deliberately brisk. "You are being retained by Mr. Leventine as his jockey—with an increase in pay, of course. You will bring the horses back in September and we start Darkie in October. The Alipore Stakes, I think, class four. Of course, he'll run away with it, then we shall see what we shall see."

"We'll see." Ted's voice was firm now. "May I ask you, sir—was it you who thought of this about my ticket?"

"Not me. Mr. Leventine."

68

"Mr. Leventine! Did this for me!"

"Wake up, Ted. Mr. Leventine didn't do it for you. He did it for himself. He doesn't *give* favours away."

That was true. Just before they had left for Bangalore, Mr. Leventine, down on the racecourse, had called Ted aside. "You have been so excellent with the horse I should like you to have this," but Ted had backed away from the wad of notes.

"Very kind of you, sir, but I don't need nothing. It's what *you* done for the Invader that counts."

"Not without you. I know. I have watched. Please, Mullins," but Ted shook his head.

"What am I to do with this then?"

"Tell you what." Ted was still haunted by what he had seen on that journey from the docks, what he saw every day as he and Dark Invader crossed the road. "Give it to the RSPCA," he told Mr. Leventine, "for the ponies and buffaloes and oxes and—oh yes—to them nuns where Mrs. Quillan goes and they feeds the old."

"Give!" Mr. Leventine's voice rose with horror. "If I am rich, it's because my money is for *use*, to reward those who are worthy, not for *derelicts*."

"Not even for them what suffers through no fault of their own?" Ted's voice oddly stern. "You rescued Dark Invader."

"Rescued? By no means. I bought him for my own advantage. I believe in that horse."

"And God bless you for that," said Ted. "But . . ." He looked at the notes again. "Give it to the RSPCA, sir."

Mr. Leventine put the wad back in his pocket.

"SUFFER through no fault of their own." It had been a terrible hot summer in Calcutta; the rains were late in breaking, "which may mean famine," said Mother Morag in dread. She had lived through two famines. Already the price of rice was high, and peasants had begun flocking in from the villages. "They hope for work or food and there isn't any." They swelled the lines waiting at the sisters' street kitchens, but the collections had lessened.

Few people went to restaurants in the heat, and, "Solomon is so slow," said Sister Timothea. It was all the sister said, but Mother Morag knew how punishing was collecting in the heat, especially wearing the habit which, though in India made of white cotton, had not changed since the days of Thérèse Hubert: long sleeves, high neck, coming down to the ankles and finished by a close-fitting muslin coif, as worn by a Belgian peasant woman in the 1840s. "But that was in *Europe*." Sister Joanna had not quite learned the utter disregard of self. "This is India! Those starched white strings under our chins!"

"They don't stay starched long," Mother Morag consoled her and laughed. "You should see yours now—spotted with gravy!"

"From the curry canister. Ugh!" It had been Sister Joanna's turn that early dawn to help carry the canisters in. "Curry of all things! I must smell."

As they talked they were storing the food, and when Mother Morag lifted her arms to set some puddings on a shelf, her sleeves fell back. The white skin of her arms was covered in prickly heat. Sister Joanna saw and was ashamed of her own small grumbling, but tactfully, all she said was, "I had better put on a fresh bonnet to go round the offices this afternoon or I shall hardly impress the young men," and tried to laugh, too.

It was no joke, though. In these stifling nights sometimes the food had gone bad before Solomon and the cart reached home. No wonder—one night it was after two o'clock. "How long have we had Solomon?" Mother Morag asked Sister Ignatius next day.

"It must be ten or eleven years."

"And he wasn't all that young when he came." Mother Morag looked thoughtfully at the dip in Solomon's back, at his legs that had thickened and were growing stiff. The hollows over his eyes were deep now, and in spite of Gulab's grooming, his coat was rough. Mother Morag sighed and a pucker, what the sisters called her worry line, showed between her eyebrows.

THE RAINS BROKE, to everyone's relief. "You can almost hear the plants drinking," said Sister Barbara and, "I want to dance in the puddles," said young Sister Mary Fanny, as the *bandar-log* did up

70

the road. There were brief furious deluges of rain, then blue skies with piled-up clouds that would presently burst again, but meanwhile the whole earth steamed. Grass, trees and flowers glistened in the washed light. All the old houses smelled dank; and mildew appeared on anything leather.

Racing began on the Monsoon Track, sometimes in a downpour. Few outside owners were there, not Lady Mehta, nor John's nawab, nor Mr. Leventine. The Monsoon Meeting was casual, friendly, everyone knew everyone else—except for John. For him, as for other trainers, the Monsoon was an anxious time; the early British had called it the sickly season, and it was sickly still. "I seem to do nothing but scratch one horse after another from a race," said John. Captain Mack was called out night and day.

"Racehorses! What about humans," said Sister Ignatius. There were "ten-day fevers", chills, pleurisy. The old people, even under the sisters' care, died as easily as flies. "As soon as a bed is empty, there are twenty waiting to fill it," and it was not only the old people; the babies died, too, and children . . . Mother Morag was too harried to think about Solomon.

Then it seemed to her only a matter of weeks, though it was almost three months when, looking down from her window to watch John Quillan's horses pass, she saw he had a greatly augmented line; augmented, too, by horses of a different quality and, after them, kept well back as usual, because his stride outdistanced every other, the big dark horse she had noticed before and the little English rider she knew was Ted Mullins.

"NERVOUS?" asked John, but Ted gave one of his rare smiles. "Not with him."

Ted had ridden in the first two Cold Weather Meetings, but not on Dark Invader. His first ride on the opening Saturday was Mr. Leventine's Pandora—one of the mares who had come out on the same ship as Dark Invader—while Ching rode her companion, Pernambuco. Pandora had won. On the second Saturday he and Ching changed mounts. Pandora had won again, while Ted rode Pernambuco into second place. The same day, to Lady Mehta's joy,

71

he had brought Flashlight up to win the mile-long Jaisalmir Plate. But the crux hadn't come yet. The crux was the first appearance of Dark Invader.

It was a Class IV race, with a huge field. "They have had to make two divisions," John told Ted. Dark Invader was in Division I with top weight, "but compared to the others, you're on a flying machine. All the same," John added, "it's often the stone-cold certainty that comes unstuck."

"He won't," said Ted. Ted had weighed out, carried his saddle and number cloths through the door and handed them to John. He himself was dapper, his breeches made as a special order by Barkat Ali in Park Street, his boots sent out from Maxwell's in London, copied from a pair he had worn in the old days. Mr. Leventine's colours were pink, with emerald hoops, and green cap, and were so bright they made Ted blink. "Pink for happiness, green for hope," Mr. Leventine had explained.

"Hullo, Rosebud!" jeered the other jockeys, but as the horses came into the paddock, there was no mistaking that Dark Invader was the best-looking animal on the course; murmurs of admiration followed him as he was led round by Sadiq, and soon he had moved up to odds-on favourite.

As Ted swung into the saddle, he met Mr. Leventine's gaze, full of a confidence and belief that had not been given Ted since Ella died, but John Quillan still had his doubts. As the horses moved out, he gave Ted his anxious final orders. "Keep clear. If they crowd you, go for the outside rail. Remember you have twenty lengths in hand. Use them."

ONLY ONCE did Ted steal a look under his elbow at the tailing field behind him. Already two lengths clear, he took the inner rail and Dark Invader kept that distance, finishing, hard held, in a time that—sure as eggs is eggs, thought Ted—would take him to Class III.

"Exactly as we wished him to do," Mr. Leventine said beaming, and even John was pleased.

It was a pattern set for the six races that followed, races that for

72

Dark Invader were little more than training gallops. Each time he got away to a good start and was never headed, which brought him from Class III to Class II. "As we expected," said Mr. Leventine, rubbing his hands.

MR. LEVENTINE did not live in one of Calcutta's ostentatious mansions. He detested waste and what would one man do with twenty rooms? One day he might marry, but now he had no time. Meanwhile he was perfectly content with a modern flat on Park Street.

Now, in his library, he moved all his racing cups to a side table and kept his mantelpiece only for Dark Invader's; already there were three, only of Indian silver it was true, but there was also a gilt quaich, or Scots drinking cup, a two-handled goblet of sterling silver and, most handsome of all, a rose bowl.

"You *are* coming up," said Bunny, drinking Mr. Leventine's excellent whisky. "You must keep a place for the gold one." Mr. Leventine, superstitious to his backbone, almost said Hush, but, "He's just doing what we expected," was all he said.

What no one had expected was Dark Invader's impact on the crowd. The whole of racing Calcutta seemed to have taken him to their hearts. It was partly his size and good looks, partly the way in which, once he had won, he let his ears flop as if to say, "That's that," tucked in his chin modestly as if to say, "It's nothing at all," and would not wait to nuzzle Mr. Leventine's pockets. He and Ted had swiftly become a legend, and stories were told of how Darkie would race for no one else; of his extraordinary intelligence; of his laziness—"He doesn't bother to try at gallops. Why should he? He knows he can when it's the real thing;" of his greediness and how the salty taste of Bengal straw had once induced him to eat his bedding and how he would have died of colic if Captain Mack had not dramatically saved him—this happened to be true and after that Dark Invader was bedded on tanbark; of his exceptional docility and good nature, as long as he was not ridden by anyone else but Ted.

Ted had difficulty, not only on race days but in the early

mornings, in getting the Invader through the admirers who wanted
to see and pat him. On race days he had to ask for a police escort and
when Dark Invader raced, there came, from the Public Enclosure
and the frenzied crowds that lined the rails, a chant for Darkie.
"Darkee! Darkee!" they would call as his great striding form showed
clear of the field along the backstretch and then, as he came
storming past the stands, they would break into a quick-fire rhythm.
"Dark Invader, Dark Invader, Dark Invader."

Mr. Leventine would be out on the course to lead him in, Ted, in
his brilliant silks, perched firmly on top, lifting his whip in shy
salute. The crowd would grow wild.

"Your horse seems to have become something of a personality,"
said Sir Humphrey; he had sought Mr. Leventine out at the club.
"You know he's now eligible for the Viceroy's Cup?"

"I know." Mr. Leventine had a new dignity.

Even John Quillan betrayed a fresh buoyancy. "I believe, Sandy,"
he said to Captain Mack at Scattergold Hall, "that the time is coming
when you may have to eat your hat."

CHAPTER V

On the eve of December 21, which, as the sisters knew, was Saint
Thomas's Day, a full moon looked down over Calcutta. It was well
after midnight and the morning mist was forming on the river,
spreading softly over the banks and the wide spaces of the Maidan.

In the bedroom of his apartment in Park Street, Mr. Leventine
lay in his large mahogany bed over which his mosquito net hung
from a vast frame. Everything in the apartment was vast. The room
was lined with massive Victorian wardrobes, the wardrobes were
full of well-pressed suits; his bathroom held a huge porcelain
bathtub set in mahogany and the lavatory pan, designed for a race of
giants, had a pattern of pink tulips and green leaves. Yet in all this
ample splendour, Mr. Leventine could not sleep. It was six days
before the running of the Viceroy's Cup.

The evening before, after Bunny had gone, Mr. Leventine, glass in hand, had stood looking at the mantelpiece. Bunny's friendliness had filled him with such cheer that suddenly he had been moved to rearrange the cups—goblets to the left, the quaich and rose bowl on the right, in the middle an empty space and, "It will be gold," Mr. Leventine had whispered.

Seldom had he felt as confident, as full of cheer; that night he had slept like a child, but tonight he was uneasy. Why? asked Mr. Leventine.

THE MOON SHONE down on the Quillan stables, lighting the blanketed forms of the syces asleep on their charpoys. The coming champion or hope of India was not asleep; Dark Invader was on his knees on his tanbark bedding, straining with a total loss of dignity to reach an odd straw that had escaped his neighbour's stall, elongating his lips till he looked like his distant South American relative, the tapir. Finally, resigned to failure, he sighed deeply, rose to his feet and slept.

The bedrooms of Scattergold Hall were empty. December 20 was Dahlia's father's birthday and, by Quillan tradition, John drove her, the children, the latest baby and Gog and Magog to Burdwan, where Mr. McGinty worked on the railway.

John's car was an old four-seater Chrysler. Its wooden-spoked wheels needed water poured on them in hot weather; its broad back seat held children, dogs, luggage, parcels, and it ran accompanied by a steady thump from the engine like an elderly tramp steamer. The children loved it and all the year Dahlia, as John knew, looked forward to this day.

Burdwan was one of the biggest junctions, and its Eurasian Club was crowded. There Dahlia saw many of her people as well as her father and mother—uncles and aunts, troops and troops of cousins and friends—because in the evening they always went to the club, where Dahlia could show off her John and their children. John joked, laughed, danced, even sang, while the *bandars* submitted to Dahlia's idea of lacy frilled dresses and sashes, white shorts and shirts and bow ties, "like little ladies and gentlemen."

With Eurasian voices still shrilling in his ears, John slept fitfully in his parents-in-law's big bed. Touchingly, they always insisted on moving out of it for John and Dahlia. She lay against him, blissfully asleep, and softly against her lay their newest baby. Prolific as her name-flower, Dahlia had just produced their eighth child. "Another little calamity," Babu Ram Sen, John's office clerk, had said, which meant another daughter and, in Ram Sen's thinking, another dowry to be found.

But John was not thinking of dowries. He was worried about the present. He should not really have left the stables this year, so much was at stake. But Ted was there. John had given careful orders; "and I shall be back soon after nine," he had told Ted. "The baby wakes us at dawn."

"Never, never should the baby be allowed to sleep in its mother's bed," said the books. But Dahlia never read books, and all her babies slept with her, "which is why they don't give any trouble," said Dahlia.

"The trouble comes later on," said John wryly, but now, carefully, he reached across Dahlia and with a deftness that no one would have believed of that fastidious and cynical young cavalry officer, tucked in the sleeping baby with its shawl. The baby blew a bubble and John thought, Ted's there. It must be all right, and he, too, went to sleep.

TED WAS NOT ASLEEP. He was sitting on his small veranda, and though he had no coat, he did not feel the cold nor the mosquitoes biting. He was past feeling anything.

It had been a bad day which was odd because the bad day should have been yesterday, the anniversary of his and Ella's wedding. Actually, he had been edgy yesterday as well. In the midst of all the excitement he had taken out their wedding photograph from his small tin trunk and put the silver-framed picture on the desk near his bed, a vase of sweet peas in front of it. The *bandar-log* had been much interested. "But why is she wearing a lace curtain on her head?" asked one of the boys innocently. The oldest girl had looked more closely, and "you told us Mrs. Ella was pretty," she said accusingly.

"She was, to me."

"Well, I think she's ugly!"

Ted had snatched the photograph away and given the little girl a slap. It was the first time he had slapped a child and it was too hard. She burst into tears, tears hurt and surprised and with one accord the *bandars* had deserted Ted. They had not been near him since and they had gone to Burdwan without saying goodbye.

To be truthful, yesterday, apart from the ritual of the photograph and flowers, Ted had not thought much about Ella until the evening. Then a strange restlessness had driven him to walk in the garden. About eleven o'clock the old Chrysler turned in at the gates, and he saw it was Mr. Quillan—and Mrs. Quillan, which was uncommon. He could not remember Mrs. Quillan going out at night, but Bunny had given a pre-Christmas dinner and insisted that Dahlia should come. She had been enchanted; John had let her buy a new dress and evening cloak at a shop on Park Street.

When John had put the car away, he and Dahlia had walked back through the garden to the house. They passed close by Ted, who had stepped behind a screen of bougainvillea; beside him was another plant that drenched the air with such sweetness he felt giddy. Dahlia paused. "What is that perfume?" "Queen of the Night," said John, "*rat ki rani*," and Dahlia had echoed, "Queen of the Night."

Ted could see her clearly: her bare arms and neck, the light where the moon caught her hair. Dahlia was always especially radiant after the birth of a child. The new dress, a confection of taffeta and lace in her favourite apricot, had a silken rustle as she moved. The cloak had slipped down as she turned to John. The two of them clung close, then John bent to kiss her. Ted could not bear to watch and had hastily gone inside.

Next afternoon the Quillan family left for Burdwan.

"I hate to go," John told Ted, "but I know you will take charge. Captain Mack will come and support you for the evening parade, His Highness, too,"—if Bunny remembers, thought John—"and you will have Ching and the jemadar. Here are the morning orders." He went through the list with Ted: which riding boy was to ride what horse, matched with whom, and for how long; even what Ted was to do with Dark Invader. "And Ted, will you do the stable night round, too?"

The night round had been the last straw. It meant Ted had to sit up late and the hours seemed endless. The servants had gone to their quarters and Scattergold Hall, usually overflowing with life, was silent, empty. At last Ted had taken John's torch and faithfully gone from one stall to the next, all around the square, careful not to disturb the sleeping grooms and horses.

When he came to Dark Invader, the Invader was too lazy even to raise his head or give his customary whinny and, with Sadiq's charpoy across the stall, Ted could not pat and fondle him. "Real old canoodler he is," Ted had often said. Now "used to be, is nearer the mark," Ted said bitterly, and jealousy came back and, added to it, hurt. Ted passed on to the next horse, but the hurt went on, and when he went back to his room, he sat at his table, his head in his hands.

Somewhere a drum was being beaten and voices were chanting in a nasal whine, utterly alien. There was a smell of dust and of pungent cooking, of hookah smoke and a waft of unbearable sweetness from that flower, queen of the night. He could hear Dahlia's soft voice saying its name after John—Dahlia's voice, not Ella's—and such desolation and longing fell on Ted that he shuddered. It was then that he remembered Mr. Leventine's whisky.

Mr. Leventine had come when the parade was over and the owners and their friends had gone. He had been put out not to find John there, because as Father Christmas, Mr. Leventine had brought wonderful presents. The Minerva was loaded.

Sadiq was presented with a gold watch, Ali with one in silver. There were toys for the children, large boxes of chocolates for everyone; for Dahlia a bouquet of orchids and a case of champagne, for John a case of whisky.

Ted helped Mr. Leventine, the chauffeur and the bearer to arrange the gifts in the sitting room, the toys and chocolate boxes piled around the cases, Dahlia's orchids on top, set off by an

78

enormous card printed in gold with a photograph of Dark Invader. Ted had one, too, and with it an English racing saddle. Nothing could have pleased Ted more. Every jockey of prestige had his own saddle, but Ted's was one John had bought for him in Dhurrumtollah Street. This one was by a leading English maker. "As if you hadn't done enough for me, sir! Too generous you are by half!" and Mr. Leventine was filled with an extraordinary glow— no one had called him generous before. "It gives me great pleasure," Mr. Leventine told Ted and, to his astonishment, found that it was true.

THE GLOW HAD FADED; in fact, as he lay sleepless, Mr. Leventine was remembering all the money he had spent needlessly and chided himself for it. "Casimir Alaric Bruce," he said severely, "you are becoming soft and silly. Go back to being yourself."

Still he tossed and turned, and then a chill wind seemed to come into his bedroom. "A warning?" asked Mr. Leventine.

Suddenly he got out of bed, and in his black satin pyjamas with a monogram, CABL, embroidered in orange on the pocket, padded into the library and hastily put Dark Invader's trophies back in their original order on the mantelpiece.

A CASE of whisky.

Ted had not touched a drop since the day Traherne put him on the Invader. But now Ted had lost Dark Invader. He forgot their new partnership, even more intimate than the companionship of horse and lad—a companionship of work. He only remembered that his Invader had not whinnied to him, that Sadiq was between them. Should be glad Mr. Saddick looks after him so well, he told himself. It did not stop the jealousy, nor the ache of loneliness, and suddenly Ted was angry. Mr. Quillan shouldn't have put all this responsibility on him. He was too old for the crowds shouting, "Darkie! Darkie!" while Mr. Quillan poured instructions into his ear. Mr. Leventine was suddenly too overwhelming, expected too much. Sadiq was a usurper and everyone had gone off leaving him, Ted, in this empty house and that child had been rude about Ella—Ella who now seemed further away than ever—and all the time the drum went on and on.

"That miserable drum!" Ted shouted, but no one heard him. His own voice echoed back off the garden wall. "Drum . . . drum."

Ted got up, went into the sitting room, opened John's case, carefully removing the orchids, and took out a bottle of whisky. "Just for a nip . . . just one. Mr. Quillan wouldn't grudge me that."

SOME TIME LATER a thought struck Ted. Haven't done the stable night round. Mus' do that. Promised. He stumbled up and again took the torch, but his hands were numb from sitting on the chilly veranda and he shook with cold. "Better have another drink to warm me," but the bottle was empty. Ted cursed and almost tumbled down the steps. The moonlight was brilliant on the lawn and track, but the shadows were dark, and trying to avoid them, Ted seemed to be going zigzag. Twice he dropped the torch, swore loudly, and heads began to lift on the charpoys.

When he came to Dark Invader, his anger overcame him and he shook Sadiq. "Out of my way, you heathen. Lemme see my hoss." Clumsily he shook the top rail of the stall, and Sadiq, barefoot, his brown-yellow eyes blurred with sleep, sprang to life. "Sahib! Ted sahib! No!" Dark Invader had woken up and was watching, puzzled. "Night round been done . . . bed now, sahib. You ride tomorrow. Please, Ted sahib."

"Oh, mind your own bloody business!" Ted shook off Sadiq and turned back, but not to his room—to the house, where he took out another bottle. He could not open it and, back on his veranda, smashed the neck against a post; nor could he pour the whisky into his glass, but he managed to put the bottle on the table, where it stood dripping while he fell into his chair. The drum was beating in his head now; the flower scent was overpowering. Ted was sick, then collapsed across the table.

It was Sadiq, touching Ted as if with a pair of tongs, the end of his turban wound over his mouth and nose to keep out the stench of vomit and, to a Muslim, the abominable smell of alcohol, who put Ted to bed.

80

THREE O'CLOCK. Half past three. Four o'clock. Sisters Ursule and Jane, Solomon, Gulab and the cart had not come in. Mother Morag had been up since midnight; twice she had sent the gate-keeper, Dil Bahadur, down the road to look for them. No sign, and for the last hour she had been pacing anxiously. Sisters Barbara and Emmanuel, whose turn it was to unload, puzzled at not being called, had risen and were with her. Presently Sister Ignatius, who seemed to know by instinct when anything was wrong, appeared too.

"What can have happened? An accident?"

"The police would have come."

"Solomon?"

"It can't be Solomon," said Sister Barbara. "He's so reliable."

"No one can be reliable for ever."

At last they heard the sound of wheels and the babble of a crowd. When she hurried to the courtyard, Mother Morag had need of all her calm. Both sisters, Jane and Ursule, were walking, their faces pallid with sweat, cloaks and habits bedraggled. With them was a band of coolies, men and a dozen or more small boys, all of them helping to hold up the shafts of the cart, and the shafts were holding up Solomon, whom Gulab held by the bridle, trying to support his head. Carefully the men eased the cart into the courtyard, unbuckled the harness and lowered the shafts.

"Mother, he fell past Dhurrumtollah," Sister Jane gasped. "We thought he had just slipped. The police helped to get him up and Gulab walked beside him. Then again, outside Firpo's, when we came out with the canisters, it seemed he couldn't move. We thought we shouldn't try to collect any more." Sister Jane was crying now. "Oh, Mother!"

Solomon was standing curiously rigid, his tail at an extraordinarily high angle, his lips drawn back showing flecks of froth between the yellowed teeth. "Aie! Aie!" the pitying voices sounded as the men pressed around. When Mother Morag made her way through, she saw with horror that the old horse was twitching with spasms, sweating, and that he could not bend his neck as Gulab tried to unbuckle the bridle.

To the sisters' astonishment she went up to the old horse and tapped him sharply on the forehead. "Mother! To punish him *now!*" But Mother Morag saw what she expected, a flash across the eyeball. She tapped again; it came again. "Unmistakable," she said. "Sister Barbara, ring Captain Mack and tell him to come at once."

"YES. TETANUS," said Captain Mack. "Poor old boy. I had thought it would be old age."

The sight of tetanus is not pretty and Mother Morag sent the, by now, thoroughly roused Community inside. "Sisters Jane and Ursule must have a bath and some good strong tea. Sister Emmanuel, will you see to that? Plenty of sugar. For Gulab, too."

"And I think you should go in yourself, Reverend Mother," said Captain Mack.

"I'll stay." Mother Morag had one hand on Solomon's neck.

"Stand away from him."

There was a short sharp noise in the courtyard, a ring of iron on stone and the sound of something soft and heavy falling. Gulab burst into loud sobs. Dil Bahadur led him away through the now silent coolies and boys. "Sister will bring him some tea," Mother Morag told Dil Bahadur.

It was she who helped Captain Mack cover the still heap with a tarpaulin the captain fetched from his car. "I'll arrange the rest," he told her.

"Thank you." She knew that with him she had no need to say more, and as his car drove away, she called the sisters. "I think it would be good if we all helped to unload the cart."

"*Unload! After this?*" The sisters were shocked.

"Of course. We're not going to let Solomon's last effort go to waste, but Sister Ursule and Sister Jane must go to bed."

"Please, no, Mother. We couldn't sleep just yet."

The coolies who had lingered for the drama came to help, and with so many people the work was quickly done. It was then that Sister Mary Fanny said timidly, "Would it be very silly, Mother, if we went into the chapel and said a prayer?"

82

"For Solomon." Mother Morag smiled down at the sister. "I don't think it would be at all silly. Come—and, child, fetch Gulab and Dil Bahadur."

"Hindus in our chapel!" Sister Ignatius was of the old narrow school.

"I think it would help Gulab," said Mother Morag, and indeed, Sister Mary Fanny found the old man sobbing in Solomon's stall. Dil Bahadur could not come because the crowd had not dispersed, but, "They pray, too," he said.

"Hindu prayers!" sniffed Sister Ignatius.

"Prayers," Mother Morag corrected her. "Sister, those men who are so poor would not take an anna for what they did for us and Solomon tonight—and don't you think we shall need all the prayers we can get?"

It was while they were in the chapel that they heard a heavy cart backing into the courtyard, then the grinding of a winch and the sound of wheels departing.

There was a fresh burst of weeping. Mother Morag gave the knock to dismiss the sisters. "Bed everyone," she said, "and this morning, meditation will be after Mass, so you will have half an hour's extra sleep."

AS THERE WAS now no more to be seen in the courtyard, the crowd dispersed. Dil Bahadur took Gulab into his gatehouse and shut the door. The sisters had left the chapel, but Mother Morag stayed on.

In all her sadness and shock, as Superior she had to ask herself the question, How, *how* are we going to replace Solomon? The convent's small savings had disappeared in the high price of rice. There was nothing to spare. "I shall have to apply to the General Fund," murmured Mother Morag. "But it has so many calls on it." Each house tried to live by donations and its own collecting, but how could they collect without Solomon? They could hire a tikka gharry, but that would be expensive and the poor half-starved animals who drew them could never stand up to the night round. "We need a strong well-trained horse with good blood in him, but that would cost perhaps several hundred rupees." Mother Morag shut her eyes.

She felt a rustle beside her. It was Sister Ursule. "Mother, please allow me. I could not sleep." Then Sister Ignatius came, Sister Mary Fanny stole in, and Sisters Emmanuel, Barbara, Jane, Claudine—the whole Community. As if moved by a single thought, they began a novena, the special prayer of the Church for a special intention—and, "God doesn't think like men and when one belongs to Him, one must not worry." Mother Morag was ashamed of herself.

The sisters were not the only ones who prayed. When at dawn Mother Morag came out into the courtyard, she saw that the dark stain where Solomon had lain was whitewashed and there were marigolds strewn over it. It had become a holy place. As she watched, a woman in the poorest of saris came, bringing more flowers and an offering of a small saucer of rice.

"Mother, that surely can't be right—in a convent?"

"I don't know if it's right, but I do know it is love and respect," and Mother Morag told Dil Bahadur to keep the gates open.

THE *BANDAR-LOG* were the first to visit Ted. They had decided to forgive him. When the old Chrysler arrived at Scattergold Hall, they tumbled out pell-mell and John drove away. The stables were empty of horses so, thinking Ted was with them on the racecourse, the children went in to breakfast, but like true *bandars* they were the first to pick up an alarm—in this case the gossip of the stables and kitchens—and soon they were at the annex.

On the veranda table was the early-morning tea tray, put down by an appalled Ahmed; beside it was the broken-necked bottle of whisky, another empty bottle on the ground. They went in to look at Ted, stealing silently up to his bed, half-fascinated, half-repelled. He was lying on his back snoring; his clothes were on the floor where Sadiq had thrown them. They tried to open Ted's eyes, but he only rolled his head and grunted, and a small *bandar* began to cry. Back on the veranda, they tasted the spilled whisky, spat it out and fled in a troop to tell Dahlia.

"Ted! My God, what have you been doing?" Dahlia shook him, trying to make him sit up, but he sank back as if he were made of rag. "Ted! John will be verree angry. Wake up, Ted. Please to wake." There was no response.

She gathered up the clothes. "Take these to the dhobi, the washerman, at once." Ahmed took them at arm's length. Hastily Dahlia searched drawers and put out clean garments. "My God, what will John say?" but John did not come back with the horses, nor did the jemadar or Sadiq, only Ching, and when Dahlia ran out to him, Ching, unlike his courteous self, turned away and did not answer. A strange quiet, too, lay over the stables, the men silently going about the morning's chores.

John did not come in for breakfast and Dahlia grew more worried. This could be nothing to do with Ted, and even when she heard the car, John did not come in. He went straight to the annex.

Ted was awake now, sitting on the edge of his bed, trying to get the walls of his room in focus. In his head the drum was beating louder than ever, and his mouth felt foul and dry. He heard John's steps and gave a small whimper.

"So!"

John was in the doorway, his face dark with rage. "So!" The word cut through the air, and Ted was suddenly aware of how he must look in one of the old-fashioned nightshirts Ella had made him long ago. He was aware, too, of sunlight. Then, suddenly more aware, he asked, "Sir, wha's the time?"

"Well after ten o'clock."

"Ten!" Ted shot upright. "Then, sir—I'm too late."

"Too late!" And John laughed, not a pleasant laugh. "You may like to know that in your absence down at the racecourse Ching changed jockeys with a character you have already met, Streaky Bacon."

"Streaky! *Streaky*—here in Calcutta!"

"In Calcutta. English jockeys do come out unfortunately." John's voice was biting. "The horse threw him and bolted, God knows where. Dark Invader has disappeared. Congratulations."

John left. If there had been a door, he would have slammed it.

"NOBODY KNOWS," Mother Morag said often, "who will be asked to do what next!" The tangled sentence was true, but she should have added, "Of course, they must have resource and courage."

At half past seven that morning a Mr. James Dunn paid his bill at the boardinghouse in Lower Circular Road where he always stayed on his visits to Calcutta. A plump middle-aged Scotsman, he was an engineer at a jute mill in Narayanganj, two hundred miles from Calcutta. So that he could travel home by river, a slow meandering that he loved, he was now on his way to where a paddle steamer waited at Chand Pal Ghat on the Strand. He would catch a taxi at the bottom of the road where it met the racecourse.

Behind James Dunn came his bearer, Sohan Lall, carrying his topee and coat, and behind Sohan Lall two coolies carried James's luggage. James himself carried Calcutta's two daily newspapers, the *Statesman* and the *Englishman*.

It was a fresh sweet morning; sunlight had begun to filter through the mist that still lay on the racecourse and the Maidan. It reminded James faintly of his native Arbroath. He began to whistle "Ye Banks and Braes o' Bonny Doon."

There were no taxis at the bottom of the road, so the little retinue crossed to the turf that edges the racecourse and turned right towards Calcutta's wide busy street, Chowringhee. It was then that they heard the sound of galloping hooves—hooves not on the racecourse but on the hard ground on which they stood. The sound came steadily nearer. Then, out of the mist, mane and tail flying, thundered a great dark horse.

Even to James Dunn's ignorant eye it was palpably a racehorse, a runaway that had thrown its rider—stirrups and reins were flapping—and jumped over the rails.

"God almighty! It's heading towards Chowringhee! The traffic! Trams!" James Dunn cried.

Already the rhythmic *ta-ta-tump* was getting louder. The horse was bearing down on them where they stood near an intersection. The coolies dropped the luggage and fled. "Aie!" cried Sohan Lall and leaped aside, and, "Ay," said James, the same sound but a different meaning, and he stepped forward, arms extended.

A thoroughbred horse travelling true and determined at some fifteen miles an hour is an awkward thing to tackle, even for an expert, and ninety-nine men out of a hundred would have jumped for safety; but James stood his ground, a folded newspaper in each hand.

"Whoa!" he bellowed. "Whoa!"

There was the sound of hooves slipping on the tarmac. For a moment James thought the horse would fall down, but it planted its feet and slid to a stop. He had a view at close quarters of large ears, wide nostrils and lustrous eyes. "Stand!" commanded James, but before he could catch the reins, the horse swerved and went past him to the stretch of turf, stopped, looked with its ears pricked forward, then, instead of dashing on to the perils of Chowringhee, turned and crossed the road. For once there were no cars, only a tikka gharry and a rickshaw, which the horse avoided. Then it began to trot purposefully up Lower Circular Road. After a few hundred yards it stopped suddenly, turned neatly and cantered in through an open gateway. James, running after it, heard the clatter of its hoofs on cobbles.

"Somebody must have guided it," Sister Mary Fanny said. "Must have been an angel," but James Dunn, in a way, was the angel. When he reached the gateway, there was nothing but the smell of horse sweat and a white scratch on the pavement. There was a gatehouse but no gateman; peering in, James could see an old-fashioned cobbled courtyard and an outbuilding containing a stall and a conical pile of straw. The horse had seemed to know exactly where it was going; indeed, he could hear the sound of munching. Food must have been made ready.

There was a bellpull beside the gateway. James Dunn did not notice the little statue set in the niche below, nor the cross above it; he was debating whether to pull the bell or not. He looked at his watch. There was the steamer to catch, and if he pulled the bell, he must wait until somebody came and there must be explanations. The horse was safe—he could still hear the munching—and so, still breathing a little hard, he walked back to join Sohan Lall and his luggage by the road.

"*Shabash!*" said Sohan Lall, which means bravo! "But, sahib," he added, "you might have been killed."

"Rot!" But as James Dunn hailed his taxi, he was not whistling, "Ye Banks and Braes," but "Cock o' the North."

FATHER JOSEPH, in his purple vestments, had just turned from the altar to give the sisters his blessing and said the final words, "*Ite Missa Est*"—the Mass is ended—and the sisters had risen to give the answer, "*Deo Gratias*"—God be thanked—when they heard a loud slither at the gates.

Father Joseph had said a special prayer not, disappointingly, for the repose of Solomon, but that the sisters would be helped in the predicament his death had left. Now, with his small acolyte walking in front of him, Father Joseph started to leave; then he stopped, the boy, too, while a controlled ripple ran along the rows of nuns as through the chapel windows came the unmistakable sound of horse's hooves on stone. The sound stopped. The priest left and the disciplined sisters knelt for the Thanksgiving, but Mother Morag quickly gave the knock, rose and led them out into the courtyard. They gasped.

In Solomon's stall was a horse. As it heard them it turned around as if to greet them, and they saw its size and splendour. The most beautiful horse they had ever seen.

It was only for a moment—Solomon's feed was not yet quite demolished—and then the only sound in the courtyard was a steady munching as the sisters stood silent in the early sunlight. Though some had tears running down their cheeks, their faces were illumined. At last Sister Mary Fanny whispered, "It's a miracle. It *is* a miracle, Mother, isn't it?"

"Not yet." The question jolted Mother Morag into action, and her voice rang clear and firm. "Wake Dil Bahadur. Tell him to close the gates and keep them closed."

IN JOHN QUILLAN'S office at the stables, Ching faced him and Mr. Leventine across the table. John had not asked the jockey to sit down. Ching had seen his employer angry but never like this; he was dark with fury and as hard as if he were made of stone. As for Mr. Leventine, he looked like a bewildered baby. "But it can't be," he kept saying. "A horse can't *vanish*."

Silence hung over the stables; the men, too, seemed stunned. Only the horses were normal, each in its stall, except, of course, Dark Invader.

"Tell Mr. Leventine exactly what happened," said John.

Ching stood stiffly, trying not to betray his dismay and shame. It is part of Chinese manners to appear cheerful in disaster. "I extremely sorry, sir," he began. "I make so unhappy mistake"—he tried to laugh—"but I think not all my fault."

"Of course it was your fault." John's temper snapped, and Ching's small black eyes looked this way and that, trying to escape. "Look at us, man," thundered John.

Ching did, and there was such distress behind the façade that John had to be gentle. "Try and tell us. Begin at the beginning."

"When Mr. Ted—Mr. Mullins—didn't . . ."

"Didn't appear, and obviously couldn't." John helped because Ching's voice had faded away from embarrassment. "Yes?"

"Jemadar sahib and I, we not know what to do, except horses must go out." John nodded approval. "Then Sadiq tell us your list of orders, sir, orders for morning, was on table by Mr. Ted's bed. Sadiq, he no want to fetch them, so—"

"Who fetched them?"

"I, Ching." And Ching shut his eyes as if to shut out the memory of Ted's room. "Jemadar sahib not read English, so I read. And we decide I take Mr. Ted's place, first riding boy take mine, et cetera, et cetera." Ching was proud of that word. "Jemadar do timing. Was that right, sir?"

"*That* was right," said John.

"I take Dark Invader. I do what you said: two circuits, like Mr. Ted. Then . . ." and Ching gulped.

"Then?"

"When we come back, there was English jockeys—five, six, standing watching horses. When Darkie come in, they all look at him. Me, I feel proud it is I, Ching, am riding him, and one of them say, 'Look. That the horse we got to beat for Viceroy Cup. Never headed this season.' I *very* proud," said Ching. "I go back to jemadar and tell him.

"Then two jockeys come over, and I knew one, sir. Him the famous Tom Bacon. I seen his photo. Now he going round pretending he no had a ride. 'Want any work ridden?' he say. 'No?' He laugh. 'Very well, I push on,' he say, and I"—Ching swallowed—"I not understand he pretending . . . and he come up to me. I pleased. English jockeys not speak much to us. He ask, 'You in charge here?'

"I say, 'This morning, yes.' Then Mr. Bacon look at Darkie and he say, 'Fine horse,' and the other man—I think he not like Mr. Bacon very much—he say, 'Come off it, Streaky. It's Dark Invader. You've ridden him.'

"Mr. Bacon he say, 'Yes, I remember. Come to think of it, I ride him his first race. Lingfield it was. He won *as* expected.'

" 'You rode him again.'

" 'Did I?' And Mr. Bacon say, 'I don't remember.'

" 'You do! Doncaster.' Other jockey, he go on. 'Sort of rode him—by all account he dumped you and ran home,' and Mr. Bacon, 'Really? I forgotten,' and, 'You must allow for a jerk or two'—I think he mean a fall," said Ching—" 'in two-year-old race.' And the other jockey, Mr. Willie, he say, 'Didn't look like a youngster's job. I behind you all the way. It look as if that horse hate your guts.'

"Then Mr. Bacon he get angry." Ching's voice grew dramatic. "He say, 'I no having that sort of talk. Never been a horse that didn't take to me.' Then . . ."

"Then?" asked John.

"He laugh up at me, so nice like and say, 'Want any work ridden?' I no understand he pretending, so I say . . " Ching choked. "I say, 'Would be an honour, sir.' He say, 'Very well, I just take him round for you,' so I dismount, sir. He say, 'Why you ride so long? That old-fashioned.' " Ching gave a reproachful look at John. "What can I say but 'Is orders.' He laugh, say, 'Like ruddy mounted policeman,' and he shorten leathers, five holes. Then he take reins and I . . . I put him up. Mr. Willie say, 'Streaky, look out,' but Mr. Bacon no

90

listening. He tell me, 'Thank you, chum.' " Ching gave another nervous laugh.

"Go on." John was remorseless.

"I think Darkie he taken by surprise. Because Sadiq and me, we holding him, he trust." Ching swallowed.

"Go on."

"Mr. Willie shout again, 'Look out!' because soon as the Streaky was on saddle, Darkie, he put back his ears. His eyes was like I never see them. Streaky gather up the reins and Darkie, he go *puggle*—mad . . ." Ching shuddered. "Other English jockeys they was watching, laughing like it was a joke, but Darkie almost standing on his head, then rearing. They laugh and shout, 'Where your magic, Streaky? *That* horse don't take to you!' and Mr. Bacon no like, and as Darkie come up again he so angry he give Darkie hard cut with his whip cross quarters and down below. Wicked cut—and Darkie made a neigh, high, like I never heard. He threw the Streaky backward. Then just bolt. Quick I take Flashlight from the syce and go after; jemadar send riding boy other way. I see nothing—only traffic roaring down Chowringhee. I look, I ask . . . at last come back. Streaky Bacon, I think he stunned. They take him back to stands. I think he not forgive."

"Nor will we," said John.

CHAPTER VI

"MOTHER, are we going to try Beauty in the cart tonight?" Dark Invader had been rechristened Beauty.

"Don't be simple, child. He's a racehorse," and "a famous one," Mother Morag might have added. "If we put him in the shafts, he would kick the cart to pieces."

"Then . . ." Elation went out of Sister Mary Fanny, "then he's no use to us."

"We'll see." Mother Morag smiled her most enigmatic smile.

Sister Ignatius said much the same as Sister Mary Fanny but in her acid way. "One mustn't criticize the Almighty, I know, but while He was about it, He might have sent us a suitable horse."

"Perhaps He means us to use our wits."

"But, meanwhile, what are we going to do with it?" asked Sister Ignatius.

"If possible, nothing at all for twenty-four hours," said Mother Morag. "That will heighten the tension."

Certain measures had to be taken, though. A track was marked out at the edge of the vegetable garden, and three times a day Beauty was to walk, "round it at least twenty times. If Gulab is too afraid, I will attend to that myself, or Sister Joanna can," said Mother Morag. "She used to hunt."

Gulab was overcome with pride at the monster now in his charge, but terrified, so "I shall help groom," said Mother Morag, a sparkle in her eyes.

Later that morning the Community watched their Superior work with Gulab, brushing the horse's brown coat, combing out the mane and tail with her fingers, sponging eyes and nose clean, and picking out the big feet while Gulab held them up. She even, and skilfully, bandaged the tail, "with our widest crêpe bandage," mourned Sister Anne, the infirmarian.

Three times that day, in her black cloak, Mother Morag led the great horse around the vegetable garden, talking to him. "What do you talk about?" asked the sisters.

"I say my prayers or the psalms. Beauty seems to like it." Walking suited his laziness, just as the piece of bread and salt given as a prize for good conduct at the end suited his greed.

But there were other problems not as easily solved. "He must be properly rugged tonight," said Mother Morag. "Solomon's blankets are not thick enough. Nor are ours." The sisters pondered. "I know," said Mother Morag. "The quilt off the bishop's bed."

The bed was not really the bishop's. A bishop had only stayed with the sisters once, but there was one room kept ready for visitors.

"Mother," Sister Ignatius protested. "That quilt came to us from France. It's handmade patchwork."

"It's warm. If that horse gets a chill . . ."

92

Another problem was food. "If I issue three or four times what we gave poor Solomon . . ." Sister Emmanuel said.

"The horse will die of indigestion." The worry line wiped out Mother Morag's smile.

"We haven't the money for corn or oats or whatever he eats."

"We can't buy them," said Mother Morag. "But we could collect them." The worry line was gone as, "Bunny," she said.

"A MIRACLE!" Bunny was ecstatic. Mother Morag had dressed the story up a little for him. "And you are asking me to take part in a miracle! Thank you, Mother Morag. Thank you."

"You haven't heard what we want you to do yet."

"Anything. Anything."

"To begin with, we want to collect from you."

"But . . ." Bunny was dashed. "I haven't any money."

As he was not yet twenty-one, and as impetuous as he was extravagant, Bunny was under the strict control of a Resident appointed by the government, "my Grey Eminence," as Bunny called him as irreverently as he called the British government P.P. for Paramount Power. "You know how tight they keep me." Only let you live in two palaces, go to London and the Riviera and play polo in India and England with a string of magnificent ponies, thought Mother Morag. "I could lend you an elephant, but that wouldn't help." Mother Morag thought of the elephant lumbering with the sisters and the canisters from restaurant to restaurant and laughed. "I know I am ridiculous," said Bunny. Then his face brightened. "Jewels! I have some from my mother. I could give you those."

"Dear Bunny, not jewels. Horse food."

"Horse food?"

"Yes, the very best, Your Highness." Now and again Mother Morag reminded Bunny of his title. "We don't want this horse to suffer in any way. Solomon did very well on what Sister Emmanuel buys."

"What is that?"

"Mixed horse food, grade three. Barley—sometimes there *are* weevils, split peas and lentils and rice-straw sweepings."

"*Ari bap!*" said Bunny, "and he *lived?*"

"Solomon did, but . . ." Mother Morag leaned across her desk. She was seeing Bunny in her office. "We need what you give your polo ponies and double that amount."

"I'll send you a truck."

"No, no, Your Highness. Could you bring perhaps two sacks in the boot of your car?"

"I see." Bunny's eyes sparkled. "I am sworn to secrecy. I will do it now."

Mother Morag, who had risen, laid an affectionate hand on his shoulder. "Thank you and bless you."

Bunny brought the sacks. Dil Bahadur opened the gates to let him in and quickly closed them again. Mother Morag was in the courtyard to see them stored, and then Bunny saw Dark Invader. "By God!" he said, then blushed. "I beg your pardon, Mother, but I can't wait to see Leventine's face."

"Leventine?"

"He's the owner, Mr. Casimir Alaric Bruce Leventine, and I think John Quillan will murder you for this. What fun!"

"I'm afraid he'll want to, but . . . one thing more." Mother Morag was serious. "Your Highness knows the people think our convent is a place of sanctuary."

"Indeed, yes," said Bunny. "It is a holy place."

"We try never to send anyone in distress away. This horse was terribly distressed. He was lathered. He had been beaten. Would you take a look at this?"

Dark Invader looked anything but distressed, but the weal from Streaky Bacon's whip still showed. Bunny bent down to look at it. "That's a vicious cut. There's blood on the sheath. You must call Captain Mack." He spoke as a horseman.

"I'm afraid so." The regret in Mother Morag's tone made Bunny look up at her. "I think you want me to do something. What do you want me to do?"

"As we can't keep it secret any longer, spread the news. How Beauty, as we call him, was lathered and beaten. How he took sanctuary here. You know how the people follow you."

94

That was true. Bunny had only to appear on the polo ground and the crowd pressed around to try to kiss his boots, his gloves, his polo stick, even his pony.

"I shall indeed spread it," said Bunny. "Far and wide."

CAPTAIN MACK usually drove in through the convent gates to the courtyard, but now, to his surprise, they were closed, and Dil Bahadur took him around to the front door. A sister opened it and asked him to come upstairs, where he found Mother Morag in her office.

"This is unusually formal," he said.

"It's an unusual occasion. Captain Mack, will you look out of the window and tell me if you see what I think I see?"

Captain Mack obediently looked. "Holy mackerel!" he said.

Below him, loose in the yard, an unmistakable big brown horse was holding court—no other word for it. Sister Barbara and two other nuns were standing in a semicircle, and he moved gravely to each in turn, nuzzling hopefully while they gave him bread and salt filched from the refectory. Gulab, who was beginning to overcome his awe, was tickling his flanks with a handful of straw.

"Greedy old devil, always was," said Captain Mack. "Even ate his bedding."

"I hope he doesn't eat Solomon's; but Captain, that is Dark Invader, isn't it?"

The rich brown coat with the dark dapple, the obvious size and strength, the loose, almost lop, ears and the placid, friendly disposition gave only one answer. "It certainly is, but who on earth brought him here?"

"No one on earth. That's what my sisters think. You see, we had no means of replacing Solomon, but we prayed." Mother Morag raised her expressive hands. "In fact, we were in chapel when we heard the sound of his hooves."

"Extraordinary!"

"Not at all. Our prayers are often answered."

"You mean the horse came of its own accord?"

"Seemingly so. He was alone, but saddled and bridled. He must

95

have thrown his rider. I sent Dil Bahadur to look, but there was no one. My sisters think the horse was looking . . ."

"Looking?"

"For sanctuary. Captain Mack, he was lathered, distressed—and marked."

"Couldn't have been." The captain did not mean to be rude, but, "He's one of John Quillan's."

"Would you come and look? I had hoped to wait twenty-four hours, but Bunny said—"

"Bunny! Is he involved in this?"

"Indeed, yes, thank heaven."

Feeling utterly bemused, Captain Mack followed Mother Morag down to the stable. "What do you say to that?" she asked when he had examined the cut.

Captain Mack looked up, his eyes dark with anger. "Someone must have indeed lost his temper and that wouldn't have been Ted Mullins, Darkie's jockey, nor any of the Quillan riding boys. Mysteriouser and mysteriouser."

He sent Dil Bahadur for his bag, gently cleaned the wound and handed Gulab a bottle of lotion. "Should be all right, but he must have exercise."

"He does. Sister Joanna and I do it ourselves." Mother Morag showed him the vegetable-garden track, and Captain Mack's lips twitched as he thought of the nuns walking the great horse around and around. They twitched still more when he saw Gulab rugging the Invader up with the bishop's quilt under Solomon's old green blanket. Solomon's surcingle would not go around the Invader, so the nuns had had to lengthen it with some more of their precious bandages. "Really you deserve to succeed," said Captain Mack.

"Then you think it's all right?"

"I wouldn't interfere with you for the world," said Captain Mack, "but you know Dark Invader is favourite for the Viceroy's Cup?"

"I know. Which is fortunate for us."

"Backed to win lakhs of rupees." A lakh is one hundred thousand.

Mother Morag's face, for a moment, seemed visionary. "Of which a few might come to us, rupees, not lakhs, I mean."

96

"Mother Morag! Wake up. As veterinary surgeon to the Turf Club, I am bound to tell the horse's owner where he is."

"Exactly what I want you to do," said Mother Morag.

Outside, Captain Mack found Dil Bahadur. The little Gurkha gateman was overflowing with pride. "You have seen our horse?" he asked.

"Yes. How did he come here?" Captain Mack was stern. "Straight now."

"God sent him."

"Why?"

"Because we prayed." Dil Bahadur was astounded anyone could doubt it. "The sister sahibs. Father Joseph. Gulab. I went to my Pujari and did a big puja for five rupees, and when I got back the horse was here."

"Holy mackerel!" repeated the captain. "Four aces and the joker!"

The captain's servant cranked the old Ford, and the captain took the wheel. There was a loud report and the car shot backwards as it was prone to do. "Hold up!" roared Captain Mack as if to a stumbling horse. He stamped on the pedals and, as he drove down the road, suddenly began to laugh.

IN THE LATE AFTERNOON Mr. Leventine and John Quillan were in the office again after a fruitless search. Tempers were getting frayed.

"It's a plot," cried Mr. Leventine. "Someone is jealous. One of your people must have been bought." He was, mercifully, interrupted by the arrival of a car, the unmistakable bang and rattle of an old Model T Ford. Captain Mack appeared in the doorway. "Good afternoon, or should I say evening." He looked at Mr. Leventine. "Och! man!" he said. "You do look depressed. Is it possible you have lost a little something?"

Mr. Leventine sat upright in his chair. John lifted his head.

"A valuable little something?"

"You have found him?" Mr. Leventine jumped up.

"Not found. I was called in to him."

"Then he is injured?"

"Had a cut with a whip, but he's quite all right—in fact, in clover."

"Clover? Where is Clover?"

"Captain Mack means he is being well looked after. Stop clowning, Sandy," John said irritably. "Where is he?"

"In the convent of the Sisters of Poverty just down the road."

"The *convent!*" They both stared incredulously at Captain Mack. "In God's name, how did he get there?" asked John.

"In God's name, precisely. That's what the sisters believe," the captain answered, but Mr. Leventine was at the door.

"I will fetch him *immediately*. Johnny, call Sadiq and Ali."

"Wait a minute," said Captain Mack. "By a strange coincidence, last night the sisters lost their only means of transport. The horse that pulled their cart."

"What has that to do with this?"

"Everything. If you knew your psalms, Mr. Leventine"—the captain was enjoying himself—"you would remember an inconvenient little set of verses. '*Every beast is mine, the cattle upon a thousand hills. I know all the fowls of the mountain. The wild beasts of the field are mine. For the world is mine and the fullness thereof*', which, of course, includes Dark Invader. Those verses are favourites of mine," added Captain Mack. "When I get sickened by cruelty and indifference, I find them reassuring."

Mr. Leventine did not. "Poppycock," he said, a word he had learned from Sir Humphrey.

"The nuns don't think it poppycock. They believe it." Captain Mack quoted again. '*Every beast is mine, and He, God, disposes.*' I, unfortunately, had to put the sisters' horse down. They had been praying for another and presto! Dark Invader takes sanctuary with them."

"Sanctuary?"

"Yes, a refuge. A holy place where a fugitive, a runaway, is safe from being taken away. Of course, that *can* be arranged, but there must be conditions."

"I'll give them conditions! John, order the men."

"Look, Cas." For once John used the detested nickname. "This

98

may be a ticklish situation. I know Mother Morag, their Superior. Let me go."

"It's my horse. Do as you're told."

The chauffeur cranked the Minerva, the engine fired, the snake horn blared; children, hens, dogs scattered as the car set off.

Never had the convent front-door bell been pulled so hard. It was followed by a fusillade of knocks, but the portress, in her clean white apron, seemed unflustered. "Yes, sir?" she asked.

"I want to see the . . ." Mr. Leventine suddenly did not know what to call her. "The nun in charge—at once."

"I'm afraid it can't be at once," said Sister Bridget. "Reverend Mother is at Vespers."

"Vespers?" Mr. Leventine made it sound like an affront.

"Our evening prayer. Will you wait in the parlour?" and Mr. Leventine found himself penned, willy-nilly, in a small room, spotless from its plain stone floor to its whitewashed walls and ceiling, and furnished only with a table, wooden chairs, a small bookcase, its legs set in saucers of Jeyes Fluid for protection against white ants, and a crucifix.

Twice Mr. Leventine rang the bell, twice the portress came. "Isn't this—what-d'you-call-it—over yet?"

"Not yet. They are listening to the reading now."

"But . . . this is interminable."

"Half an hour. That is not much."

The second time—"It will not be long. They are singing the Magnificat?"

"The Magnificat?"

"Our Lady's song of praise and thanksgiving." The portress broke into a smile. "That has a special meaning for us today. We have been given a horse."

"Given!" Mr. Leventine did not ring the bell again.

"SO YOU REFUSE to give him back."

"Under present conditions, yes, and I should have to think very carefully before changing my mind." For a moment the hazel eyes looked down. It was difficult for Mother Morag to keep a spice of amusement out of them, but she knew she must look directly and seriously at Mr. Leventine, and she raised them again. "I might even have to consult our Mother General in Bruges."

"Bruges! That's in Belgium! Madam! The horse is due to race in five days."

"What a disappointment for you."

Mr. Leventine seemed to swell. "Madam, I am not accustomed to being disappointed."

"What an exceptional person you must be," said the cool voice.

"I am going straight to the police, to Lall Bazaar."

Mother Morag inclined her head. "Then I will not keep you."

IN THE RAILED red-brick building of the police headquarters in Lall Bazaar, the chief commissioner looked dispassionately at Mr. Leventine. Under the bland considering gaze, Mr. Leventine faltered and his blustering grew quieter, but still, "No action. No response," he cried. "Good God, Mr. Commissioner! My horse has been stolen."

"I think the Sisters of Poverty do not steal. I am sorry," the commissioner said, "but for the moment it is better we do nothing. Police do not, on principle, interfere with religious premises or disputes."

"This is not a dispute. It is a fact . . . a *fact*."

"Disputes," the commissioner went on as if he had not heard. "Hindu, Muslim, Buddhist, Christian—unless there is violence, and I find no violence here. The Sisters of Poverty are the most deserving of all charities. We know because we often send them the destitutes we pick up from the streets and old people who have been living in hovels. I expect you have passed them thousands of times on the other side." Mr. Leventine drew his breath in sharply. Why should he, the injured party, be preached at? First Captain Mack, now this officer, who was going on, "They do this city a great service and ask nothing in return."

"Except my most valuable horse."

"Not for themselves, Mr. Leventine. For you to lose that horse means you forfeit the chance of winning perhaps a great deal of

100

money and prestige. For them the loss of theirs spells hunger, not just for themselves, but for the two hundred or so people in their home and, if I know them, many more. Have you ever been hungry, Mr. Leventine? I don't think so. Of course, you can, if you wish, involve the law, but it will bring you a great deal of odium. Also it will take time."

"Time! The race is in five days! No, it is almost four."

"Then I strongly advise you to settle with the sisters yourself. Good evening, Mr. Leventine."

After Mr. Leventine had gone, more quietly than he came, the commissioner, smiling, pulled a writing pad towards him. "Dear Reverend Mother," he wrote. "I have just seen Mr. Leventine, and this is to tell you I endorse . . ."

MOTHER MORAG did not open the letter until the next morning. By the time it had arrived, the sisters were saying Compline, the last liturgical prayer of the day, after which no outside business was allowed, no letters or even telephone calls, except in an emergency. "This is an emergency," she could imagine Mr. Leventine saying. "Not to us," she would have replied. The telephone had sounded two or three times. There had also been a hammering on the front door, and in spite of her calm, Mother Morag had passed another sleepless night. "So how glad I was to have your note!" she wrote to the commissioner.

Two tikka gharries had had to be hired for the night round. "We dare not let the collecting drop."

"But Mother, the expense!"

"It won't be for long." I hope and pray, she added secretly. Though Mother Morag seemed completely in command, confident and serene, inwardly she was in turmoil, most of all because, "Is what I am doing right?" She would have given worlds to be able to talk to Father Joseph, but he was a timid man; worlds to have consulted her Mother Provincial and Council.

After the canisters had been carried in, the food put away, again she went into the chapel, which was in darkness except for the glow of the tabernacle light. That was steady, and, "I must be steady,

101

too," she told herself. But she was not too tired to pray except for what perhaps is the best prayer of all, to be still, thinking of nothing only, "Lord, Lord help me. Help me to do what is right under the circumstances. Lord."

Then, as dawn broke, she heard a bird singing and went to the window. The garden was still in darkness, but there was light in the sky and she could just see the bird on the convent gable. It was a magpie robin boldly marking its territory before the other birds began to sing, and she knew that the lovely liquid melody was her answer. It was not only prayer, a paean of praise, but defiance; not thanksgiving, but aggression. What I have I hold for my nest, my helpless ones, and, "Thank you," said Mother Morag and knelt down again.

MR. LEVENTINE was beside himself. "That Mother Morag! That nun!" Yet suddenly he seemed to see her again; her dignity, the clear bones of her face, the hazel eyes, her hands. She must have been a beautiful girl, he thought illogically—appreciation does not generally mix with anger—and he was furious.

"If it wasn't for the Viceroy's Cup, I would let them keep the horse. That would teach them a lesson. Let them try putting Darkie between the shafts. If it wasn't for the Cup . . ."

"But there is the Cup," said John.

"I know." Mr. Leventine's voice rose almost to a shriek. "Johnny, you must get me out of this, you must. Each day that horse will be going down."

"I don't think so. Captain Mack . . ."

"From all I hear, those women could never afford to feed him."

"They can't. The food is being given by Bunny Malwa."

"The young maharajah! *That* young reprobate?"

"He is a great friend of Mother Morag's."

"But . . ." Mr. Leventine was getting more and more bewildered. "I thought nuns were saintly people."

"I think you'll find that saints never minded whom they mixed with. It's the rest of us who do that," but John was getting weary. "All right," he said. "I'll try."

102

"A HORSE forced to race against its will"—from the *bandar-log* Mother Morag had heard every detail of Dark Invader's dramatic story—"ridden by a jockey it dreaded. Who knows what pain he once inflicted? Handed over to him again by your man, and when it rebelled, given the cruellest of cuts—ask Captain Mack, or I'll show you myself—bolted blind with fear and pain. . . ."

"Have you finished?" asked John.

Mother Morag smiled, and before he could explain, she went on. "You're quite right. I knew it was a chain of seeming accidents."

"Seeming?"

"Yes, I said 'seeming', but that is the story and it will spread as long as Dark Invader is here."

"Which is to your advantage."

"Of course. Also, we Sisters of Poverty take an extra vow beyond the usual three: the vow of hospitality. We cannot turn anyone in distress away—not even a horse." John could have sworn there was a mischievous glint in her eyes. "And do you know, Mr. Quillan, that yesterday, the twenty-first, happened to be Saint Thomas's Day, when anyone in need has the right to ask alms?"

"Mother Morag!"

"It is true." Now the eyes were candid, innocent.

"We could get an injunction."

"I doubt it. I had a letter from the commissioner of police this morning."

"So you have him in your pocket, too."

She ignored that and went on. "In any case, if you succeeded, I doubt if the crowds would let you get Dark Invader to the racecourse. You know what mobs are, particularly Indian ones. Your stables might be invaded. Mr. Leventine's beautiful car might be stoned. There could be a riot."

"Are you spinning me another tale?"

"This time not. There has already been an encounter between two of your men, the syces who came with Mr. Leventine for Dark Invader, and our gateman."

Dil Bahadur had spoken to Sadiq and Ali first through a grating in the gates. "What do you want?"

"We have come to fetch our horse."

"*Our* horse," contradicted Dil Bahadur.

"Ours!"

Dil Bahadur opened the wicket and came out onto the pavement, closing the door behind him.

They had confronted one another, the two Muslims—Sadiq's upturned moustaches were fierce—and the little Gurkha in a starched drill tunic and medals, which included the Indian Distinguished Service Medal and three chevrons. A pillbox hat in black velvet cut in patterns sat firmly over one ear, and his shaven skull, crisscrossed with the scars and weals of old wounds, gleamed in the evening sun. Dil Bahadur's face, which could be so genial, was wiped clean of all humour. His mouth was a thin line, his eyes like brown stones. "You will not enter. No one will enter. It is the Mother sahib's orders. I, Dil Bahadur, say so. With this kukri"—he held up his wicked, curved, flat-bladed cutlass—"I will cut off your heads if you do not go away." He began to crowd them along the wall. "This is a holy place," he said.

"Which is what saved the situation," said Mother Morag now. "But Muslims and a Gurkha, that's dangerous and you know how inflammable the people are. It only needs a little agitation."

"Which you will provide?"

"We?" The eyebrows lifted. "I am doing my best to prevent it. It's not I who can start or stop it."

"Then who?"

"Mr. Leventine."

"And if he won't move?"

"A little pressure from Bunny . . ."

John had forgotten Bunny and his power. Against Bunny, Mr. Leventine would not have a chance.

Mother Morag bent her head. Her hands were on her desk— beautiful hands, Mr. Leventine had thought, but John noticed how toilworn they were—held together now in the attitude of prayer. What he did not see was that their tips were tightly pressed together. Then she gave a smile that was tender. "Yes, Bunny," she said. "Fortunately His Highness believes in miracles."

104

"So that's what they are beginning to call this!"

"Yes."

"But you?" John was astute.

Mother Morag smiled again. "What most people call miracles are to us perfectly normal. We have a need—in this case, a horse—and by God's providence a horse was sent."

"Then your God doesn't know much about horses."

"His ways are certainly sometimes difficult to understand," she admitted, "He helps us, but we also have to help ourselves. Suppose you bring Mr. Leventine to see me again."

"He is outside, fuming."

"THIS IS BLACKMAIL," said Mr. Leventine.

"Isn't it, rather, nemesis?" But that was another word Mr. Leventine did not know. "For thirty-five years," said Mother Morag, "first as a sister, then as Superior, I have helped to organize the collecting by which our old people live—scraps of food, Mr. Leventine, scraps of money to rich people like you. Our sisters go round the offices, and most firms are generous; but yours is one of the few where, every time, they get a rebuff. It seems Leventine's cannot afford to spare an anna."

"Afford!" That affronted Mr. Leventine. "Madam, we are one of the most successful firms of our size in the city."

Out of your own mouth, thought John. He was enjoying this.

"Then perhaps it really would take a miracle to change your heart?"

Mr. Leventine looked at her. He knew he was beaten. His heart, which Mother Morag had spoken of, also knew, under his ornate waistcoat, that it had had enough. His bewildered eyes were sharp again as he asked, "How much for Dark Invader?"

"Money?" The eyebrows went up. "Not money, Mr. Leventine. The people would never understand that. To them, though, one horse is much like another. If you would give us a carriage horse used to harness, strong yet tractable, a horse not too young but not too old. . . ." Her voice faltered; she was thinking of Solomon. "One that Captain Mack and Mr. Quillan would approve."

Mr. Leventine was affronted again. "Madam, I think you will find I am as good if not a better judge of a horse than they. *They* would not have bought Dark Invader."

"YOU HAVE twenty-four hours," John told Mr. Leventine. "Today is the twenty-second, and I must have three days to get Dark Invader wound up." John had not tried to gain time with Mother Morag—by now he knew her too well—but Mr. Leventine had. "If I give you my promise . . ."

"Promises won't do, Mr. Leventine. Think of the people. A horse can leave, certainly, but there must be a horse here."

"I only hope," said Captain Mack, "that he doesn't think he can get away with rubbish, something that takes the eye. He's probably sure that a nun can't know one end of a horse from another."

"Let things take their course," said John and almost smiled.

THAT AFTERNOON Mr. Leventine was outside the convent, stamping his foot imperiously on the bell of a smart Cee spring buggy. In the shafts was a handsome bay horse, by his appearance, English-bred. Mr. Leventine waited with every satisfaction for Mother Morag to appear.

"Certainly rather good-looking," she said. She seemed, to Mr. Leventine's dismay, to take in the whole of the horse with one glance. She walked to its head, rubbed the nose and lifted the upper lip with a deft finger. "No, thank you," she said.

"No, thank you?" Mr. Leventine was dazed.

"How can you, Mr. Leventine!" Mother Morag was stern. "You are wasting your time and mine. This horse has been raced. At some time he has sprained a tendon and the injury has calloused. That wouldn't interfere with his work, but I said, 'Not too young,' also, 'Not too old.' This horse is twenty."

"Madam, you must be mistaken."

"Perhaps I am; perhaps he is even older. Look at that corner tooth, Mr. Leventine. It will tell you his whole story. So—no, thank you."

Mr. Leventine was chagrined but challenged, too. "Why not

106

settle for that roan country-bred, Raj Kumar, belonging to the nawab?" asked John. "I actually have him in the stable. No good for racing but broken to carriage work—strong, docile, six years old. Ideal. The nawab would let you have him for a thousand rupees."

"A thousand! Five hundred is the price for a country-bred."

John shrugged. "He won't let it go for less. Still, do as you like, but remember, every hour is precious."

Mr. Leventine could not resist trying again. This time it was a dapple grey—"a colour ladies seem to like"—and a true carriage horse, belonging to a Greek, Mr. Petrides, who drove sedately to his office every morning, sedately back every evening, and was now retiring so that his Bimbo was for sale. Bimbo was ten years old but had been little used. "An advantage in a car but not in a horse," said Mother Morag. "Overfed, too, and listen, Mr. Leventine." She lifted her arm suddenly so that her sleeve flapped, startling Bimbo into the loud grunt that spells a broken wind. This time Mother Morag had no need to say, No, thank you. She simply looked at Mr. Leventine in reproach.

Mr. Leventine found himself with a curious new feeling. Half of him was filled with chagrin, because for once he could not make a bargain, half of him filled with admiration for this nun.

"Cas, why not give in?" said John. "Take her the roan."

"But the price! A thousand rupees."

"I'll pay half," said John. "After all, the whole thing is my fault," but, for some reason Mr. Leventine did not understand, he declined the money. "Have I ever before refused to bargain?" He did not know what was the matter with him—it was like having teeth drawn—but an hour later he and the buggy drove into the convent again. This time, between the shafts was an upstanding red roan with the arched neck, corkscrew ears of an Indian country-bred, and a splendid Arab tail. He was strong, vigorous, but obviously tractable with an intelligent, docile eye.

"Ah!" said Mother Morag. She examined him as carefully as she had the others, but this time her eyes were bright. Then, putting the last hoof down and giving the right flank a pat, she said, "I should like to try him."

"Try him. You mean . . ."

"I mean that while he may seem suitable, until he is driven . . ."

"I will take you gladly. Let me help you up." He joined her and Sister Ignatius, who was accompanying them, in the buggy. "Now, where shall I drive you?"

"I will drive." Mother Morag had already gathered up the reins. Mr. Leventine had never thought he would be seen being driven round Ballygunj in a buggy by a nun, but he soon forgot his embarrassment as he saw how Mother Morag drove, with what skill she coaxed response from the strong roan.

"But how," he asked John when he got back to the office, "how does a nun know about horses?"

"Simple," said Captain Mack, who was there with Bunny. "She was born to it. Her father was Rattler Dawson, the leading horse dealer in Dublin."

"Yes," said Bunny. "That's how I met her. My father used to buy horses from her father."

"And Mother Morag—Helen Dawson as she was then—used to show hunters when she was still at school," said John. "I believe that did wonders with the young cavalry officers from the Curragh. Couldn't bear to be bested by a brat in pigtails," and he added, "She knows all right."

"She certainly knows," said Mr. Leventine gloomily.

"That *was* satisfactory," Mother Morag had said as she jumped down from the buggy like a girl. Mr. Leventine was left to help stiff old Sister Ignatius. "How I enjoyed that! Of course, we still have to try him in the cart."

"The cart?"

"Yes. It's much more difficult than a beautifully sprung buggy. Also we must see if Gulab, our driver, can manage Raj Kumar, who is not yet as well-trained as Solomon, but you'll see."

"You mean, I am to come with you? In that?" Mr. Leventine recoiled at the sight of the cart, but mysteriously found himself seated next to the driver.

The cart did not run, it trundled. Its roof was of canvas so old that obviously it had let in the rain and it stank of mildew. The flooring

108

was of rough planking on which some dozen canisters, as large as dustbins, rattled. The lights were two hand lanterns that swung from hooks on each side of the cart; another was hung inside. There were two small wooden seats for the sisters, while in front a wide plank set on battens and covered with carpet made the driver's seat.

"This is impossible," said Mr. Leventine. He hoped, almost prayed, that nobody he knew would see him perched up beside the old Hindu bundled in his ancient coat. What if Sir Humphrey should pass? Mr. Leventine shrank back under the hood. "Impossible," he repeated.

"It is what we have." Mother Morag was serene. "And it has been possible for years. Would you believe, Mr. Leventine, that this old cart has been the means of feeding hundreds of people every day? But sometimes I do not know how Gulab manages."

"Nor do I," said Mr. Leventine.

"It will be easier with Strawberry." By now she and Sister Ignatius had abandoned the grand name of Raj Kumar for homely Strawberry. Back in the convent courtyard, she patted him gratefully. "Poor old Solomon's mouth was hard," and, "better with Strawberry," she told Gulab, who was already gleaming with pride.

"And better still," said Mr. Leventine, "you will have the buggy. It is yours, too."

That took her by surprise. "But, dear Mr. Leventine, what should we do with a buggy? How would it hold our canisters?"

"You could use it for errands."

She shook her head. "The poor don't have buggies, and we are Sisters of Poverty; we do our errands as they do, by bus or tram, or on foot when we can't afford fares. We have the cart only for collecting, and Strawberry must pull that. It is most kind of you . . ." She paused, then a look came over her face, a shrewdness, twin, he recognized with unexpected comradeship, with his own. "Of course, as you are so generous, perhaps the cost of the buggy could repair our cart."

"Repair *that!* You shall have a new cart." Mr. Leventine seemed unable to stop himself and at once wanted to retract. He should have added "one day", which would have meant never; he was just

110

going to say it when Sister Ignatius spoke up. In a deep and impressive voice she said, "God bless you, Mr. Leventine," and a strange feeling of happiness that seemed to come from outside himself warmed him. He had never been blessed before.

STRAWBERRY'S papers and certificates had been handed over. "Now all we have to do," said Mr. Leventine, "is make our amicable exchange," and another, even stranger, sensation filled him, a feeling of deep gratification; though why he should be gratified when he had been forced—yes, forced—to spend a great deal of money, he did not know.

The Quillan syces arrived to fetch Dark Invader, and a crowd gathered outside the gate, a crowd that was growing larger. Mother Morag said suddenly, "It would be wise—I think imperative—that the people see the horse goes willingly."

Dark Invader would not go willingly. After these two halcyon days he had no intention of returning to the effort and stress of the racecourse. The quiet walks around the vegetable garden while he was talked to gently, the tidbits of bread and salt that came like manna from heaven at unexpected times, Gulab's and Mother Morag's gentle grooming, none of that thump and slapping, all suited his lazy and greedy self. When Gulab led him out of the stall, he thought at first it was for another quiet wander or some more bread and salt. Instead, he saw Sadiq and Ali advancing. Dark Invader stopped, laid back his ears and when Sadiq took the halter rope, gave a sideways swing of his head that hit Gulab's face and drew a gasp from the crowd.

Then the crowd, Mr. Leventine and the nuns were given a display of horse fireworks such as they had never seen or imagined. Dark Invader kicked, reared, beating the air with his forefeet, bringing them down on the cobblestones with a crash and going up again. Sadiq, helped by Ali, manfully held on, dodging the flashing hooves, shouting and cursing, while Mr. Leventine wailed. It was only the appearance of Sisters Barbara and Joanna bearing, like handmaidens, slices of bread and salt, calling in their cooing voices, "Beauty, Beauty, Beauty," that made Dark Invader stop. As if

111

nothing had happened, he accepted their tidbits and let Sister Joanna lead him towards the vegetable garden, leaving the two grooms out of breath, furious and shamed.

"Allah! Ismallah! Shaitan!" Sadiq muttered while Gulab staunched his nosebleed. "Do you think," the shattered Mr. Leventine asked Mother Morag, "that the sight of Sadiq could have brought back this famous fear?"

"Not at all," said Mother Morag. "The horse was not sweating or trembling. He simply wanted his own way—but poor Sadiq and Gulab."

"Of course." Mr. Leventine slapped his thigh. "Of course, that fool Johnny should never have sent the syces," and he bellowed, "Why didn't he send Ted Mullins? Telephone Quillan and tell him to send Mullins at once. No, wait," and Mr. Leventine added majestically, "I will fetch him myself."

"MULLINS. *Mullins!*"

Ted raised his head. He was sitting where he had sat for most of the last two days, at the desk in the darkest corner of the darkened room. He had kept the shutters closed. There was nothing on the desk now; the photograph of him and Ella in her "lace curtain" had been shut away in the drawer, as had been the framed form of his new licence.

At night he had gone to bed only to lie awake; at dawn when he heard the jemadar's call, he got up, shaved and dressed, but as he heard the horses go out, he took a cup of tea from Ahmed's tray, leaving the toast and bananas untouched, and shut himself in the room again. "He will die!" Dahlia wept in her distress. "For two days he has taken nothing but that cup of tea. He will die."

"No one dies from going without food for two days," said John.

"Papa, you must forgive poor Ted. You must." The *bandar-log* were frantic. "Papa, *please*," but, "Mr. Mullins," John had said, "is going straight back to England." He had trusted Ted. There were few people he trusted, and Dahlia knew he was not only angry but deeply hurt. "I don't want to see him again," he said.

Ted knew it and shut himself out of sight.

112

Now came the voice of authority. "Mullins, open up." Dazed, Ted rose and opened the shutters, wincing at the light.

"And what do you think you are doing?" asked Mr. Leventine. "Why are you not with your charge? With Dark Invader?"

"The . . . the Invader, sir?" Ted croaked. "I knew he had been found, thanks be. Mr. Quillan sent me a note. But I thought . . . thought he was out of the race, that he wouldn't race now."

"And what business have you in thinking? Who says he's out of the race?"

"Then, he isn't?" Joy lit up Ted's face. "You mean he's fit! But . . ." And the shame came back. "Anyway, I'm out."

"Who says so?"

"Mr. Quillan."

"Who employs you? I, or Mr. Quillan?"

"I suppose . . . you do, sir."

"Exactly," said Mr. Leventine. "You will take your orders from me, and at this moment they are that you will come with me in my car and get this . . . this animal out of this ridiculous situation and bring him immediately home."

"Me?" Ted sounded as if he could not believe his ears.

"Who else?" and Mr. Leventine, looking down at the little man who seemed to have shrunk even more and aged by twenty years, put a plump hand on the rigid shoulder and said, "I think no one else but you can do it, Teddy."

Far from grating on him, the nickname heartened Ted as nothing else could have done. No one since Ella had called him Teddy, and Ted took his clean handkerchief out of his pocket—by habit he had a clean handkerchief every morning—used it, put it meticulously away and said, "I'm ready, sir."

"WE CALL him Beauty," Sister Joanna told Ted, and Ted's chivalry rose to the occasion. "A good name for him, ma'am." It was an emotional evening for Ted, but that did not prevent him giving Dark Invader a thorough rating. "You shocker! That's what you are, a shocker."

A secret fear had been removed from Ted; he could not help

remembering, even though he had been fuddled, how Dark Invader had not greeted him that night. "Thought he had gone off me for Mr. Saddick," but when Ted gave his whistle across the convent vegetable garden, Dark Invader pricked his ears. There was a loud whicker of welcome, and the Invader tried to break away from Gulab and Sister Joanna. Ted had gone quickly to the rescue. "Shocker! Putting it on for these kind ladies. Never heard of such a thing, but don't think you can get away with it. You've been too kind to him, ma'am," and, "You're coming home, my lad," to Dark Invader, who looked at him lovingly, a cabbage leaf dangling from his lips. Nothing had been nicer than the nibbles of fresh vegetables in the convent garden. "Home." Ted said it sternly and, recalling his war years in France, "Toot de sweet and the tooter the sweeter."

"But how will you get him there?" asked Sister Joanna.

"Ride him, of course. Would you ask that man of yours to bring the saddle and bridle?"

John Quillan appeared with Gulab. He did not speak to Ted but gave him a leg up when Dark Invader had been saddled. The big horse had not objected even when Ted tightened the girth. "He's wise enough to know when the game's up," Ted told Sister Joanna. He took the reins. "Say goodbye and thank you."

"Wouldn't it be safer," Sister Ignatius said, "if we opened the garden gate and he went out that way?"

"That wouldn't do," said Mother Morag. "He must leave through the crowd. It will probably be *with* the crowd."

The crowd was getting bigger, they could hear the rising hum. "Can you manage him?" asked anxious Mr. Leventine.

"Gawd almighty!" said Ted. Back in the saddle with Dark Invader under him, that was almost the power he felt. "The Invader and I, ain't we used to crowds?" And he ran his finger in the familiar Ted gesture up the long line of Dark Invader's mane, but there was a doubt in Ted's mind. John Quillan had given Ted his chance, almost equally with Mr. Leventine, gone along with him all the way, and though John now was silent, hostile, Ted was not taking Dark Invader out without his permission. "Mr. Quillan, sir?" asked Ted. It was a beseeching.

114

John raised his head and perhaps only Dahlia could have told what the quirk of a smile he gave Ted meant. "Go to it, Ted," he said.

There was no trouble, no Invader antics. Mother Morag pulled his ears and gave him a most un-nunlike slap on the rump, and Ted rode him out of the vegetable garden, past the rows of nuns, past Gulab, who, with a swollen nose, was standing guard over the stable where Strawberry was eating his supper, past Dil Bahadur, who saluted, and into the crowd, which parted respectfully, then, as Mother Morag had predicted, accompanied them up the road.

Bunny had driven up to control the concourse, but Ted sat easily, using the long rein. Only once did he jerk it when Dark Invader nosed too eagerly for the sweets that were offered. Marigolds were thrown, too, and both were garlanded. Dark Invader put his head down graciously as if flowers were his due, but Ted turned a deeper bronze and hunched his shoulders. Sadiq and Ali followed, chastened, and as they neared the Quillan stables, the *bandar-log* came dancing down, and as Ted dismounted, Dahlia, waiting by Dark Invader's stall, threw her arms around Ted's neck and kissed him.

"A little fast work tomorrow morning." John gave Ted his orders as if nothing had happened. "You can take him as far as the four-furlong mark. Ching can pace you with Flashlight. Repeat on Christmas Day, then, on the morning of the race, a two-furlong sprint just to clear his wind. Got that?" asked John.

"Yes, sir," said Ted.

SIR HUMPHREY met Mr. Leventine the next day in the billiard room where both had taken refuge—sanctuary, thought Mr. Leventine.

"Well, how are you, Leventine?"

"Thank you. I'm in clover."

"Hear you had some trouble with your horse down on the track."

"Just nemesis." Mr. Leventine waved his hand. "We were foolish enough to let another jockey try him."

"Doesn't answer so close to the race. Hope it hasn't impaired his chances."

"We still hope to turn a nimble shilling on him."

The judge looked slightly astonished but only said, "Well, Merry Christmas."

"Bless you, Sir Humphrey," said Mr. Leventine.

THE SISTERS had made a small crib in the chapel—tomorrow was Christmas Eve—and Dahlia took the *bandar-log* to see it. They had brought with them two small clay horses, one painted dark brown, the other dark red. "Mohan, our friend in the bazaar, made them for us. Aren't they pretty?"

"Very pretty," said Mother Morag. Mohan, in the way of Indian potters, had added a few painted daisies and golden necklaces.

"They are to stand close to the Jesus," said the eldest boy.

"Oh, no! They can't." Sister Ignatius was shocked.

"Why not? You have an ox and an ass."

"And they must. Darkie has come to say thank you. Strawberry has come to say please," explained the eldest girl.

"No, they have both come to say thank you. They both have come to say please," said the *bandar* who was the youngest except for the two babies. At that moment, with his big blue eyes turned up to look at Mother Morag, he looked less like a monkey, more like a wise little owl. "Yes, put them close to the manger," said Mother Morag, "and both of them shall say thank you *and* please. So shall we." And that night in chapel she announced, "Tonight we shall sing Te Deum."

We praise thee, O God . . .
All the earth doth worship thee . . .

DARK INVADER was back unharmed at Quillan's. Strawberry was in the convent stall. Mr. Leventine had promised a new cart. John Quillan was mollified, Bunny was enchanted, but Mother Morag's knees felt weak. "I don't want to see or hear a magpie robin again," she told Sister Ignatius. Then she stopped. "But magpie robins . . . they don't come till March. That one I heard"—she almost said, "spoke to me"—"was singing out of season."

116

CHAPTER VII

The start of the Viceroy's Cup was in front of the stands. It was the greatest day of the racing year. Flags flew, and banks of potted dahlias, chrysanthemums and cinerarias were everywhere. No lawns were ever greener, no ropes and rails whiter, and the track itself stretched like a wide emerald ribbon in the golden sunlight of the Bengal winter.

The governor had arrived in state; after him, in greater state, the viceroy, both in four-horse landaus, shaded by scarlet and gold umbrellas, and accompanied by the lancers, their horses matched, pennons flying below glittering lance points, red coats, white breeches, and dark faces bearded under a pride of turbans, starched in blue and gold; the whole noiseless on the grass, except for the clink of bits and chains and the creak of leather. There was a fanfare of trumpets while the stewards stood in an array of grey morning suits, white carnations and white topees, which would presently be replaced by grey top hats.

The Members' Enclosure was filled. The women's dresses and hats were worthy of Ascot or Longchamps, but for beauty and elegance they could not match the exquisite shimmering saris of the Indian women nor the turbans of the visiting princes. Bunny's was of pink gauze with an emerald in front. "Your colours," he told Mr. Leventine, "happiness and hope. I'm not allowed to bet," he said ruefully, "but I would have put twenty thousand on your Invader."

"Don't be too sure yet," said Mr. Leventine. He was still superstitious, and John added, "This *is* the first real test. Darkie won't be able to gallop away with it as he has so far—not with this lot."

It was time for the big race, and for the first time Ted was nervous. In the changing room his stock would not come right. Then the jockeys who had ridden in the race before came in, unbuttoning their silks and putting on new colours. Among them were Streaky Bacon, Willie Hunt and three other English jockeys.

Streaky saw Ted. "Hullo. Here's Father Christmas." He looked

117

closer. "Seen you before. Weren't you one of Michael Traherne's lads?" He straddled the floor. "What are you doing here, may I ask?"

"Riding," Ted said briefly.

"Riding for Quillan, Mr. Leventine's Dark Invader," put in one of the others.

"Cor! The comeback of all time! Methuselah in person. Riding Dark Invader!"

"Which is more than you can do." Willie's voice came across the room. "Remember Thursday morning." Bacon turned away to go into a huddle with his friends.

Ted had expected this. "Watch out for Bacon," John had said, but what Ted had not expected was the crawling feeling in his guts, the sudden cold sweat that broke out on his neck and hands. This was the first time Dark Invader had appeared since his encounter with Streaky. Ted was going to race against him. Would there be trouble? Ted looked at the order on the race card. "Thank God I didn't draw next to him."

Ted fastened his silks, tucked them into his breeches, picked up his whip, saddle and weight cloth and went onto the scales for a final check.

They were singing at him now, a ribald version of "John Anderson My Jo."

> "Now your brow is bald, Ted,
> Your locks are like the snow,
> But blessings on your frosty pow . . .
> pow pow pow"

"Blessings! I don't think," said Streaky Bacon.

Ted could almost feel the grizzle among the fair tuft on his head. He tried not to hurry as he pulled on his cap. His legs felt so clamped with terror that he seemed to swagger as he walked. If only there had not been the bad luck of Streaky's appearance. If only Streaky had not got near Dark Invader. If only . . . Then Ted remembered the sister who had been leading Dark Invader. At

118

parting she had said, "Oh, I do hope you'll win." Then she had caught herself. "I suppose one mustn't pray for racing."

"Prob'ly not," Ted had said. He was not used to talking about praying, but in the strangeness of the convent he had been led to add, "You can pray for the Invader and for me." Must have been out of meself, Ted thought afterwards, but standing on the vegetable-garden path, the young sister had looked so appealing, "Oh, I will. All of us will," she had said fervently, and, "That's the way for us to win," Ted had said.

Now a little knot seemed to form inside Ted. "If you've got the jitters, whatever you do, don't pass them on to the Invader. He's going to need all he's got, so you forgets about your blinking self," Ted Mullins told Ted Mullins.

As THE CROWD watched, the first little brightly clad figure came through the door of the weighing-room veranda and sat down on the bench. The judges in the judges' box identified them. Blue silks, orange cap, that would be Quarterback, a grey five-year-old from Bombay. White with red sleeves, red cap—Backgammon, ridden by Streaky Bacon, the visiting crack brought out especially by the rajah of Raniganj. Here was another, a chessboard effect, black and white checks, scarlet cap, Lady Mehta's Flashlight. Then Volteface, red with brown sleeves and black cap. Then pink and green, green cap—a small man, even smaller than the others—Ted Mullins on Dark Invader.

There were eleven runners, six more to come: Racing Demon, Postillion, Bezique, Tetrazone and Moonlighter. Last of all Ching, peacock jacket, white sleeves and cap, having his first run in the Viceroy's Cup on Greensleeves, owned by a syndicate and trained by John Quillan. At the bell they came into the paddock where the trainers were gathered while the grooms led the horses round and round.

Then came orders to mount, and quick hands swung the little men up. A last tug at girths and a look at stirrup leathers. Streaky's powerful legs were tucked under him until he seemed almost to kneel on the horse's withers. Mullins sat Dark Invader calmly. On

119

the grey, Quarterback, was a solid little chunk of a man, snub nose, blue jowl—the English jockey Tim Stubbs. Then Flashlight, little head, little short ears, bit of white in his eye—a sporting print racehorse—and his English jockey Syd Johnson on top. Willie Hunt was nearby on Racing Demon.

It was time for the parade. The horses walked down in single file past the stands and crowds—it seemed half Calcutta was gathered on the far side of the rails—past the finish in order of the race card, Dark Invader five behind Backgammon and Streaky. He heard the cries of "Darkie! Darkie!" as they came back, one by one, at a fast canter with a slap of the reins, a flutter of silk and the smell of horses and bruised grass.

At the start a stream of orders came from the starter, who had horses facing the wrong way, breaking out, sidling around. Mr. Leventine, sweating under the hat he had exchanged for his topee, mopped his forehead, his rosy face growing purple. John's was white. Never had Ted looked so small, hunched and old; Dark Invader never as big and intimidating. Yet John noticed Ted's easy seat, the quiet rein, the horse's pricked ears. Dark Invader was eager. Eager! thought John, marvelling.

The gate went up. The timekeeper pressed the button on the watch before the sharp bang of the rising barrier had time to reach him.

The next moment the field surged past with thunder of hooves and shouts as they raced for position on the first bend. In a matter of seconds the mass of manes, nostrils, faces half-glimpsed, resolved itself into a procession of strong quarters and jockeys' white bottoms bobbing away into the distance.

The senior judge began to call the race to the other judges. "Volteface leads, followed by Quarterback. Mullins has Dark Invader tucked comfortably on the rails in fifth place."

The field strung out along the backstretch, coloured beads sliding along above the whiteness of the distant rail, the white domes of the Victoria Memorial behind them. The judge went on. "Racing Demon, Postillion, Quarterback, Backgammon, Volteface, Dark Invader, Bezique, Flashlight, Tetrazone, Moonlighter and

120

Greensleeves." Then, "Same order. Moonlighter and Greensleeves tailing off."

They were racing now two furlongs out, fighting for position, and then it happened. John, watching through his binoculars, drew a quick breath. On the Calcutta racecourse the final bend is sharp, before the short run in.

"But I had seen," Ted told him afterwards. "Seen what them bunch had cooked up. All of them got together to look after me. Streaky, Joe, Syd Johnson, Tim, the lot—'cept Willie. They knew it, that bend, and what they done was, they draws together to block it. Strewth! For a flash I thought I'd have to pull the Invader, but . . . as if I'd told him, he followed our pattern."

"Our pattern?"

"What you told me the first time, sir—go for the outer rail, only he did it hisself!"

John had seen something dark swing clear of the mass of horses to take a line of its own, exactly on that outer rail. "Yes, went round the outside and, s'help me God, if he wasn't so bloody good they couldn't catch us," said Ted.

The main body of the race came thundering down the straight as the judge's voice rose in excitement. "Backgammon, Volteface, Racing Demon," and, to the timekeeper, "Get Backgammon's number ready," but the dark horse on the outside was gaining ground with every stride, bright colours, pink and green, pink and green, and the cries of "Darkie!" "Darkie!" grew to a roar.

"Now it's Dark Invader, Backgammon, Volteface—get Dark Invader's number ready and hold it—Dark Invader, Backgammon, Racing Demon, Volteface." Then, in ringing tones, "One, Dark Invader; Two, Racing Demon; Three, Backgammon. Four and Five, Volteface and Postillion. Two lengths, half length, short head, short head. Right. Time?" he asked the timekeeper. "Three minutes, four and three quarter seconds. Agreed? Right. Dark Invader."

"Dark Invader," and with a rattle and squeak of pulleys an attendant hoisted aloft the numbers of the first, second, third and fourth horses in the Viceroy's Cup.

MR. LEVENTINE gave a dinner at Firpo's for forty people. His guests included Sir Readymoney and Lady Mehta, the commissioner of police, Bunny and Captain Mack, who both left early for another engagement. John Quillan and Dahlia were asked but did not go. Sir Humphrey proposed the toast.

It was a banquet of eight courses in the Edwardian style, with hors d'oeuvres followed by turtle soup. Next came local crayfish doing duty for lobsters and echoing Mr. Leventine's racing colours on a bed of green salad. Then quails, stuffed, on saddle-shaped pieces of toast, and a guinea fowl with almond sauce.

There was a needed pause for a pink and green sorbet, accompanied by brown Russian cigarettes before, with new energy, the diners attacked a saddle of lamb. Then came a cake with a portrait of Dark Invader in chocolate icing, and an enormous replica of the Viceroy's Cup in golden foil which, cut open, revealed an ice pudding.

They finished with devils on horseback—bacon wrapped around a prune—so suitable, thought Mr. Leventine. The wines, beginning with dry sherry for the hors d'oeuvres, ran through Chablis, a Rudesheimer 1929, claret, Château Cheval Blanc, to champagne, Veuve Clicquot, ending with Madeira and Malmsey.

There was a band and a cabaret.

Ted gave a supper party on his veranda for the *bandar-log*. John and Dahlia were invited and came. The menu was sausages and ice cream; for John and Dahlia there was whisky and champagne, but when Dark Invader was led around by Sadiq and Ali for the toast, it was drunk in sherbet by the children, Sadiq, Ali and Ted. The entertainment was fireworks, which Bunny and Captain Mack were in time to let off.

NO ONE SEEING Mr. Leventine rise in all the glory of his evening tails, white tie, diamond dress studs, his florid yet innocent happiness, could have suspected he had spent the evening in a battle, a battle with himself.

He had led in his winner to tumultuous applause and an uproar from the crowd. Ted's face was screwed into a hundred delighted

wrinkles. Dark Invader lopped his ears, inclined his head and looked calm and unembarrassed.

Later in the afternoon Mr. Leventine was graciously given the golden cup by the viceroy and made an almost equally gracious speech, impeccably modest, paying tribute to John Quillan and Ted and Dark Invader himself.

Then he had made his announcement. Dark Invader, he said, would probably race again next winter, but he would then be retired and sent to stud, but not in England. Here Mr. Leventine gathered himself to his full size and extended his hand to Lady Mehta, who was standing by him. The stud farm would be here in India for the encouragement of Indian breeding and racing. A farm newly built and run on model lines, a venture made possible by the cooperation of his, Mr. Leventine's, dear friends, Sir Prakash and Lady Mehta and—he extended the other hand to Bunny—His Highness the maharajah of Malwa. The applause was tremendous, but Mr. Leventine held up his hand for silence. "You will be glad to hear that with Dark Invader goes his inseparable other half, his jockey, Ted Mullins, who will be our head stud groom. No one," said Mr. Leventine, "can think of one without the other."

No speech could have been more welcome, none more heartily endorsed. Mr. Leventine would be in the company now of people. "*People*," he said reverently, and it was sure that he would be a steward now.

When he left the racecourse, he had gone straight to the stables to see Dark Invader comfortably bedded down and rugged. The cup meant nothing to Dark Invader except that he was tired. He only raised his head hoping for a tidbit. He still had a hankering for bread and salt, but Mr. Leventine gave him Kulu apples and large pieces of sugarcane. There was a bonus of a hundred rupees for Sadiq, fifty for Ali. Then Mr. Leventine went to the annex to confirm his present to Ted.

"I hope you are pleased. I should have asked you before I made that announcement," but Ted had heard no announcement; he had been too overcome and too full of pride in Dark Invader to listen to any speech. "A stud!" he said when Mr. Leventine had explained and John endorsed it. Both John and Bunny were with Ted. "You . . . you, sir, are going to have a stud farm?"

"Indeed yes." Mr. Leventine waved his hand. "Land has been bought, building commenced. It will be a model, financed by me, Sir Prakash and Lady Mehta and . . ." He was not quite sure what title to give Bunny—Highness or just maharajah. "And . . ."

"And me," said Bunny. "Yes, the Paramount Power are letting me put money in. They actually believe one of my ideas is sound."

"And if we succeed," said Mr. Leventine, "Mr. Quillan may join us. It will not be a paltry stud."

"And you want me . . . as head groom." Ted could hardly say it.

"Who else?" Mr. Leventine had reverted to his "who". "Don't forget who will be the first to stand at stud—Dark Invader."

Ted had a sudden vision. Green grass and white-railed paddocks. Dark Invader, a portly, heavy-crested patriarch, and he, Ted, his companion to the end of his days. The whole, in the true tradition of visions and memories of childhood, suffused with golden sunlight. "Gor blimey!" And then Ted said aloud, "If only Ella could know."

WHEN Mr. Leventine left to go home and dress for his banquet, the brief Calcutta twilight had come and gone; lights were twinkling across the Maidan with smaller pinpricks from the beggar camp-fires. This time of dusk always made him feel a little sad and lonely, as if something were lacking in his busy successful life, but not tonight, thought Mr. Leventine. Surely not tonight, but, even half an hour later, dressed and standing as he liked to do in front of his library mantelpiece, it persisted. Dark Invader's cups were safely rearranged, there had been no need for that moment of panic; three cups were on the left, the goblet, quaich and rose bowl on the right and, in the centre, the golden cup. Tomorrow it would be taken to be engraved, but now the library lamps caught the gold, sending soft rays into Mr. Leventine's eyes. The cup would go with him to the banquet, where it would be put on a stand; he had thought of filling it with champagne and passing it around, "like a loving cup," he had told John—"loving cup" had sounded beautiful to Mr. Leventine—but John had said he thought it might be ostentatious.

In all Mr. Leventine's life there had never been a more happy and successful day; then why should this annoying thought come up that something more was needed to complete it? That something was lacking? "Nonsense, nonsense," Mr. Leventine told himself. "This is nonsense," but, though he said it aloud, the feeling persisted. Worse, he knew what it was as surely as if another voice had told him, "the stake money".

"But it's mine—I earned it!" argued Mr. Leventine. "And I need it," but that truly was nonsense. That very morning Mr. Leventine had rounded off an extremely cosy deal—cosy was his word for the swelling of his already swollen bank account.

How the thought about the stake money had come to him he did not know; perhaps it was those mean little beggar fires; perhaps because, passing the convent, he had thought of Mother Morag and the sisters, and had wondered if they were warm enough. He was almost sure not. "But what is that to do with me?" he asked himself. "Look what they have extorted from me already."

"Not exactly extorted," said this other inexorable voice, and he could hear again what Mother Morag had told him. "Of course we would have given you Dark Invader back in the end. We just wanted to see if you were generous."

"And wasn't I generous? That horse cost me a thousand rupees, a thousand for a country-bred! And I would have given the buggy as well. Is it my fault they refused it?" But the refusal had stayed in his mind. "We couldn't have that expensive buggy. We are Sisters of *Poverty*. The poor don't have buggies, though they might have a cart for work." He winced as he remembered his drive in the cart. "Well, I have given a new cart. Enough—enough!" said Mr. Leventine and he clapped his hands. A servant was always nearby to answer that clap. "Bring me a large whisky and soda," said Mr. Leventine, and lit a cigar.

The whisky made him more comfortable. The stake money had certainly been earned. "Look what I have spent on that horse," but, "Not very much;" the voice might now have been John Quillan's. "You got him as a bargain. You said that yourself and, as it turned out, you got Ted Mullins too."

126

"Well, I have not been mean. I have given lavish presents."

"Were you trying to buy goodwill?" That was a hard thought, and Mr. Leventine blinked almost as if tears had come into his eyes, and it was not entirely true. He had enjoyed choosing those Christmas presents, and in thinking about the people the presents were for, particularly Ted's saddle, he had felt enormous pleasure about that; still more in telling Ted about the stud farm, in seeing a gleam of real hope and enthusiasm in John Quillan's eyes and in hearing Dahlia's ecstatic, "Oh, John! It would be so wonderful for the children." It made him, Mr. Leventine, feel like a magician, the sort of feeling he had had when the old sister had said, "Bless you." But "it's an infernal nuisance being a blessing," said Mr. Leventine, "and so expensive."

"Sahib, it is almost eight o'clock. Car is waiting. Time to go." Relief filled Mr. Leventine and he threw his cigar in the grate. His head bearer was holding his coat and white silk scarf, and the butler reverently went to lift down the golden cup and its stand, which he would take to the banquet. The Viceroy's Cup, but the stake money . . .

Mr. Leventine saw the menu which had been propped beside the cup, a gold embellished card with pictures of little horses. Wines, hors d'oeuvres, langoustines . . .

"Have you ever been hungry, Mr. Leventine?" It was the voice of the chief commissioner, whom he would meet in a few minutes.

"Hellfire and damnation," cried Mr. Leventine and, to the servants, "Wait," and he went to his writing desk and took out a cheque book.

"DO YOU SEE what I see?" asked Mother Morag.

She pressed her hand over her eyes, then looked again and, "Do you read what I read?" she asked Sister Ignatius.

Sister Ignatius read and had to sit down suddenly.

After a stunned silence Mother Morag whispered, "Fifty thousand rupees!" and, presently, "We can pay off the mortgage on the new infirmary," she said.

"Perhaps we could install fans."

127

"Open that new kitchen."

Next day, Sister Ignatius, who was not given to such things, cut out a newspaper photograph of Dark Invader and framed it in passe-partout. Mother Morag allowed her to hang it in the chapel.

EPILOGUE

IT WAS two years later. A telegram came to Mr. Leventine, a duplicate to John Quillan, from Bangalore. It read, FAIRYTALE'S COLT BORN JUST AFTER MIDNIGHT. ALL WELL, and Ted, in his enthusiasm, had added, STRIKINGLY HANDSOME. DEAD RINGER FOR DARK INVADER, which meant, Captain Mack explained to Mr. Leventine, "that it's Dark Invader all over again."

"How does Ted know?" asked John. "He wasn't there when Dark Invader was born."

"Here's hoping," said Mr. Leventine. "Our first foal."

"By Dark Invader out of Fairytale," Captain Mack said thoughtfully. "I think you should call him Dark Legend."

Rumer Godden

The story of Dark Invader is taken from an event that happened in Calcutta some fifty years ago and has since become a legend in Indian racing circles. There are several versions of the story, but Rumer Godden's is based on one told to her by Sir Owain Jenkins, who was a distinguished member of the Royal Calcutta Turf Club in the thirties.

It is no wonder that this writer's evocation of the rich glamour of the Indian racing world seems so authentic; for many years she was part of that society herself. Life for Westerners living in India was both hectic and gay, and the winter "season" centred around racing. The Godden family had always been fond of horses; her father was, she says, "horse mad", and her three sisters were all good horsewomen. "I was the only rabbit."

The Godden sisters were brought up mainly in India, spending most of their childhood in a small town on a Bengal river. Their idyllically happy life there was interrupted when they were sent back to school in England. But when the First World War broke out, back they went to India for five years, a blissful reprieve Rumer Godden describes delightfully in the autobiography, *Two Under The Indian Sun*, which she wrote jointly with her sister Jon.

When Rumer was eighteen she started training in England as a dancer, returning to India three years later to teach dancing. She found then that glamorous Indian society could be intolerant; she was totally ostracized because she worked for a living. She was not at all put out by this. "I rather gloried in it," she says, "and they just had to accept it in the end."

All the time Rumer Godden was writing, and many of her novels are set in India: *Black Narcissus*, about a community of nuns in the Himalayas; *The River*, loosely based on her childhood and made into an outstanding film by Jean Renoir; and, among others, *The Peacock Spring* and *Kingfishers Catch Fire*.

After living in many parts of India, and later in Henry James's house in Rye, Sussex, Rumer Godden has now settled quietly in Scotland, where she is happy to be close to her two married daughters.

STILL MISSING
Beth Gutcheon

ALEX SELKY, age 6

Last seen May 15th, 1980, 8:50 a.m., corner of Fremont and Beacon
Wearing blue jeans, red and white T-shirt, blue running shoes
Persons with any information, call 966-3411

A condensation of the book by
Beth Gutcheon

Illustrated by Ted Lewin
Published by Michael Joseph

Alex Selky was nearly seven. He knew he must not dawdle on the way to school, must not talk to strangers. He knew he had to come straight home afterwards. He had done it many times. He was a big boy now. Then one morning, after waving goodbye to his mother, Alex turned the corner— and disappeared.

Was he lost? Had he been kidnapped? Was he still alive? For his mother, it was the beginning of a nightmare. Others shared Susan Selky's anguish: her estranged husband, Graham; Detective Menetti, whose hunt for Alex became an obsession. Friends, even concerned strangers, took to the streets in a relentless search.

But as the days turned to weeks and Alex was still missing, it was Susan who never lost faith. Somehow, somewhere, she knew her child would be found alive and brought back to her.

You could hardly get to age thirty-four without learning something about loss. By thirty-four you're bound to have lost your Swiss army knife, your best friend from fourth grade, your chance to be center forward on the starting team, quite a few of your illusions, and certainly, somewhere along the line, some significant love. Susan Selky had in fact recently lost an old battle, for her marriage to the man she was in love with, and, with it, her dreams of more babies and of holding his hand in the dark when they were old.

It may be that one loss helps to prepare you for the next, but the truth is that life is not something you can go into training for. There was nothing that Susan Selky could have done to prepare for the breathtaking impact of losing her son.

Susan Selky, bright, loyal, stubborn, shy, accomplished. If you knew her professionally, you probably wouldn't have guessed that she thought of her narrow brick house on Fremont Street as if it were a shell, guarding the heart of her life, her private days and nights with Alex.

Alexander Graham Selky, Jr., age six and three quarters, a free-lance spaceman. A small, sturdy child with a two-hundred-watt smile and a giggle like falling water, a child who saw *Star Wars* once with Mommy, twice with Daddy, and once again with

135

TJ, the original owner-trainer of Taxi, an oversize Shetland sheepdog.

Taxi was a near total loss in the training department. He had only managed to learn to start barking with joy when Alex got home from school, a full minute before any human could have heard his feet on the stairs, and to smuggle himself soundlessly onto Alex's bed at night against orders. Most evenings when Susan went to kiss Alex one more time on her own way to bed, she found Taxi burrowed against her sleeping boy, still as a statue except for the wistful eyes that begged, Pretend you don't see me.

"He thinks he's my brother," said Alex. "He thinks he's a fur person."

Alex Selky, going on seven, so eager to grow up, kissed his mother good-by on their front steps on the hot, bright morning of Thursday, May 15, 1980, and marched himself down the street to the New Boston School of Back Bay, two blocks from his corner. He never arrived at school, and from the moment he turned the corner, he apparently disappeared from the face of the earth.

It was only two fifty in the afternoon when Susan jogged down Fremont Street. She'd been held up after her seminar by a chatty student, and she was worried that she wouldn't get home before Alex. The entryway in her house was dark; the tenant of her ground-floor apartment was at work. Alex's bike lay against the wall by the stairs that led up to the two floors Susan and her son occupied. As she unlocked her upstairs door, she could hear Taxi flinging himself against it on the other side, howling with delight that one of his people had come back.

Inside, Susan bent over him fondly. "Hush, lovely Taxi. Can't learn not to bark my ears off, can you, poor Taxi?"

She found her morning *Globe* and settled herself in a deep chair by the window. Sunlight flooded this front room in the afternoons, slanting in across the bright blue chairs and sofa, the fading Persian carpet, and the dark, wide polished floorboards. What a pleasure it was to have the room in ticking silence for a minute or two.

It was almost three thirty before something caused her to look at her watch. That was the moment it began. It was thirty minutes since school let out. It took seven minutes to walk home from the schoolyard. Where was Alex?

She went to the window and leaned out over the sidewalk. The street lay silent in the sunlight. She watched for a moment or two, knowing that if she refused that quiver of fear starting under her rib cage, Alex would sprint around the corner bouncing his green knapsack.

"I won't dawdle," he had said manfully when he asked permission to walk home alone from school. "You can *count* on me."

"Okay," she had said, reaching across the supper table to shake on it. Alex shook, and with his elbow overturned his milk.

Susan kept her eyes on the corner, trying to make Alex appear by force of will. Just do it. Just come around the corner, panting, with your cheeks flushed and your brown hair flying and your totally plausible six-year-old's explanation. Just show up right now, my good little man, before I allow this feeling to have a name, and panic, and make a fool of myself. (Yes, I know I said he was missing, Officer, but you see he was actually at his friend's house reading Batman comics. Yes, he *is* here now. He just . . . But you see, he promised he wouldn't dawdle. . . . Seven. Well, almost seven. But he's very responsible. Well, I'm sorry. Yes, I know I inconvenienced you. . . . No, I'm not a hysterical woman. I'm a tenured professor of American literature at Harvard. . . . I *said* I was sorry.)

The street was so strangely still that Susan went to the phone and called Jocelyn. "Hey," she said. "It's me."

"Hey. I'm glad you called. I'm really having a swell day, let me tell you. I waited four hours for the plumber to get here. I was late to pick up Justine and everything."

"Oh, Justine's home?" asked Susan.

"Finally. I had to stop and feed her on the way, though, because she traded her lunch at school for a Catwoman doll."

"Oh, good, okay. Actually Alex isn't home yet, and I was wondering would you just ask Justine if she remembers if he stayed to play ball in the yard or anything?"

"Alex isn't *home* yet?"

That was a bad moment. The moment when you have to admit to another mother that you don't know where your child is.

"Hold on a sec," said Jocelyn.

Susan could hear her calling Justine.

It took a long time. It took such a long time that while she was holding on, Susan died and went to hell and came back a soul in torment. It took such a long time that before Jocelyn picked up the phone again, Susan already knew.

"Susan, Justine says Alex wasn't in school today at all."

Later Susan actually remembered hearing a crash at that moment. She remembered the words accompanied by a noise as if a giant tree were being shattered by lightning. There was a bright lurid flash, too, like the kind of frightening light you see in a thundersquall just at twilight.

He didn't go home with a friend? He didn't stop to read comics? She was still reaching for reasons for him not being home yet. She couldn't begin to grasp the idea of him not getting to school at all.

"Susan," said Jocelyn, "I'm coming over. Call the police."

Call the police. *Call the police.*

In the quiet room, in the sunlight, Susan felt herself sink into a well of horror so great that it was all colors, all light and all darkness, scalding heat and killing cold. The sensation was beyond anything you could feel and not be seared along every nerve and cell, altered forever. But you couldn't feel that way long without it stopping your heart. By the time Susan picked up the phone again, she had passed through the first shock. She was certainly not a hysterical woman as she called the police.

She didn't know what precinct she lived in. She dialed 911. "Yes, it's an emergency. My son has disappeared."

"What address?"

"Fremont Street. Back Bay."

"That's the Fourth District. I'll connect you."

The phone was answered on the first ring. "Fourth District."

"Yes. Hello. I want to report a missing child."

"That's Juvenile. Hold on."

The line went numb, then came alive again. Another voice said, "Detective Menetti."

It shook her to have to begin a third time. "Yes, I want to report . . . This is Mrs. . . . My son is missing. He's six years old."

"Name," said the toneless voice on the other end.

"My name is Susan Selky; his name is Alexander."

"Your address, Mrs. Selky?"

"Sixty-three Fremont Street. That's between Marlborough and Beacon."

"You last saw your son . . . when?"

"At eight fifty this morning. I kissed him good-by and watched him to the corner. The school is only two more blocks."

"He was last seen at eight fifty *this morning?* Why did you wait so long to call us?"

"Oh, please . . ." she said very softly.

"Never mind. I'll be right there." Lieutenant Menetti hung up.

The doorbell rang. Jocelyn and Justine. Taxi greeted them fervently but was a little surprised. *They* weren't Alex. He did his best to welcome them anyway. Justine, in a white leotard and a red peasant skirt, looked grave and held her mother's hand.

"He never *came* to school today," Justine started explaining to Susan while still climbing the stairs. "I waited outside for him until the bell rang. He has my red pencil."

Far in the distance, Susan heard a siren. It whined louder and louder through the streets toward them until at last it pulled up at the front door with a threatening wail. Jocelyn held Susan's hand as they listened to the footsteps on the stairs.

Susan felt weirdly calm, as if she were outside her body, picturing the scene. There she was, standing at the top of the stairs, holding her door open. She was slim, tall, with fine dark hair and light blue eyes. There she was in her bare feet; her sandals were by the chair where she had curled up with the paper an hour ago. There was Jocelyn, with her fashionably wild brown hair streaked with gray, looking bony in her ancient blue jeans and work shirt, but, as always, carefully made-up. Here were the two detectives. This one was big, dark, fifty, with a flushed face and creases around his mouth and eyes. Detective Menetti. This other one was younger. Pale. Heavy.

Detective Menetti introduced himself and the other officer and registered Jocelyn's and Justine's names. Susan told him again what she'd told him on the phone.

"He never got to school at *all*," Justine kept piping up. "I waited for him. I waited and waited."

Menetti said, "Tell me a little about him, Mrs. Selky."

She hesitated. How can you tell a little about your whole child? "He's very responsible," she said. "The school's only two blocks up Beacon Street." To one side, the second detective was watching her.

"Can you let me have a more complete description?" Menetti asked. He had his pad out and his pen poised.

"Oh. Yes. He's, um, he's almost seven years old; he has straight dark brown hair. He's very friendly and happy, and he loves soccer . . . and riddles."

"How tall is he, Mrs. Selky?"

"How . . . well . . . he comes to right here on me." Her arms curved outward, as if to embrace her missing boy.

"He's exactly Justine's height," said Jocelyn softly.

Menetti looked at Justine. "I have a seven-year-old myself," he said to her. "I bet you weigh, what, fifty-five pounds?"

"Alex is a pound or two lighter," said Jocelyn.

"Wearing?" They looked at Susan.

She took a deep breath. "Wearing. Blue jeans, red-and-white T-shirt, and blue running shoes. He was carrying a green knapsack on his back."

"Okay, got that. Mrs. Selky, is Alex the kind of kid who talks to strangers?"

140

Susan shook her head. "We went over that when we decided he could walk to school by himself. We talked about strangers and what they might say, and the ways Alex could handle it."

"Okay. Now, when you say 'we decided'—you mean you and Mr. Selky?"

"I mean Alex and me. Graham and I are separated."

A look passed between the two detectives. "And how long have you been separated, Mrs. Selky?"

"Three months."

"Uh-huh. And where is Mr. Selky living now?"

"In Cambridge." Then she asked tartly, "Do you want to know with whom?"

"It was a painful separation, then?"

"Painful? Of course it was painful— May I ask why this is important? Couldn't we be doing something?"

"In just a second. Just a second. You had a custody fight, did you, over Alex, when you separated?"

Susan shook her head impatiently. "No, nothing like that. Graham and I didn't separate to hurt each other; we were trying to *stop* hurting each other."

"I see. Mr. Selky sees Alex when he wants to, then?"

"All the time. They adore each other. Graham's a wonderful father." Her voice was starting to tremble.

"Could we have your husband's address, Mrs. Selky?"

She recited it, and both detectives wrote it down.

"Good. Got it." Menetti snapped his pad shut. "Now, listen, Mrs. Selky. I know you're feeling anxious right now, and I don't blame you. I'm going to radio from my car for some extra help, and we're going to cover the neighborhood here. I have seven kids of my own, and I'll lay you odds we'll have your rascal back here for you by bedtime."

He smiled at Susan, and she felt a sudden thaw of hope. Could he be right? Of course he could.

"We'll canvass the neighborhood," Menetti went on. "There must have been people going to work that time of day who saw him. You and Mrs. Norris here can help out, if you would."

141

"Anything," said Jocelyn. "You name it."

"You can start phoning the parents of Alex's classmates. Find out if any of them saw him, tell them that he's missing, and tell them what he was wearing. Ask them to pass it on."

"You got it," said Jocelyn. Susan, mute, just touched her on the arm. Then Jocelyn went to the kitchen phone.

"I'm going down to my radio," Menetti said to Susan. "Do you mind if Detective Sachs looks over the house?"

Susan shook her head.

"Good. Now, remember, kids do *not* disappear into thin air. Sometimes we can't *find* them for a while, but they do not just disappear. Can you remember that? Keep calm." Menetti went downstairs.

Detective Sachs put away his pad and came forward. "Before we go over the house, Mrs. Selky, do you have a good picture of Alex you can let us have?"

Susan put her hand to her mouth nervously. "The most recent is . . . six months old. . . . Children change so fast. Maybe Graham has some more recent ones. Oh, God, I've got to tell him." She started for the phone.

"Mrs. Selky, please hold off doing that for a while."

"Doing what?"

"Calling your husband. Or your relatives. No need to alarm them yet, and it will make our job easier if you delay that."

"Really? But you told us to call our friends."

"I know, but we prefer to do it this way."

"Oh," Susan said vaguely. She felt taut as a harp string, one quivering thread of gut, and she was easily distracted. She sat down. Stood up. Said, "I'll get the pictures."

Detective Sachs followed her; then he went methodically from room to room, showing particular interest in the bathrooms. He opened the hamper in Susan's bathroom and took everything out, socks, towels, and underwear. In Alex's he did the same thing. He opened doors, checked closets. He studied the pictures on the mantel in Susan's bedroom. "This your husband?" he asked, pointing to a dark-haired man in a smiling family group.

142

"No," said Susan. "That's his brother, Robert. The blond one is Graham. They're twins, but you'd never know it. Fraternal."

"Good-looking guy," said Detective Sachs. "Your husband."

"Yes," said Susan, snatching snapshots from her mirror frame. "These are Alex." She laid them on the mantelpiece beside a large picture of Alex at five, his head thrown back in the sunlight, laughing. There were snaps of Alex in his Camp Woonsocket T-shirt, with a balloon at his first-birthday party, Alex on Graham's shoulders on Boston Common.

Detective Sachs tapped the mantel with his hand. "Must be nice, a fire in the bedroom." He crouched down and peered up into the chimney. He opened the flue and closed it again. Then he stood and asked, "Do you have a laundry?"

"Yes. In the basement. It's this way."

As they trooped downstairs, Sachs asked about the tenant in the ground-floor apartment.

"She's a widow named Margaret Mayo," said Susan. "She works at the MIT library."

"Does she have children?"

"Two. Grown up. They live in California, I think."

"I'd like to look around her apartment, if I may."

Susan got the key, and Detective Sachs went all through Margaret Mayo's apartment, opening closets, checking under the beds, looking into the refrigerator and the oven.

When they were finished, they turned off the lights, locked the door, and went on down the stairs to the cellar. Susan followed Detective Sachs patiently, feeling hopeful and curious. She didn't ask herself what he was doing. She simply clung to the simplicity of minutes passing and somebody doing something.

Detective Sachs was very thorough in the basement. He looked in the washer and the dryer. He took out his flashlight and checked behind the machines. In one corner he opened a crate full of place mats, cheese boards, and fondue pots still in gift boxes. He examined them, then straightened, saying, "You have a lot of fondue pots."

"It was the year of the fondue pot, the year I got married."

"My wife loves fondue pots," said Sachs. "She enjoys eating things with those little forks."

"I bet your wife feels safer having you work in Juvenile than on the Bomb Squad or something," Susan offered.

"Oh, I'm not on Juvenile," Sachs said. "I'm on Homicide."

As THE afternoon light began to deepen into evening in the corners of the living room, so did Susan's horror. It was past Alex's suppertime. His package of chicken breasts lay in the refrigerator. Jocelyn had called family after family, but no one she had spoken to had seen Alex from the moment he turned the corner onto Beacon Street. It was as if he had walked out of sight and out of this life.

Jocelyn had gone home at six to continue her telephoning, because Detective Menetti had decided that they should keep Susan's line clear in case of a ransom call. Now Susan wanted to call Graham. In three months she had only called him at his office at Boston University, never at his girl friend's.

As she was trying to make herself go to the phone and dial the number, to say to a girl on the other end, This is Graham's wife, the phone rang. It was very loud, and Susan jumped. Detective Menetti gestured to her to answer. Upstairs, she knew, another detective would silently pick up the extension.

Susan picked up the phone, said, "Hello," and started praying.

"Susan?" said a woman's voice, very young and low and tense. "This is . . . Naomi, Graham's friend."

Susan stopped praying. It took her a moment or two to whisper, "Oh."

"The police were just here, looking for Graham. They searched the apartment, and they kept asking me questions about Alex. They wouldn't answer any of my questions, but I suddenly felt so afraid for you. Susan . . . are you all right?"

Oh, please, thought Susan, don't let me cry.

144

She said, "Alex has disappeared, Naomi. He hasn't been seen since nine o'clock this morning. Where is Graham?"

"He . . . he told me he was having dinner with TJ, but I called there, and he isn't." Naomi paused, and Susan felt something in her heart go out to this younger one. "I would find Graham for you if I could," said Naomi simply. "I don't know what to say."

"It's all right. I know." Oh, I do know, she thought.

"Susan, could I tell you something?"

"Yes."

"I always wanted to tell you that I first introduced myself to Graham to tell him how I admired your study of Willa Cather."

Susan didn't answer. Her throat at that moment was aching with anger. She tried twice to speak again, but found she couldn't, so she just hung up.

Almost immediately the phone rang again. Menetti had to signal her twice to pick up the receiver.

"Susan. TJ. Look, did you know the police were looking for Graham?" His voice was big and deep. Susan pictured him, his tall, long-waisted body, in jeans with a hole nearly through his back pocket where he carried his keys. She began to cry.

"TJ, they're not looking for Graham; they're looking for Alex. He never got to school this morning, but I didn't know it, and he's been gone all this time. TJ, can you help me?"

"I'm on my way," he said, and the phone clicked down. TJ was Graham's closest friend and Alex's godfather. He was smart and wry and absolutely true. If you were facing the longest night of your life, TJ was the one you'd want to face it with.

By the clock it was less than eight minutes between the time she hung up and the moment she heard TJ's ancient Porsche screech to a stop in front of her house. He used his own front-door key and took the stairs three at a time, with his plump little girl friend, Annie, scampering behind him. Annie waited while TJ wrapped Susan in a long, speechless embrace. Susan kept a tight grip on his hand even as she then kissed Annie. With them in the room the blue glow of the last light outside the window seemed less evil.

145

After introductions, Detective Menetti questioned both TJ and Annie about Graham. They had no idea where he was.

"This is going to take him apart," said TJ. "He thinks Alex makes the sun rise."

"Can you help me find Graham, Mr. French?" asked Menetti.

"Dr. French," said Susan.

"TJ," said TJ. "Sure, I can help find Graham, but I'd rather find Alex. Have you got any leads at all yet?"

Menetti and Sachs exchanged glances. "We've got a lot of people who recognize the boy," said Menetti. The police on the street were now carrying copies of the photograph of Alex in his camp T-shirt. "We've got a dozen who know they see him most mornings, and we've got a couple who think they saw him today."

"What does that mean, they *think?*"

"Well, in a case like this, everyone wants to help, to turn in the big clue. Pretty soon they're positive they saw him this morning, only it turns out that they saw him last week."

"In other words, you don't have anyone who definitely saw him after he left Susan?"

"Not at this moment, no. But we'll check out every lead we get." Almost as if talking to himself, Menetti continued, "He could have wandered off and fallen down and gotten hurt and taken a while to come to. He could be in a hospital, and eventually he'll identify himself. If he doesn't, we'll see the report, an unidentified patient. Or he could be afraid you'd be mad at him for getting lost, so he doesn't want to come home."

Susan absorbed this picture. However wrenching the thought was, it was something to hope for. That her sweet, good boy, trying so hard to help, somehow (But how? *How?* Don't think about it. . . .) did in fact take a wrong turn trying to walk up Beacon Street to school, and that he didn't ask for directions because he'd been told not to talk to strangers, and that he felt more and more bewildered and embarrassed until finally he just sat down somewhere and decided to wait for help. It could be worse . . . there could be worse things. . . .

"And if he's not lost?" asked TJ.

146

"Well, there are other possibilities," said Menetti. "One is kidnapping. For money. Mrs. Selky tells me that her father is comfortable and Mr. Selky's parents are fairly wealthy. In other words, she could raise a ransom if she had to."

"But wouldn't a kidnapper go for some Rockefeller kid?"

"Listen," said Menetti. "Kidnapping isn't a crime for pros. Unless it's political, your kidnapper is probably on his maiden voyage, and he may do things that you and I would consider stupid. Like picking a kid whose family doesn't have big money. Also, there are plenty of people who would look at this house and this street, and to them that is big money. Kid in private school. Both parents professors. They might just have hung around and seen that here was a pretty small kid who always walked the same two blocks every morning, and just picked him because it would be easy."

Susan put her head in her hands. TJ went over and knelt in front of her chair and lifted her arms around his neck. "Don't think it," he said, holding her with both arms. "He *is* old enough to walk two blocks by himself. You didn't risk him; you gave him room to grow up, by trusting him."

"Room to grow up?" She wept, so softly that only TJ could hear. "This is very hard. . . ."

"Don't cry yet," TJ whispered. "It's not time for that. It's time to have faith." He felt her quiet herself.

Menetti said, "I'm finding it pretty hard to figure out how a kid could disappear so fast or completely unless he was taken into a building right near here, or into a car—"

The phone rang. Susan ran for it. It was Alex's teacher, distraught because she hadn't called Susan immediately when she learned that the school nurse hadn't received a call to explain Alex's absence. "I never *thought* . . ." The woman sobbed. "Parents often forget to call us when they keep a child home."

"It's all right," Susan kept murmuring to her. "It's all right. It's not your fault." What am I talking about? her head said while her mouth spoke. It's *not* all right.

When she came back to the living room, Menetti was saying,

"Something that happens more often than you think is a kid getting stolen by someone who just wants a kid. We've seen an increase in those cases since the abortion law was passed. There are less babies around now to adopt, and some people really want children."

"What kind of person *does* that?" asked TJ.

"You name it. Can be a lonely woman . . . or man . . . a frustrated grandparent. They sit around the park, they watch the kids, they hear the mothers complain. They start telling themselves young people aren't taking proper care of the kids, and the next thing you know they've adopted one, as a public service.

"We had a case last year of a teenage boy who stole a little two-year-old he'd been baby-sitting for. We picked them up in Texas after almost a month. The kid said he just felt like hitting the road, and he wanted a traveling companion.

"See, with that kind of situation, they just want the kid; they don't really think about what it's going to be like, how long you have to hide him, how you do it, where you go, what a kid needs."

TJ and Susan looked at each other, and TJ could almost hear her thinking that it sounded much more likely than some amateur ransom job—the idea that someone, some lonely person, could look at her lovely, jaunty little boy and just want him so badly, she took him.

"Of course," said Menetti, "it's a long shot that we're ever going to seriously face that kind of possibility."

"Why do you say that?" TJ asked.

Menetti frowned. "Look, you gotta understand. What is it—some sixty percent of murderers know their victims? Now, usually, when a child disappears, you've got a runaway or you've got custodial interference. You know."

"I *don't* know," said Susan, staring at him.

"Look," said Menetti. "You just separated from your husband, right? You're still pretty ticked off at him, right? And he's pretty ticked off at you. I know you say, 'Not my husband, *he'd* never do a thing like this,' but nine times out of ten, when a kid disappears, the person you look for first is the other parent."

148

"I am not ticked off at Graham!" said Susan sharply. "And he is not ticked off at me. Oh, God. You *can't* be doing all you can to find out what really happened if you're seriously wasting men on looking for Graham. I thought you were trying to reach him to tell him about Alex. I thought you just wanted to ask him for his help."

For the first time TJ, too, showed signs of his own anger. "Look, sir, you are way off the mark—"

The phone rang. Everyone froze. Susan picked it up. "Hello?"

"Hello," said a woman's voice. "Is this Mrs. Selky?"

"Yes, this is she." Susan had to push to make her voice come out at normal volume. Who are you? Do you have my son?

"Mrs. Selky, this is Maureen Laugherty with the Channel Eleven news team, and we understand that your six-year-old boy has vanished into thin air."

"Oh!" Susan wailed in frustration. "It's some woman from the news. . . ."

Menetti took the phone from her. "This is Detective Menetti," he said. "The situation is that the child is missing, and we have no more information whatsoever. There will be no more comment at this time." He hung up, then called up the stairs to the officer listening on the extension and told him to cut in on all press calls with the word that there was no comment at this time and that police orders were to keep the line clear.

"Okay," Menetti said to Susan. "Now we'll be in for it. I'm surprised we stayed clear this long, with my men in the neighborhood and your Mrs. Norris calling everyone in the city. I'm going to order a cordon in the street, so no one can get close to the house, but we can't keep the press from camping all up and down the block or from interviewing your neighbors. I'm afraid that with you and your husband both professors and Alex such an appealing kid, you're going to look like awfully good copy."

The phone rang again. Susan picked it up, but before she even spoke, the voice said, "This is 'News Center Four' calling," and she heard the officer upstairs take it, so she hung up.

Alex hungry and frightened. Alex out there in the dark, crying.

149

Alex in a hospital, unconscious, no identification for them to notify her. Alex threatened by criminals . . .

"I want to know where he is," Susan said to Menetti. "I want to go on TV. Whatever it is, wherever he is, I want everyone to see me, to know that I love him, and that I just want to know . . ."

Menetti looked surprised. "Are you sure?" he asked. "Do you know what it's going to be like to face the media? It's not Walter Cronkite out there. It's some very ruthless garbage hounds."

She shrugged. "Doesn't matter. Couldn't hurt any more. It's the one thing I can do."

The phone rang again. Again, the caller introduced herself; it was Vivienne Grant with Channel 5 News. She wanted to know if she could do a live interview with Susan, in the missing boy's bedroom. "Yes," said Susan. "Yes, you can."

The phone rang again. It was Jocelyn. "How are you, baby?" she murmured. "Is there anything new at all?" Susan said not. "Well, I've got Katherine Abbot and Martina Rolley calling, too. I think we've reached every parent from Beacon Hill to Porter Square. People are praying for you. I've got a whole army out here ready to help, if there's anything they can do."

"Thank you, Jocelyn. Thanks for what you've done already. Just a minute, Detective Menetti wants to talk to you."

Susan listened to Menetti saying, "Mrs. Selky wants to go public . . . the eleven-o'clock news. It may be that we'll flush something out pretty quickly. If nothing happens, if you've really got some volunteers lined up, let's have a meeting with them right here at ten tomorrow morning. Can you get that word out? Okay. Yes, she's all right; she has some friends here. . . . No, we're still looking for Mr. Selky. . . . Yes. Good-by."

As he hung up, Annie went to answer a light tapping at the door, and came back, followed by Margaret Mayo, Susan's tenant. She was a graceful sixty-year-old woman with iron-gray hair and brilliant eyes and one of the world's readiest smiles. She somehow introduced herself to everyone in the room while moving straight to Susan. She took her hand and gave her a strong, steady gaze. "I want to know how I can help you."

150

"Margaret, thank you. I don't know. There doesn't seem to be anything we can do."

"Well, tell me this, have you called your father?"

Susan looked at her.

"You were hoping any moment Alex would be found, and *then* you could let him know you'd had a scare."

Susan nodded.

"But you can't just let him hear it on the news," said Margaret. "Why don't I call him for you? I'll call Graham's parents, too. Where are the numbers?"

Susan pointed to the list in felt-tip pen on the wall above the telephone. "Margaret, thank you." It was all in her voice— she so much didn't want to make those calls.

"You're welcome," said Margaret. "First, would you like a big hug?" Susan actually smiled for the first time in hours. Margaret's hug was warm and firm and deliberate. Susan hadn't felt that particular brand of comfort since her mother died.

Menetti thanked Margaret, too, and asked her to make the calls downstairs, from her own phone. "Certainly," said Margaret. "In fact, why don't you always use my phone for making calls out? That way you can keep this number free."

The phone rang twenty-two times in the next hour. It was getting on toward eleven. Some of the callers were friends wanting news. The other calls were from news personnel. Reporters and camera crews had now gathered outside. Huge lights illuminated the façade of the house, and the sidewalk was a snake's nest of cables from lights and microphones. Presently an officer in charge of the press chose a small group to come inside for the live interview.

Susan felt numb as technicians tested connections and the lighting men ran up and down the steps. She could hardly think of Alex. There was so much confusion that she was finding it hard to recapture some concrete detail of him. The smell of his hair warm from the sun. The perfect roundness of his head, how it fitted the curve of her palm when she stroked it. A woman with a large black case kept asking her something she couldn't understand. Finally Margaret Mayo intervened. "No, she doesn't want any makeup," she said gently. "She feels like hell, and she might as well look that way."

Vivienne Grant wanted Susan sitting on Alex's bed, holding something that belonged to him. "Get the dog in the shot," the cameraman kept urging. Taxi, thought Susan with a stab of worry. Had anyone fed him this evening? Taxi came into the bedroom and lay down by her feet, looking bewildered, but got up and ran out of the room as they switched on the brilliant lights. "Damn," said the cameraman. "Can you call him back?"

"No," Susan said. "It's too bright."

"Well, could you hold something of the boy's, then? How about a teddy bear?" Susan looked at the threadbare plush rabbit that was lying, as always, on Alex's pillow.

"No," she said. "I think not." She felt strangely calm. Now Alex's room was a movie set. Alex was nowhere. Alex had been gone for years. There had never been a real Alex.

Suddenly Vivienne Grant began to speak, looking intently into the camera. "We're here on

152

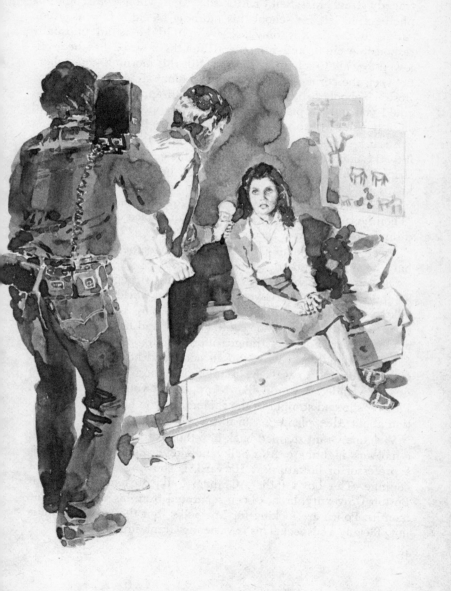

Fremont Street at the home of Mrs. Susan Selky, where today, tragedy struck. Mrs. Selky's little son, Alex, whom you see in this photograph, left for school this morning at eight fifty as usual. Although the boy is only six, we're told he is an unusually responsible child, and for several months now he has been allowed to walk to school by himself. But this morning, somewhere between the corner of Beacon and Fremont streets and the New Boston School, two blocks away, Alex disappeared. Mrs. Selky, could you tell us, please, exactly what happened?" She stepped slightly sideways so the camera could move in on Susan.

Susan's voice was clear and calm. "Alex left the house at eight fifty this morning. He was wearing blue jeans, a red-and-white striped T-shirt, and blue running shoes; he was carrying a green knapsack. I watched him walk to the corner, and he turned and waved to me." He waved to me! I forgot that, until this second! "Then he turned the corner," Susan's calm voice continued, "and disappeared. He never reached school."

"I see," said Vivienne Grant. "Tell me, Mrs. Selky, would Alex have been on his guard against strangers?"

Of course Alex was on his guard against strangers. Of *course* he understood that there were people in the world not to trust or talk to. And don't say again that he was "only six." He's known since he was two that traffic could kill him, and he certainly knew not to wander off with a stranger offering lollipops.

"He is friendly but wise," Susan said, "and he was very proud of being trusted to walk by himself. He doesn't dawdle and he doesn't wander. I would like to appeal to your audience. . . . Please," she said straight to the camera, "if you have any information about Alex, please get in touch with the police."

Vivienne Grant stepped back into the shot. "In Boston tonight, a mother's nightmare. Alex Selky, missing at age six. His mother, a professor of literature at Harvard, is showing a great deal of courage. The boy's father, Graham Selky, teaches English at Boston University; he has been separated from his wife for three months. Police are looking for Mr. Selky, but they say that he is not officially a suspect. This is Vivienne Grant, in Back Bay."

154

The moment the scene was finished, Susan shot up from where she was sitting and made her way through the equipment back to Menetti. He was on the phone, confirming a special police number for viewers to call, to be broadcast before the end of the program. He said, "Right—got it," then hung up. Menetti was beginning to look haggard, and the thought occurred to Susan that he wasn't just doing a job—he really cared about Alex.

"Detective Menetti . . ." she said.

"Look, why don't you call me Al?" he said to her wearily.

"Al, I know you don't have all the men in the world. Will you *please, please* not waste time chasing Graham. We may have had problems, but this isn't a crazy family. We're normal people, and some lunatic has done something . . . to our . . ." She could feel the hysteria welling up in her chest.

"I know how you feel," Menetti began.

"No, you don't. Excuse me, but you cannot possibly know at this moment how I—" The phone rang.

"Susan?" said the anxious voice. "This is Robert."

"Robert!" Graham's brother? Detective Menetti asked her soundlessly. She nodded yes.

"I'm in Boston. I just saw you on the news. Susan, is there anything I can do?"

"But you're never in Boston. What are you doing here?"

"I came up last night. I can't believe this is happening. Where is Graham?"

"Robert, we don't know where he is, really."

"I'm coming right over there," said Robert.

"Okay," said Susan. She hung up.

"Robert's in Boston?" asked TJ. "That's weird."

"It *is* weird," said Susan.

"Robert's one of those types who brags about never stepping in the provinces except to change planes," TJ explained to Annie.

There was some kind of commotion downstairs, an increasing murmur of raised voices. Then one voice soared to desperate volume. "Just get the hell out of my way. *I want my wife!*"

"Graham!" TJ and Susan cried at the same time.

155

Menetti threw open the door and yelled down, "Let him up!"

In another moment Graham burst through the door. The expression on his face was something Susan felt she'd never forget for the rest of her life. She ran to him and held him as hard as she could, knowing that the first shock was burning through his heart and mind like acid, as if it would literally kill him.

"I was in a taxi," he said into her hair. "The driver had the news on the radio." His voice sounded as if he were strangling. Susan felt his anguish as he tried not to cry.

TJ put his hand on Graham's shoulder, then wrapped an arm around him and clasped him hard.

Graham gave TJ his hand. "Thank you for being here, man," he said. "Annie"—over TJ's shoulder—"thank you for coming." The two men looked very alike, both tall and muscular, but Graham had thick honey-blond hair. He wore a dark blue shirt and a tweed jacket, and looked almost exactly the same as when Susan had fallen in love with him twelve years ago. Except that his eyes no longer glowed with that generous joy that he had back when he was young and thought he couldn't lose. That didn't stop Susan from feeling a surprised burst of love at the tilt of his head and the swing of his hips every time she saw him.

Tonight his eyes were dull with fear. She could feel him staring around, as she had for hours, unable to believe that Alex wasn't in the next room. Soon he would feel the numbness begin. Soon he would be with her in the unreality.

"Mr. Selky," said Menetti firmly, "could you please tell me where you have been for the last six hours?"

Graham made a face as if he couldn't answer. "All this time," he said, and his arms went around Susan, "all this time, and I could have been here and *done* something. . . ."

"Mr. Selky? I really must know," Menetti pressed.

"I was visiting a friend." Graham didn't look at him.

"Mr. Selky," said Menetti, "I have had police officers who could have been otherwise occupied looking for you for six hours, and I want to know *exactly*—"

"I was in Charlestown trying to seduce a nurse!" Graham

yelled. "Do you want to talk to her? You'll find it delightful; she's got a vocabulary of at least forty words." Then he did begin to cry, and Susan, stricken for him, held his bowed head against her cheek and began to cry, too.

"I'm afraid I will have to talk to her," said Menetti.

Graham shook Susan off and covered his face with his hands, furiously stripping away the tears. Then he began searching his pockets, which, she knew, were always an owl's nest of receipts, deposit slips, and scraps of paper with phone numbers. Suddenly he threw them all on the floor. "I don't have her number. What the hell does it matter? *Where is my son?*"

"Hey, Graham," said TJ. "Cool down. Menetti's only trying to do his job."

"So why isn't he out doing it?"

"He's asking you where you were because they thought you might have taken Alex."

"They thought what?"

"Look," said TJ, "they don't know you. You've got to let them check out your story so they'll believe you."

Graham groaned. "I met her on a bus. Her name is Claire. She works at Mount Auburn Hospital. That's all I know."

TJ stared at him. "If I didn't feel so frightened for you right now, I'd wring your neck, man."

"Please," said Graham. "Please."

"Call Naomi," said TJ.

Graham looked at Susan. "She called me," said Susan. "The police were at her apartment looking for you—and for Alex. She was very worried."

"Okay. I'll call her."

"You can use Mrs. Mayo's phone downstairs," said Menetti. "We're keeping this line clear."

After Graham, followed by a policeman, had gone out the door, Robert arrived. Menetti watched him closely as he greeted Susan and TJ and was introduced to Annie. Smaller, darker, with something soft about him, he looked nothing like his brother, and yet he had a kind of presence. Perhaps it was his self-absorption,

Menetti thought; but there was something about him that seemed not precisely restful.

"Susan, it's *unreal*," Robert kept saying. He was right about that, so Susan nodded. Just then Graham returned, and Robert cried, "Graham, I can't believe it!" They shook hands.

"Robert. It's strange to see you in Boston."

"Well, it was last minute; someone got sick, and I was asked to fill in at a conference on public broadcasting."

Graham seemed to tune him out, saying to Menetti, "There must be something we can do besides standing here. Couldn't TJ and I take the dog or something and go out there?"

"I had a team of trained men on the street for as long as we had light," said Menetti. "There just isn't anything to see now."

"I want to help. I want to do something."

"I think you're going to have to help each other get through tonight," said Menetti.

"Are you going to stay?" Susan asked the detective. She realized she was beginning to have problems with time; she wasn't sure if it was midnight or four in the morning.

"Yeah," said Menetti. "I guess I'd have to say the odds are with ransom now. If we're going to hear from the kidnappers, my guess is the first contact will come in the next six hours."

"What about hospitals?" Graham asked suddenly. "Did you think of that? Supposing he's hurt and unconscious and—"

"We've checked them all," said Menetti. "Nothing."

"Oh," said Graham.

FOR the first two hours after the news broadcast the phone seemed to ring every time it touched the cradle. Susan's father called; Graham's parents called. Students and colleagues of Graham's and Susan's called; total strangers called, offering help. Others called to offer psychic information and tips from God.

Margaret took all the calls, while an officer listened in upstairs. Menetti thought it would be best, psychologically, for a woman to answer a ransom call. Susan's frantic jittery feeling had worn off, and she felt muffled and numb again. She just wanted to sit still and try to make her mind remember what had happened. The major fact kept escaping her, like a dream in which you know you're in prison for life but can't remember why.

She would suddenly have a vivid picture of Alex still and white. An arm broken and bent the wrong way. Dry brown blood at his nose and mouth. His eyes were open, glazed in an expression of horror, the first knowledge of terror, coming into his life at the moment it ended.

After three a.m. the phone calls began to taper off. For Graham's benefit and Robert's, Menetti went over the possibilities again. Alex might be lost and for some reason be afraid or ashamed to ask for help. . . .

"But he knows to look for policemen," said Graham. "And he knows his phone number, and he always carries a dime."

"How would he reach a phone in a phone booth?" asked Robert. "A little kid, he couldn't reach the dial."

"He would ask someone to lift him up," said Susan. "Or to dial for him." But she was picturing big hands picking Alex up. Big hands, grasping and crushing.

"He could have asked the wrong person for help," said Robert. "We've got to face it."

We? thought Susan. Suddenly she wished Robert would go away. She started to cry.

Quite a while passed in silence. Annie, sitting with TJ in one big chair, settled her head on his shoulder and fell asleep. Graham and Susan sat side by side on the couch. Graham held Susan's hand. Margaret sat at the table by the telephone, playing solitaire. Menetti, in the chair by the window, slept sitting bolt upright. TJ fell asleep. Robert got up eventually and went up the stairs. From the creaking on the floor above as he walked, Susan knew he'd gone into Alex's room and stretched out on the bed.

In the darkest hours of the night Susan thought, If it's kidnap, if it's ransom, then he's not dead. If he's not dead, then the phone will ring. What I must do is make the phone ring. People say you can make something happen by making an image of it happening. So I am picturing the phone ringing, right now. I am hearing the

159

voice on the other end. "Hello, Mrs. Selky?" or "Hello, Mommy?"

I am picturing the phone beginning to ring. In the next second it is going to ring. I can feel it; you sometimes hear it a second before it actually starts to ring.

They sat in that room like stones, until the gray morning light started leaking in like the death of hope.

TJ and Annie woke up. Menetti went into the kitchen and made instant coffee. Margaret put away her cards and folded her hands in her lap. Graham stood up and began to pace around the room.

Menetti said, "Now that it's light again, we can do something."

"What?" asked Graham.

"We can get out there, and we can find every human being who was on the street yesterday morning."

Robert came downstairs, grunted hello at everyone, and went into the kitchen for coffee. Menetti stood staring down at the street. Suddenly he turned to Graham and said, "Well, I'll tell you this. A kid cannot disappear into thin air. Especially at eight fifty in the morning. Another thing, it's easier to hide a live kid than a dead one."

Susan came up behind them. "What did you say?"

"I said it's easier to hide a live kid than a dead one. A body is a real problem, especially in hot weather."

"He has a very small body," said Susan.

Graham put his arms around her. She leaned against him and closed her eyes. Everything went away for her except touch and sound. Warm, dark. Shirt against her cheek. Sound of someone— Robert—going up the stairs. Footsteps. Faint hiss. The shower.

IT WAS hardly past first light when the phone rang in Jocelyn's darkened bedroom on Marlborough Street.

"Hi, it's Martina. I'm sorry, did I wake you?"

"Who could sleep?" Jocelyn answered groggily.

"I couldn't," said Martina. "I got up and went running. I kept thinking he's *out* there. I wondered if you'd heard anything."

"Not since about three thirty this morning. Susan was too wrecked to come to the phone, but her tenant, Margaret, said they hadn't heard a thing."

"Did you see Susan on the news? She was incredible."

"No, I didn't. I heard about it. I was still on the phone, but everyone said she was totally calm."

"She was incredible. My little boy has been stolen and he's probably been raped and murdered, and I'm not going to fall apart as long as there's a single thing I can do to help him. It was like that. If it were me, I'd have been on there *screaming*."

"No, you wouldn't," said Jocelyn. "You think you would, but when it's happening to you . . ."

"She had dignity. She was like that all through that mess with Graham, too. So in love with him and so angry and sad, but she was always fair. She just kept saying, you know, that it had been hard for Graham to feel stalled on that book he's been trying to write and to have people make such a fuss about *her* book."

"Did you hear they couldn't even find Graham until eleven thirty last night?" asked Jocelyn.

"I know," said Martina. "It must have been killing her. Well, I ought to call Susan now. I'm sure they're up."

"Yes. Look, Menetti's holding a meeting of volunteers at ten o'clock. Help get the word around, will you?"

"Right. It was good of you to do all that phoning yesterday," said Martina.

"Oh, it's not just about Alex, you know. If there's a pervert kid killer out there, it's about all of us with children."

"I know," said Martina.

WHEN the first editions of the Boston *Globe* and the *Record American* hit the morning streets, they carried the story of Alex's disappearance on page one. The *Record American* ran a front-page picture of his laughing face. The three national networks carried the story on their morning news broadcasts. About eighteen million people heard of Alex's disappearance over breakfast.

When Al Menetti walked into his kitchen in Saugus, his wife, Pat, had the "Today" show on. Eugene, Eileen, and Roberta were watching it while they ate. "Hi, Dad," they all mumbled.

Al's wife kissed him hello. She noticed his ashen face and gave him a look, but he turned to give his small children a hug and a kiss each in turn. Then he went upstairs to shower, shave, and change. From the bathroom window, he watched the three children walk to the corner to meet the school bus. Eugene lagged far behind the others, swinging his book bag. Al could tell from the little skips he took that Eugene was singing to himself.

Pat poured him a cup of coffee when he came downstairs. She made toast and brought it to him, then sat down with a cup of coffee for herself.

"See the news?" he asked her.

She nodded. "They had a picture of the little boy on."

"He's a few months younger than Eugene," said Al. "I saw these drawings he did, all taped to his wall. They look just like Eugene's." He stared into his coffee cup.

"How's the mother?" Pat Menetti asked. She was wearing blue jeans and one of her husband's shirts with the tail out. Al had a pure moment of seeing her suddenly not as the woman who kept serving frozen codfish cakes and who fell asleep in the movies, but as the pretty girl who met him when he was seventeen and never knew she would raise his seven children.

"The mother's good," he said thoughtfully. "She's amazingly good." He stared into space for a while, then spoke again. "I made a mistake last night. I put a lot of men on finding the separated father. Should have been able to tell from the mother that it wasn't a custody thing. She told me it wasn't, and it wasn't. I should have had the bloodhounds on the job right away. There's not much point now. They can't do much after eight hours."

"The thing I wonder," said his wife, "is, if you only have one child, and something happens to him, it must be the worst thing in the world. But then, when you have seven, don't you just worry for them seven times as much?"

"If you don't know, who does?"

162

"*I* don't know," said Pat. "But I don't see how she went on television like that. I couldn't have done it."

"Yeah, you could," he said, looking at her. "If you believed you could help Eugene, I bet you could."

"Are you sure there's nothing funny about her?" his wife asked.

"What do you mean?"

"She was so cool," said Pat.

Uh-huh, thought Menetti. Now it starts. Pat is thinking, It can't happen to me. That mother lost her kid, but if there's something funny about her, then there's a reason it could happen to her but it couldn't happen to me.

"There's nothing funny about her," Menetti said. He finished his coffee and stood up regretfully. "I have to be back in the city at ten. The Selkys have some volunteers, neighborhood parents and friends, coming in to see what they can do. I'll start them putting pictures of the kid around. After that, if anything's moving, I'll stay. Otherwise, I'll come home for dinner."

"Roberta's slumber party is tonight," Pat said.

"Good," he said wearily. "We can all sit around the TV with curlers in our hair."

WHEN Susan was growing up in Quaker Village, Ohio, a suburb of Cleveland, she thought of Boston as a place where people lived wider, richer lives than in Ohio. The Boston of her mind's eye with its Public Garden and the elegant sweep of Commonwealth Avenue seemed like a European capital. It was a place for people of character and wit, people who acted on principle.

By the time Susan and Graham moved to Boston, the city's first families had gradually sifted out of Beacon Hill and Back Bay to the rural comfort of the suburbs. The flavor and charm of the city neighborhoods had changed. Vast mansions along Commonwealth and Beacon had been converted to offices and schools. When Susan and Graham found their narrow town house on Fremont Street in Back Bay, it had been badly used by generations of students from the scattered institutions that Graham called collectively Unknown Junior College. It had taken the

Selkys seven years to fix up the house again, and it still had two unconverted rooms in the attic and was a little short on furniture. But for neighbors they had a Chinese scholar from Peking, a poet who worked for the *Atlantic Monthly*, and a curator from the Boston Museum of Fine Arts.

With one of the highest per capita student populations in the world, Boston seemed simultaneously very young and very old, a city full of diversity, experiment, tradition, and transience. To Susan it felt like a feast. There was a high-caste Hindu teaching assistant in her department, and a Boston Brahmin in Alex's play group, and her kitchen shelves were built by a carpenter from the South End who had a Ph.D. in philosophy. The South End, just across Copley Square from Back Bay, was a neighborhood in the midst of what Boston called gentrification. Row houses that had fallen into ruin were being restored by a mixture of young professionals, academics, and artists. The Fourth District police headquarters was on one seedy edge of the South End.

Menetti, driving in from the suburb of Saugus, had to remind himself that it takes all kinds. He'd worked his butt off to move out of Boston and to raise his kids in a place where everybody tried hard to stay married and keep the lawn cut. A city to him wasn't a place for people, especially kids. There was no center there. People moving in all the time, other people moving out. A city to him was more like a big zoo with cement floors and all the cage doors left open.

When Menetti arrived at the Selky house for his briefing of the volunteers, he was surprised to find more than a hundred people crowded into the living room, quietly waiting for him.

Susan saw him and rose from the chair where she had perched on the arm, leaning on Jocelyn. She couldn't seem to light anywhere for long; she had felt terribly restless and bereft while Menetti was gone. "They're being wonderful," she said to Menetti, gesturing around the jammed room.

Menetti surveyed the group. There were women in peasant dresses; there were women in jeans; there were slender women with delicate necks who looked like dancers. There were several

164

men among the women. One was a well-known chef who lived
in the South End with his lawyer wife. Another turned out to be
a jazz clarinetist Menetti had admired since Police Academy days.

Graham stood and faced the room, clearing his throat for attention. "I want to thank you all for coming today. It means a
great deal to Susan and me. Now I know you must have questions, so Lieutenant Menetti will try to answer them."

Menetti moved to the center of the room. What people wanted
to know was whether their own children were in danger. There
was a darting, stricken look in the eyes of the mothers.

"Do you have any idea," asked one woman, "if this was a crime
committed by somebody Alex knew?"

"Well, we don't know yet that a crime was committed at all,"
said Menetti. "The boy may be lost."

"Are you saying that's what you think?" asked another mother.

"No, I'm not. I'm saying we don't know yet what's happened."
A hundred attentive pairs of eyes were fixed on him. "We have
leads. We're not in the dark. I don't want to be more specific,
because of the press. But at this point, I want to make clear, our
department has *never* had a case of a child this young disappearing without a trace."

"Lieutenant Menetti," asked Susan's friend Martina, "if you
were raising a young child in this neighborhood, what would you
go home and tell him? How would you handle this?"

Menetti had been waiting for this question. "Well," he said,
"I'd have a talk with him about strangers, if you haven't already.
But I also would supervise him pretty carefully."

"Meaning?" "What do you mean?" a dozen voices asked.

"Meaning, I don't think for the time being I'd let a young child
out of the house without an adult."

"What do you mean by young?"

"I'd say . . . under twelve."

There was something awful in hearing him say something so
specific. Why twelve? Why not eight? No one asked. Instead,
Graham said, "Lieutenant Menetti, a lot of us would feel better
if we could help."

165

"Absolutely," said Menetti. An officer who was waiting at the door came forward now with a stack of handbills. Menetti held one up. It showed two snapshots of Alex, one of his smiling face and the camp T-shirt, the other of him standing on the grass, holding a baseball cap and a mitt. Under the pictures was a description of what Alex was wearing, his age, and the exact time and place of his disappearance. Across the top of the paper was the bold headline MISSING.

Menetti asked them all to take handbills everywhere they went in the next few days. To staple them onto trees, tape them onto lampposts. To get permission from every shop they could to post the handbills in the windows.

"Somewhere, somebody knows something," he said. "Somebody's seen something. If anyone gives you information directly, please write it down and get the source's name and address. Call the number on the handbill with anything you get, day or night. And . . . I think it will help to move fast."

As the volunteers left, Susan thanked each one for coming. She stood at the door, as if it were a receiving line. Some kissed her or touched her cheek as they passed. "It's remarkable how kind people are, really," she said when they were gone. She mused on the strangeness of this, the sense of community. Then she drifted into trying to picture Alex. Trying to bring back a round, scented image of him, of his touch. All she could see was his photograph on the poster. MISSING. Yes.

By sundown it seemed that there were posters of Alex in every drugstore, butcher shop, luncheonette, and boutique from the Charles River to Boston Harbor. The six-o'clock news on all stations carried interviews with volunteers. "Mrs. Norris, you've been walking for two hours now, putting up handbills of the missing boy, Alex Selky. Why are you doing that? . . . I see, and are you worried for your own child? . . . I see. . . . From Boston, the scene of a truly stirring volunteer effort to find little Alex Selky, missing now for thirty-three hours. This is Vivienne Grant . . ."

There was an interview with Susan, too, taped early in the afternoon. "We're very grateful to the community for their help and support," she said calmly. "My husband and I feel very hopeful that something or someone will lead us to Alex very quickly."

"You believe, then, that your son is alive, Mrs. Selky?"

"Absolutely," she said to the camera.

Susan sat on her bed in the dusk, watching the broadcast, and wondered, How could I? How did I ever stand so straight and speak like that?

IN SAUGUS, Detective Menetti turned off the news and got up to refill his glass. Roberta and her friends were in the kitchen making fudge. Eugene was listening to records upstairs.

"You look like you've been worked over by Nick the Bouncer," said Pat, glancing up from her needlepoint.

"I hate this case," he said.

"Do you think you're going to get an early break?" asked Pat.

He ignored the question. "You should hear the kinds of leads we have. A neighbor near the school is *sure* he saw the boy yesterday afternoon, unless it was the day before. A woman claims she saw him alone at ten a.m. walking on Newbury Street. She can't explain why she didn't think anything about it, a kid that age wandering around by himself during school hours.

"A man living on Beacon Street, around the corner from the Selky house, claims he saw a woman waiting in a car for about ten minutes the morning in question. He cannot describe the woman; he can sort of describe the car. But he never saw Alex; he just saw this car, and when he finished shaving and went downstairs at nine o'clock, it was gone. Then I've got a guy who thinks he saw Alex in a Cambridge food store at noon. He thinks he was with a punk with bad skin and peroxide hair. Now, why would a smart little kid who knew not to talk to strangers be pricing Twinkies with some pimply jerk instead of screaming his head off? Tell me the truth, would Eugene do that?"

Pat nodded over her needlepoint and went on working.

"I'm serious," said Menetti. "Is there anything some geek could say to Eugene that would get him to wander off shopping with him? Think about it. I want to know."

Pat thought about it. She shrugged. "If he promised to take him to meet the real Batman?"

"I hope you're kidding."

"I don't know if I am or not."

"Pat, what exactly have you told Eugene about strangers?"

"I've told him not to talk to them. I've told him not to go anywhere with them."

"Still, do you think some guy could talk Eugene into going with him, even though you've warned him about strangers?"

"Al, Eugene is seven years old. A seven-year-old is not a responsible person, no matter what you tell him. Not if he has to handle something that hasn't come up before. Sure, I think a reasonably bright grown-up could talk him into anything."

"I'll tell you where Alex Selky is," Menetti said suddenly. "His neighborhood is one block from the Esplanade, and these hot mornings the riverbank is full of people from sunrise on. Drunks, creeps, perverts . . . the whole mixed grill."

"Meaning?"

"Meaning, he was a beautiful little boy. Real beautiful, with a great smile. If he's not dead by now . . . It would probably be better if he was." As Menetti said that, tears came into his eyes.

Pat studied him from her chair, her hand over her mouth. "Do you want dinner?" she said at last. The sounds from the kitchen suggested that Roberta and her friends had reached the pot-and spoon-licking stage.

He wiped his eyes. "No . . . bed," he said.

AT MIDNIGHT the street was gleaming with a slow, cold, steady rain. Susan stood at her bedroom window, looking down. Alex, are you out in this? Alex, my baby, I know it's May, but won't you take your jacket? Alex . . . The gooseflesh on your arms when you're cold. O Lord, deliver me. Christ, deliver me. O God, help me. How do I bear unbearable loss?

In the church in which Susan was raised, there is a moment in the service when the choir rises and slowly marches down the center aisle, chanting. The rector walks behind them. He chants,

"O God the Son, Redeemer of the world"; and the choir and congregation respond, *"Have mercy upon us."* He chants, "From lightning and tempest; . . . from plague, pestilence, and famine; from battle and murder, and from sudden death," and the people respond, *"Good Lord, deliver us."* It is the Litany, the oldest chant in the prayer book, and tonight it was reverberating in Susan, a primitive longing for ritual.

Downstairs in the living room, the bright blue couch had been pushed against the wall to make room for a long table the police had brought in. There were now three telephones on it, Susan's and the special police phone with an extension. Three uniformed officers sat at the table in a row, smoking cigarettes and drinking coffee from paper cups, logging in every telephone call. The phones seemed to ring incessantly. There had been nearly four hundred calls between noon and midnight.

By midafternoon Menetti had had more than three hundred uniformed officers in the streets, searching every house and store and garage and warehouse. Helicopters cruised overhead, scanning rooftops and piers, looking for a place a small boy could have ventured out and become stuck or trapped. Blue-and-white patrol cars drove slowly through the streets, broadcasting through PA systems on the car roofs. "We are looking for a white male child, age six. He is wearing a red-and-white striped T-shirt, blue jeans, and blue running shoes. His name is Alex. Anyone with information concerning this child, please call the police."

Menetti was downstairs most of the time keeping in touch with searchers through a communications van parked in front of the house. Graham and TJ were out in the streets all day, going everywhere Alex would go, doing everything Alex did. Two blue-coated policemen followed them, taking notes, asking questions. They reported to Menetti on walkie-talkies every ten minutes. Nothing so far. Nothing yet. Nothing.

By dinnertime neighbors had dropped off homemade bread and casseroles at the house. Susan tried hard to swallow some soup Margaret prepared, but she only felt nausea boil up in her.

"I can't eat," Susan said, putting down her spoon.

170

Margaret understood. "I can't always eat. We'll try later."

The police were eating Big Macs at their table and continued to take phone calls while they chewed. The room seemed to be filled with racket. All evening the phones rang and rang, and it was torture. Then they began to ring less, and that was worse.

Susan had to wait until very late that night before she could say to herself, I was wrong to let him walk by himself. I was wrong. He was so young . . . too young. It was me.

There had been plenty of calls like that. The police didn't say so, but she knew. A six-year-old child wandering down the street by himself? What do you expect?

Susan sat in the darkness, feeling like an open wound.

She thought, It's days since I had any sleep. I should sleep, or else I'm going to hallucinate. This is much worse than last night. I can't even trace for myself what has happened in a clear linear way. Maybe I can be in the past again. I can be together in time with Alex, before . . .

The phone might ring. It could ring anytime. Couldn't it?

It's been fifteen years since I went to church. I stopped going because religion was the opiate of the masses. Tonight I see that faith isn't a drug. It's an active practice, an act of will. *Now* I see.

To have faith that Alex is alive—it has nothing to do with belief, or thought. Do I think he's alive? I commit myself to his being alive, as an act of will.

Lord, I believe; help thou mine unbelief.

I'm beginning to have longer stretches of my mind going blank. I think I'm beginning to slow down. I wonder if I could sleep.

SATURDAY morning, seven o'clock. It had been full light for over an hour. Hundreds of uniformed police were still carrying on their house-to-house search across Back Bay. Menetti had been downstairs in the street since dawn, directing the operations by radio from the police van.

"One of the largest manhunts in city history," said the morning news. "Police say they will keep up their exhaustive efforts until they find out exactly what happened to little Alex Selky, age six, missing now from his home in Boston for two days." Then the pictures, the phone number, the appeal for information.

Susan could hear the phones shrilling as she lowered herself like a brittle old woman into a tub full of steaming water. On the edge of the tub lay Alex's blue plastic dolphin that swam around by jerking its tail back and forth when you wound it up. Alex, flushed and wet and slippery in his bath, winding it over and over again. Alex's giggle. Alex learning to wash his own hair, rubbing the lather on his head with his little blunt fingers, his eyes and lips ferociously clamped together to keep out the soap. The smell of Alex's clean soapy skin, his warm breath on her cheek as he kissed her good night.

At eight o'clock Al Menetti came inside with two paper cups of coffee and two gelatinous Danish pastries wrapped in waxed paper. When Susan joined him in the living room, he said, "Share this with me." She obediently sat down and slowly managed to eat a whole sweet roll.

Once again there were dozens of policemen all over the house. One of the officers on the telephones this morning was a woman. "Could I speak to you for a minute, Lieutenant?" she called across the room. Menetti gestured to her to join them.

Officer Hines, a tough, bottom-heavy woman, pulled a chair up to the dining table. "Getting an awful lot of dreams the last two hours," she said.

"Adding up to anything?" Menetti asked.

"Maybe half say they see him near a body of water."

"Great," said Menetti. "How much of the earth is covered with water?"

Officer Hines shrugged. "You ever work with Jennifer Busch?"

"The woman in Providence?"

Officer Hines nodded. "She's not exactly batting four for four, but she hits it now and then."

"Isn't she the one who was consulted in the Patty Hearst case?

172

She kept saying Patty was in a small dark place? There are a lot of closets in California."

"Yeah, but I worked on one case she was in on, where a guy disappeared one night between work and home. Jennifer Busch kept seeing him *under* water. There was a place along his route home where the highway ran by a river, and, sure enough, we finally found a clump of trees she kept describing, and there was the car, in about eight feet of water, with the guy in it. He'd had a heart attack at the wheel."

Susan looked sharply from one of them to the other.

"She won't work on just any case," continued Officer Hines. "She'll only get involved if she thinks she can actually help. I could give her a call for you." She looked at Susan.

"Do it. Yes, please do it," said Susan.

The woman said heartily, "No problem," and went back to her place at the telephones.

Susan and Menetti sat silently in their chairs for some minutes listening to the phones ring. The officers took names, addresses, phone numbers. They copied down descriptions seen in dreams; they recorded messages from Ouija boards.

"Lieutenant, I think I've got something," one of the telephone men shouted excitedly across the din. "A third sighting of a boy who fits our description, on Newbury Street Thursday morning."

Menetti crossed the floor in two steps. He scanned the facts of the conversation; then he sprinted down the stairs to the communications van, with Susan at his heels. He called for a dozen men to get over to Newbury Street, to go into every store, to get names of every single employee and deliveryman. He gave orders for his men to stay there till noon, stopping everyone, until they found other people who were on Newbury Street at ten on Thursday morning who might also have seen Alex.

"Okay," he said with a smile, turning to Susan. "Now the next thing I want to do is to get in a hypnotist to talk to the people who reported these sightings—and why don't we have you go under hypnosis, too, and the guy on Beacon Street, to see what more you can remember about the street that morning?

"You know," he said with new energy as they walked back up the stairs, "a case like this is like dominoes. You get nothing, nothing, nothing, and you feel like you're looking at a brick wall, and then suddenly one brick falls, and in a second you've got them all tumbling one after another till the whole case falls into your lap. I can feel it."

THE Newbury Street sightings were a false alarm. Under hypnosis the two people who claimed to have seen Alex gave completely divergent descriptions. One described a child of at least twelve; the other could give no details that were not in the handbill, and in fact had almost surely seen nothing at all. Next Menetti had the man from around the corner put under hypnosis to see if he could remember anything more about the car he saw parked on Beacon Street, or if he could remember seeing Alex approach it. The man identified the car as a light blue Oldsmobile, vintage 1963 or 1964, with rust spots on both doors and one whitewall—on the front-right tire. He insisted he had seen the car parked in exactly the same place at least once earlier in the week, but at no time had he seen Alex approach it. He hadn't seen Alex at all Thursday morning; he'd evidently gone back to shaving before Alex came around the corner.

The police hypnotist came to Susan next. They sat facing each other in two kitchen chairs that Menetti had carried up to Susan's bedroom. "Just relax," said the young doctor. "Focus your eyes right here," and he tapped the bridge of his nose. Susan looked at the spot. In a moment it seemed to glow brightly. They sat in silence. Menetti, behind her on the bed, was perfectly still.

The doctor spoke again. "Now I'm going to count. With each number your eyelids will grow heavier. When I reach ten, your eyes will close."

He began to count, and by the time he reached five, her eyelids dragged downward like lead. At ten, they irresistibly closed.

"Your arms are growing heavy," said the voice. "They are as heavy as lead now." Her arms hung at her sides. "You cannot lift your arms." Susan sat still.

"Try to lift your right arm." She tried. The arm didn't move.

"Good," said the voice. "Now it's the morning of May fifteenth. It's eight forty-five. What are you doing?"

"I'm in the kitchen, putting my students' papers in my folder."

"Where is Alex?"

"He's beside me. He's putting an apple into his lunch bag." Alex brushed his forelock out of his eyes and put the brown lunch bag into his knapsack.

"You ready to go, honey?" asked Susan.

"Yep," he said.

"What about tying that shoelace before you take a trip down the stairs?" Alex giggled. He put down his pack and dropped to his knee to struggle with the lace.

"Honey . . ." said Susan, a little impatient after almost a minute.

"I got it; I can do it," said Alex. He stood up.

The doctor's voice: "All right. You are leaving the kitchen. What do you do?"

"We go downstairs."

"Very good," said the doctor. "Now you are outside. On the front steps." They are. The morning sun, suddenly bright and hot, warms her face and arms. She has to squint a little when she first opens the door and steps outside.

Alex is looking up at her, and the sun makes his hair gleam like polished wood. "Have a good day, sweetheart," she says.

"By, Mommy." She bends down to kiss him, and he puts his right arm around her neck. His left holds his knapsack. His cheek, cool as satin, is against her lips.

"Now, Mrs. Selky," said the doctor, "look down the street to your left. Tell me what you see." She turned her head inside her mind and saw the whole street. As she watched, a truck came around the corner. Two men in running clothes jogged up the street toward her. Then the doctor told her to turn to the right. She described every tree. Every door that opened. The people who passed. It took nearly forty-five minutes to describe it all. She did not see an old blue car; it must have passed her house and turned the corner.

What she could see with staggering immediacy was every lilt of Alex's last steps as she watched him to the corner. The swing of his arms. The turning at the corner to see if she was still watching, the wave of his small right hand. She came out of the trance with a terrible sense of loss, and began to cry.

"It's all right," said Menetti. "The odds are that the car isn't important." Susan didn't bother to explain that that wasn't what she was crying about.

Jennifer Busch, the psychic, arrived in the middle of the afternoon. Her hair was dyed jet black, and she wore a jumper and soft ballet slippers. Her large dark eyes were liquid with sympathy.

"Well, I hope I can help you, dear," she said to Susan. "I'm glad you called; you've been on my mind."

"Do you have an idea . . . do you think you know what's happened to Alex?"

"Don't know yet. I'll tell you one thing, though. When I can see, I know it. When I can't, I say so."

Mrs. Busch asked to be taken to Alex's room. Susan had been careful not to go in there more than once or twice since Alex disappeared. She was saving his room, like a secret cache of something, to be felt with intensity only in deepest private.

Mrs. Busch went straight to the bed and sat down on it, and remained very still a moment or two. "There's been a great deal of loss in this house," she said pointedly to Susan. "A great deal of pain in the little heart that slept here."

"Alex's father and I separated three months ago."

"Um. From the feel of things, I'd say you fought it hard."

"We did," said Susan.

"You feel a great sense of failure."

"Yes."

"Could I have something Alex played with or used when he was happy, please?"

"What? Oh, yes. Sure." Susan looked around, then scooped up Alex's soccer ball from beside his bookcase. Mrs. Busch took it between her plump, short-fingered hands and said, "Good. He played with this with his father?"

"Yes."

Mrs. Busch closed her eyes and sat for some time. Now and then Susan would see a certain flicker or strain cross her face. At last she opened her eyes.

"I can see *him*," she said. "I can't see much else that's any use. He's standing by a window, and the window has cheap venetian blinds, and there's a large road or highway outside, so I'd say it's a motel room."

"You mean, that's what he's doing right this minute?"

"Yes."

"You mean you're sure he's alive, and he's standing by a window? You can tell that wasn't yesterday or . . ."

"Yes," said Mrs. Busch. "I can tell that much."

"Oh, God, he's alive!" said Susan.

"Oh, yes," said Mrs. Busch. "Of course he's alive. I wouldn't have bothered to come if I didn't know that."

ALL afternoon and into the night Susan and Graham were questioned over and over by Al Menetti and a dozen other detectives. Susan had to find names and numbers for virtually every person who ever baby-sat for Alex. They named all the friends they saw regularly, and then the ones not so regularly.

"But why do you want to know about them?" Susan would ask at first. "We haven't seen them for years. Besides, they're perfectly nice." The detectives just kept writing.

One name kept coming up through the afternoon, the father of a child named Bina whom Alex had played with in a day-care center. Bina's mother, Maeve, was a weaver, Susan said. She was very lovely, but once or twice when Alex went to Bina's to play and Susan came to pick him up, she had found that Maeve had "had to go out," and Bina's father, Richard, was there with the children instead. He seemed nice enough, and she never thought more about it, except to wish that Maeve would explain her plans beforehand.

At this point Menetti interrupted. "Susan, you're going to find that a community like this, where people are always coming and going and everyone's allowed to be slightly unconventional, is not always a nice place for people like you." Susan bristled, but Menetti didn't notice. He continued, "For instance, Bina's father, Richard, is a junkie. He's been booked a dozen times for dealing cocaine and heroin, and twice for armed robbery. The last time, he did four years in prison in New Mexico."

Susan felt a cramp of nausea. She had taken pride in her utter tolerance, but she was shocked now—and frightened.

She remembered Richard patiently crawling around on the living-room floor to help Alex find a lost mitten. She remembered prompting Alex to say, "Good-by and thank you." And Richard solemnly coaching Bina to say good-by to Alex and Mrs. Selky.

Susan had passed her teenage years in distress at her stepmother, who greatly simplified her life by dismissing people who were not "our kind." Susan had thought this a very ungenerous and self-limiting way to be. It was chilling to come to understand there are greater kinds of evil than the narrow mind.

It was somewhere around the middle of Saturday afternoon. Graham finally decided to go home to his apartment for an hour to get some clean clothes. When Menetti assigned a detective to go with him, Susan realized that both she and Graham were essentially under house arrest. She hadn't left the house since Thursday evening, and by Saturday she was developing a malaise of physical restlessness like a slight fever. That afternoon she announced that she would go to the supermarket, in spite of a light rain that had begun to fall. She put on her raincoat, and then she went to the pad in the kitchen where she and Alex wrote down items for the shopping list. On the pad was written in Alex's irregular printing, CHEERIOS, BANANANAS.

Her expression didn't change. Her eyes filled and she stood very still, deep in tears. Alex must have written that Thursday morning. He must have copied the spelling from the Cheerios box—he usually spelled it with one *e*.

She carefully tore off the shopping list and put it in her pocket, and left the house in the company of a policeman. Along every

178

step of the route to the supermarket she saw the streets honeycombed with basements and shafts and alleys and stairwells where a small body could fall or be thrown, hide or be hidden. This was a new horror, a great horror. To see the familiar streets and sidewalks now as sites of danger, scenes of crime.

In the gray of the rainy afternoon the market's yellow fluorescent glow gave the impression of shelter. But the shelves were filled with things that were for Alex, or else not for Alex. The Sugar Pops he could eat at Justine's but not at home, the little snack packs of raisins she never kept enough of in the cupboard. Popcorn—she was out of that—and lemonade now that the hot weather had come. The aisles were also full of people who recognized her. Who felt the same indiscriminate thrill they would feel if she were an actress on a soap opera. And now there she was, in the flesh, the woman who had lost her little boy, the woman they had seen on TV with Vivienne Grant.

Many were discreet, but a surprising number talked loudly to each other about her, or pointed, or stared. A total stranger came up to her and told her she was real sorry about Alex. That they were all praying for him. Then another and another and another spoke to her. Susan thanked them calmly, surprised that her voice was perfectly steady. "Thank you. No, we haven't heard anything. Yes, I feel terrible. Yes, please pray."

A small old woman with an angry face pushed her cart close to Susan's and lit a cigarette. Smoking is illegal in supermarkets, and Susan turned. The woman was staring at her coldly.

"Think you're going to get away with it?" she asked suddenly in a loud voice. "You think you're so smart; you think you can kill your own little boy. How do you feel now, that's what I'd like to know." The woman's eyes were calm, sane, full of hate.

At first Susan barely felt the words land. She just shrugged and moved quickly away, the policeman helping to hurry her cart toward the checkout counter.

But as she walked home the shock began to wear off, and she found her knees and hands shaking. Was that what was going on in people's minds? Those people that you see on the street every

179

day, those people who drop litter on the ground and smoke in the checkout line, with their set resentful faces, is *that* what's going on in their minds? That anger, that twisted loathing? Is that what's all around us?

IN THE weeks that followed Alex's disappearance, Susan had no idea when she slept or how long, or if she was really asleep; and when she did sleep, her dreams were so full of torture that it seemed to drain her more than staying awake.

She had one persistent dream in which she and Alex were walking down a street and they saw Graham coming toward them, hands in pockets and whistling. He had a wonderful swinging walk, and she watched him full of love, waiting for him to notice her and wave. But he did not. Instead he stopped at a strange house and let himself in with his own key. Susan followed him in, and there she found a woman bathing a baby. The baby was Graham's, and the woman was Graham's other wife.

Sometimes Susan woke up heavy with dread and anger, unable to remember what she had dreamed. Whatever it was, the dreams were never as bad as the reality.

She knew she was losing weight, so she refused to weigh herself. But she bathed every day and washed her hair. Her cheeks were often flushed, as May turned to June and the heat rose. Very hard to hide a body in the heat, because of the smell.

The constant noise and the milling of scores of people in and out of the house were a true torture. She often had to fight panic at finding her home completely invaded, finding no room that was hers, no place ever to be alone. To have her house and her heart exposed to the public at this moment, to be robbed of the personal and private in tragedy, was particularly bitter.

For the first two weeks Graham was there every day from eight in the morning until late at night, when he went back to his own apartment to sleep. He'd been good about insisting that his parents stay away. The police had been to West Hartford, Connecticut, to question them, and Susan knew they had found it an ordeal. Alex was their only grandchild, and his disappearance was

180

the most shattering thing to have happened to them in their long lives. If they came, he and Susan would have to spend energy comforting them, and they couldn't afford it.

And Graham was bitter, so angry and guilty. It was terrible for him not to be able to do anything to bring Alex back. He didn't have Susan's numbness. He'd get into fevers of activity, and activity would seem to give rise to hope, and he'd run here and there, call this one and that one, and be suddenly surprised by a great explosion of pain. It was the way he was wired up, the way he'd always been. This day up, that day down, then *boom!* He knew he needed the explosions, but, oh, they hurt when they came. Picking fights, leaving clues to his infidelities, pushing Susan till she fought with him. "That's the last time," she'd finally said. "You need the release, but I don't need the pain. Take it somewhere else. I love you, but you hurt too much."

It was bad enough to be the way he was; was it fair that he should lose so much more because of it?

ONE day at the beginning of the second week, four different people, self-styled psychics, called in to report a similar vision. The first saw Alex in the front seat of a car. The car was moving, and it was a light blue color, and Alex was eating raisins. The second caller also saw Alex in a light blue car, an old-model American sedan. Alex was asleep in the back seat. Policemen were dispatched with pictures of automobiles from 1955 on, to see if the callers could identify the make and year.

Fifteen minutes later a third caller described almost the identical scene. She had had a trance, she said, and she had seen the missing boy lying on the back seat of a blue car. The car was moving, and the driver was a woman, but the caller couldn't see her face in the vision. By that time the first and second callers had each identified the car as an American make from the early 1960s, but even under hypnosis, neither could see the license plate nor describe the driver.

Late that afternoon they had a report from Jennifer Busch. She saw Alex asleep on the back seat of a four-door sedan, a blue or gray car about fifteen years old. The driver was a woman. Mrs. Busch could not see a license plate, but she could see the car pass under a big green sign with white letters: CHARTER OAK BRIDGE. Mrs. Busch had no idea where it was.

But Graham and Susan both knew immediately. "The Charter Oak Bridge is the toll bridge right outside Hartford," Graham said. He wanted to get in a police car and speed up and down the New England Thruway until he found the car himself. He flooded the room with energy and hope.

Menetti contacted highway police in Massachusetts, Connecticut, and New York, and a dragnet was ordered across the three states. On every highway, at every toll plaza from Boston to Bridgeport, police and highway personnel were on the alert for a light blue four-door sedan, American model, year 1963 or 1964, driven by a woman, and carrying a six-year-old boy. Alex's picture was also sent by wire, but it wasn't needed. Every police officer in the East had studied it for the last eight days.

Graham and Susan were sick with hope. They paced up and down the living room and spent much of the evening standing near the bank of telephones, listening to the officers taking the calls. Their eyes met often, speechless and prayerful. They gripped each other's hands. By midnight they were sagging.

In the intervening hours they had learned to think of hope as a vicious tease, the enemy, for in all that time there had been absolutely nothing to confirm what the psychics had seen. There was not a toll collector or highway patrolman who remembered such a car, or boy, or driver. The odds seemed to Graham and Susan too cruel. How on hundreds of miles of highway, in eight hours, could there not be even one woman driving with a six-year-old boy in an old blue car? Susan was more devastated than she had been the night Alex disappeared.

Menetti, who was beginning to look haggard himself, went home about one in the morning, but Graham made no move to follow. Instead he and Susan climbed the stairs together. There were lights still blazing all over the house, with people talking, making coffee, and smoking cigarettes. They lay down together

182

on the bed that had been theirs. Susan sobbed and Graham began to cry openly as well.

After a while Graham whispered, "Susan, let's have another baby."

She held him in the dark, shaking her head vehemently, clenching trembling closed lips. It was so familiar, so bitter, to be hugging his warmth in the dark, her lover, her enemy. She had a piercing headache from crying, and she could feel Graham's tears slip along her collarbone as he cried against her shoulder.

Another baby, because Alex is dead. No, no, no, her head shook in the dark, and she went on crying.

THE next morning Graham was up early. After having a cup of coffee, he went upstairs to Susan's darkened bedroom and looked at her lying prone and still, her face turned away from him. He put a hand on her shoulder in the darkness. "Susan, honey?" he whispered. "Philippe is downstairs. Do you want him to stay?"

"Yes. Tell him I'll be down soon."

Philippe was Jocelyn's "gay cleaning guy," who had been coming to Susan's every other Tuesday for two years. Jocelyn had talked all her friends into trying him. He was easily worth six dollars an hour to Jocelyn, because she dined out on merciless Philippe stories. He cleaned the stove as if it were a fetish. ("When I came home and found him unscrewing the knobs on the stove so he could clean that gunk that gets behind 'em, I asked him to *marry* me," Jocelyn would drawl to an amused audience.) Philippe also read palms and tarot cards and gave his clients a Christmas party every year.

"You're crazy not to use Philippe," Jocelyn had said to Susan, with a look around the kitchen that hinted she thought Susan's housekeeping could stand the improvement. "If I can afford him, *you* can afford him. I'll ask him if he has a free day."

Susan had found Philippe to be everything Jocelyn claimed—sweet, funny, good company, and utterly honest and reliable.

Now she heard a tap on her door. "Suusan," a low voice murmured. "It's Philippe. Do you want me to come iin?" Philippe seemed to stretch and sing all the vowels in his words. He pronounced his own name "Feeleepe," with a long French accent.

"Oh, yes, Philippe. Come in!" Susan sat up on the bed.

"It's so daaark in here," he said, bustling in the door. "Do you mind if I open the curtains?" The sunlight cut painfully across the room in a brilliant ribbon.

"Honey, you are a wreeeck! You look like my dead aunt! Do you know what you should do? You should soak cucumbers in milk and put them on your eyes for fifteen minutes. It just takes the red *right out*. Do you want me to do it for you?"

Susan smiled. Before she could decide what to say, he had bustled purposefully out of the room. Soon he was back with a tray bearing a cup of hot coffee, a glass plate with translucent slices of peeled cucumber, and a bowl of milk. He darted into the bathroom for a towel, which he spread over the pillow.

"Now, lie down flat, and this way the milk won't get on the pillowcase." She closed her eyes and felt something wet plop onto one eyelid, then the other.

He laid a damp washcloth across her eyes and pressed lightly on each eye. "I'll time you. This works *wonders*."

From under her wet bandage she could hear the clink of cup on saucer as Philippe drank his coffee, sitting carefully on the side of the bed. "And he's so good-looking," she could hear Jocelyn saying. "What a waste."

Philippe was short, solid, and muscular, with curly graying hair; he *was* good-looking.

"Now, Susan," he said. "What do you want me to do today? Your house smells like a smoker. Do you want me to do the living room? I don't want to get in the way of the police."

"Would you mind very much just dusting and washing the ashtrays in the living room? Don't bother to vacuum. Then do up here and the kitchen."

"Okay. Do you want me to do anything in Alex's room?"

She stiffened. "Just leave it."

"All right. Time's up." He took off the cloth and scooped up the cucumbers. "There! Much better!"

184

She smiled and got up to look in the mirror. "Well, Philippe, I don't know what they looked like before, but . . ."

"*And,* you're smiling!"

"Yes, that's true."

"See?" he said proudly. "And your coffee's ready downstairs." He put the things back on his tray and returned to the kitchen.

LATER that morning there was another meeting of the Volunteers to Find Alex Selky. They decided to concentrate this week on getting posters taped inside car windows, so Alex's face would be moving all over the city and the message would go out onto the highways as people began leaving for vacation.

Susan felt the kind of fatigue that leaves you too dragged down to do anything for yourself that might help. All afternoon Menetti questioned her over and over about Graham, Robert, Philippe, everyone. It all seemed to be ground they'd covered before, and she found it boring. Now for the fifteenth time Menetti wanted to know how many people knew she was separated.

"I don't know. A lot."

"What do you mean, did you advertise it?"

"Well, no, but a friend of mine, a psychologist, asked me to be on a TV panel show to talk about how kids adjust to divorce."

Menetti looked as if he needed to spit. "You mean you went on a show where they said, 'This is Professor Susan Selky, she lives in Boston, and her husband has left her'?"

"Well . . ."

"So basically you said to ten thousand people, or fifty thousand, whatever it is, 'I'm a pretty woman, I earn a good salary, I live alone with my young son, and you can find me by looking in the phone book'?"

Susan felt a cold, nauseous twang in the pit of her stomach, followed by a flash of defensive anger. Did Menetti expect a normal person to monitor every decision in terms of the harm that could *conceivably* come of it, one chance in a thousand?

"Why is this so important?" she asked in a much smaller voice, already knowing why, and what he was thinking.

185

He shook his head. "Never mind. Forget it. Now, can you remember anything else you haven't told me? Any little thing, no matter how small?"

She could not think of anything. It was so sad, so exhausting. She was upset that Menetti was upset.

"DEAR George and Marianne," Susan wrote to Graham's parents. "As I said on the phone, I was glad to get the copy of the sermon you sent me. There has been such a lot of mail—hundreds of letters a day—and a lot of prayers and hopes for Alex. So many people have been kind. If prayers will help, we have them.

"I'm writing because I didn't want to tell you on the phone—the police feel they have a real lead. It is *very* important that the press not get wind of it, because they think they may be able to locate the person quite soon, if nothing alarms him."

The reason she gave for writing was a half-truth. Susan had found to her pain that several things said to friends in her living room had turned up in the Boston papers. The half that was false was the implied hope that her sweet, gallant boy might soon be back in her arms. She just wanted the comfort, however wishful, of saying to someone somewhere that there was good news.

Susan's father used to say you should try to learn something new every day, and that would keep you young. But what she had learned in the last two weeks had changed her to a weary old woman. And then today Menetti had been explaining to her, reluctantly, about a ring of men who produced pornographic photographs and films of little boys. Of course the men didn't kidnap all the boys they used. They didn't have to. Often these men were apparently normal people who made friends with neighborhood kids one way or another—through a Boy Scout troop, a touch-football game. Sometimes the little boys were drugged or forced, but the men were rarely afraid to let them go home afterward. It was not that difficult to convince six- or

186

seven-year-old children that they were profoundly bad and that if they ever told what they had done, they would be punished.

Susan thought of Alex with his Batman cape. All his games and fantasies about power and triumph against evil, the fantasies of a person who feels weak and small. Menetti had said how curious it was that often these sick men did not have to use force on the kids. The man needs the child, and the child realizes that his fantasy has come true—that he's in a position of power, he's got some kind of control over an adult he's never had before.

On the rare occasions that the men were caught, the children were amazingly sly about what had been going on. "He told me my mother and father had moved away and didn't want me anymore, and that I was supposed to live with him now." "He was very nice to me. I called him Dad."

Of course there were the ones who drugged and tortured, and sometimes killed. Less likely to be part of any porn ring. If you catch them at all, you catch them for good. Gacy in Illinois, a man his ex-wife described as kind and gentle. Who turned out to have murdered thirty-three young men and boys and buried them around his house and yard.

Many parents of boys who were ultimately found in Gacy's yard had reported their sons missing and had asked the police for help. But in many states when a child of seven or over disappears, he is presumed a runaway. Two months older, and Alex, too, could have been shrugged off as a runaway.

Menetti had had men combing their records for known child molesters, especially those who specialized in boys. Two days ago they'd come up with a lead pointing to a man called Neil Mooney, twice convicted of sex offenses. Child molesters are the lowest scum in the prison pecking order, and prison officials have trouble protecting them against other inmates. Mooney had been given early parole after being nearly beaten to death in prison. He had been released at the beginning of May.

Mooney had come straight to Boston, and two days after Alex disappeared, he had missed his meeting with his parole officer. That was the lead Susan had written to her parents-in-law about.

187

Police were working as hard and as fast as they could, trying to trace Mooney's movements without letting the news get around. An ex-con with no money and very few friends would have trouble traveling far, especially if he had a small child with him. He might be underground someplace nearby.

The end of the second week, at seven in the morning, one of the police called Susan to the phone.

"Susan! This is Una Wright, you know, Una Smith!" (A girl Susan had liked very much in college.) "I'm so happy for you . . . I'm trying not to cry. I had to call you the minute I saw the paper. I went to pick it up a few minutes ago, and when I saw the headline, I burst into tears on the doorstep."

"Una . . ." Susan did not know what to say. "It's good to hear your voice, but I don't know what you're talking about."

"You don't?" said Una. "The headline in the New York *Herald* this morning says the case is solved."

"It says *what?*" Susan had a wild, irrational moment of hope.

188

Maybe it was solved and she didn't know it. . . . No. "Una, exactly what does it say? Please read it to me."

"I'll get it." Una sounded chastened and scared. "Here. 'A source close to the family revealed tonight in New York that police are ready to announce a happy ending to the case of little Alex Selky, missing from his home in Boston for fifteen days. Police do not wish to reveal details of the mystery yet, but an announcement is expected later today.'"

Susan felt overcome by a great wave of anxiety. What would this mean? "Thank you for letting me know, Una. It really *was* good to hear from you, and I wish it had been good news."

By the time she dressed and got downstairs, the phones were ringing like banshees, and she could tell from the police response that it was media from all over New England calling to confirm the *Herald*'s story.

Menetti arrived at eight, and Susan knew from his face that he was upset. "It's bad," he said. "It's not going to help at all. We're going to have phones tied up all day undoing the damage, and we're going to lose a lot of momentum." He went to Susan's kitchen phone and put in a call to the New York *Herald*.

They wouldn't, of course, reveal their source. They said they hadn't checked the story with the police because their source was very reliable and they had no reason to doubt him.

Menetti was furious. He told Susan, "I'll have to get the Boston papers to run a story about the *false* story. Otherwise I'll have trouble keeping the department on the case." He was dialing. "And you'll lose your volunteer corps," he said over his shoulder to her. "Yeah! Menetti! Get me the Public Relations office. Look, we've got a big problem here with the Selky case. . . ."

Susan could hear from the next room that the phones were swamped with congratulations. Her heart sank, for, exactly as Menetti had predicted, many calls were from the committee of Volunteers to Find Alex Selky. Those who called could be told, but what about those who did not? What about those who got the story thirdhand, in the bank, at the supermarket? It's all over, he's found; thank God, we can ease our minds. The grateful willingness to be excused, to forget it and return to their own concerns.

When Menetti hung up, he was furious. "This is a mess. I want to know who the reliable source was. Did you tell someone something? Who do you know in New York?"

"I don't know anyone in New York except Robert. We've got a couple of friends there, but none who would hurt us."

"I told you not to tell anyone anything. Didn't I?"

"Yes."

"And did you tell someone? College roomie? Robert?"

"*No!* I wrote a note to my parents-in-law. All I said was things weren't as bad as the papers made them look, but we couldn't afford to have any details get out."

"In other words, you hinted we had a lead."

"I said there was a lead, yes. They're Alex's grandparents! They're worried sick. I didn't see how it could hurt. . . ."

"Didn't it occur to you that the first thing Mrs. Selky would do would be share the good news with Robert?"

"No. It actually didn't."

"Well, think about it! I'd say we got a leak in New York, and we've got Uncle Robert in New York, and I'd check it out."

Susan stared at him. There was so much dislike in his voice when he spoke Robert's name. Why? She actually had opened her mouth to ask him when she stopped herself. A cold new Susan realized for the first time that there was no longer anything she wouldn't believe. In fact she was gradually coming to see the world as the police saw it.

She went to the kitchen and put a call through to Robert.

He greeted her with concern. "Susan! How are you? Is there anything new?"

"There's a story in the morning *Herald* that says that the case is solved. The case is not solved, Robert. I wonder if you can tell me anything about where the paper got that idea?"

"How should I know? Why are you asking me?" He went on the defensive so fast that she knew in her heart that Menetti had guessed right.

190

"Robert, did your mother tell you we had a lead?"

"I spoke to Mother yesterday."

"Did she tell you we thought there was a lead?"

"Well, she was so encouraged. Why? Did you tell her not to tell me?"

"I hardly told her anything except that I wanted her and Dad to be optimistic, and I didn't want anything about it to turn up in the papers!"

"She didn't say anything about that."

"So what did you do? Did you phone in the story to the *Herald*, or what?"

Robert's voice turned angry. "Wait a minute, Susan. It happens I was at a dinner party last night and I happened to mention that there was going to be a break in the case. One of the gals at the party does book reviews for the *Herald*, which I had forgotten. Besides, it didn't occur to me that she'd tell."

"It didn't occur to you! If you couldn't keep your mouth shut, how did you expect her to, when it's her job?" Susan hung up and started to cry.

The phone rang at once. It was Public Relations for Menetti. At the end of the call he reported to Susan. "They've contacted all the papers and notified the radio and TV stations. None of them will repeat the *Herald* story, but no one will run a story to stop the rumors, either. The news that there's no news doesn't interest them."

When Susan went out late in the afternoon to walk Taxi, she noticed that two of the posters of Alex, with the headline MISSING, had been taken down from windows on her block. The glad tidings were spreading.

In the middle of the third week the police took out their bank of phones and left the house. The taxpayer is entitled to that kind of expense for only so long, and Susan had had her allotment for the search effort. In the sudden quiet that fell on the house as the police departed, Susan felt that she was experiencing Alex's death.

Menetti was still with her, and there were, he assured her, a dozen detectives still committed full time to the case. But the house was quiet again, as quiet as it was the afternoon she had sat by the window and waited for Alex to come home. That analogy kept recurring to her, and in midafternoon she went into the living room, placed the chair as it had been that day nineteen days ago, and sat down again to wait.

The phone rang.

It was the afternoon Alex disappeared, and the phone was ringing. If she answered it, her life would wind back, like a movie run backward. Then it would start forward again, but sane this time, the world a sunlit place. On the phone would be the school nurse: "Hello, Mrs. Selky? Alex had a tummy ache, so we thought he should lie down in the office until you could come for him. Yes. Oh, he's fine. Would you like to speak to him?"

"Hello, Mommy?"

Or simply Alex, with his dime, at the deli on the corner. He's stopped to read a comic and lost track of the time. He is kneeling on the seat in the phone booth, so he can dial.

"Hello," he says, quick and stern, "Mommy?"

Or it would be Menetti. "Susan? It's Al. I've finally got some good news for you."

Then the voice on the other end, so sweet and small. "Hello, Mommy?"

The phone is not Menetti.

"Mrs. Selky, this is Mrs. Feldman in the office of the English Department. Dr. Lynn asked me to call you, to tell you how sorry he is. . . ."

"That's kind of him." It was kind of him. It just didn't happen to help. "Tell him I thank him, and—"

"Oh, Mrs. Selky, wait," the secretary cut in, sensing that Susan was going to hang up. "Dr. Lynn, um, wants to know if you're planning to teach your summer courses this year."

"Oh," said Susan. "Tell him that I am not planning to teach."

"I see," said Mrs. Feldman.

"Good," said Susan.

192

"Have you talked to Susan today?" Jocelyn asked Martina, without preamble, when Martina answered the phone. "The police took out the special phone lines this morning. The house must feel like a tomb after what it's been like."

"No, I haven't. I forgot that was today. I've been so busy."

"I don't know, she seems so distant," Jocelyn went on. "She hasn't seemed like herself to me at all for a week or so. Do you think she's all right?"

"What do you mean, all right? How all right can she be?"

"Well, you know, Philippe was here yesterday. He said the police have searched his apartment twice, and they got pretty rough with him the second time."

"He mentioned that," said Martina. "He said they even gave him a lie-detector test."

"Yes, he was in a total panic when he told me. But you know what he did? He said he took one look at Susan when he was over there for his day and decided she was such a wreck, he never even mentioned the test to her. He said he didn't want to upset her any more. So he spent the whole afternoon in the kitchen scrubbing the oven. Isn't that sweet?"

Martina agreed. She said she was sorry she couldn't get to see Susan before the weekend. She would speak to Jocelyn soon.

It was midmorning, four weeks to the day since Alex disappeared. The mail continued to pour in for Susan and Graham, and the phone rang often. Menetti was still constantly in and out of the house, and there were still a dozen detectives working on the case, but Susan saw far less of them.

She was opening the mail, sorting it into piles of notes from personal friends, well-wishes from strangers, visions from the Lord, and lunatic abuse. She was surprised that she heard so much less from people she knew than she did from strangers.

She didn't know yet how to field the attacks. She dropped the notes into the wastebasket without reading more than a line, the way one hangs up on an obscene phone caller after the first few words. But they yammered at her with their malicious voices when she was too tired to knock them away. You killed him yourself. Your husband killed him. You killed him together and you're pretending to be separated so the police won't think you're conspiring. You're guilty because you did it. You're guilty because you were negligent; you endangered your own child's life to save yourself walking a block. You're an unfit mother who deserved to lose your child. Have you learned your lesson? God has done this to show you. And I'm so happy you got what you deserved.

In the late nights, alone, she sometimes crossed the line and believed that she was guilty, that she had risked his life to save herself walking a block, that she did deserve to lose Alex.

Menetti buzzed her from downstairs, and she let him in. "All alone?" was his first question. Yes, she was, today. Graham came over only when there was a really promising lead. Margaret Mayo was at work, and Susan's friends were very busy.

"I'm having this root canal done, but I'm thinking of you. . . ."

"As soon as I get the boys off to summer camp I'll be free again. I'll try to drop by on Sunday."

She could understand. Their lives did have to go on. She only wished hers could. They *had* given tremendously of their time.

"Yes," she said to Menetti, "I'm holding the fort. Has anything happened?"

"Well, we found Neil Mooney."

"And?" Susan's heart was cold with fear.

"And it's a dead end. His parole officer called me last night at home to say Mooney had walked into his office at five in the afternoon. He's been in Belmont all this time and had no idea we were looking for him. He told us exactly what he's been doing since his release from prison, and we checked everything out. His story stands up."

"Oh," said Susan. What was she supposed to say? No news was good news. No news was bad news. All news was bad news.

THE Volunteers to Find Alex Selky called a meeting at Susan's house for the following Wednesday. Susan phoned several television stations to see if they'd like to cover the meeting. It was essential that people remember Alex and that they see his face, that people keep looking for him. Are there new leads? the producers wanted to know. There were not. Oh, said the producers, then we'll pass.

The meeting of the volunteers attracted a smaller group than in the beginning. Jocelyn and Martina were there, of course, and perhaps two dozen others, including Graham, Margaret Mayo, TJ, and Annie. It was an awkward hour. People entered in twos and threes, no longer in the stunned, frightened silence that had filled them all at the first news, but now chatting with each other about work, play, vacations, camp, and kids. Susan could hear their voices on the stairs; then she'd hear them suddenly hush themselves as they reached the landing, as if they'd caught themselves telling jokes at a funeral.

At the meeting it was agreed that the main objective now was to keep people interested. Graham said, "I saw a guy on the street the other day look at a poster as he passed and say to his companion, 'Whatever happened about that kid? They must have found him by now.'

"What we have to do," Graham continued, "is demonstrate that the search is active. If people only see that same first handbill, they will stop seeing it, or stop believing it."

Muriel Kopp spoke from the depths of the blue sofa. "Graham, if you'd like to go to a four-color poster, my office will donate the graphics. I can have my printer do the job at cost."

"Muriel, thank you." Graham turned to Susan, who was sitting in a chair behind him. "Should we?" he whispered.

"Absolutely," she agreed.

"And until we can get new posters ready, Susan has an interim plan." Graham held up a brown paper bag. "We had a dozen rubber stamps made up that say STILL." He reached into the bag and held up a stamp with a wooden handle. "And we've got a dozen red ink pads. If each of you would volunteer to be responsible for an area of the city, we could get around and stamp the handbills in red with the word STILL above MISSING."

"I'll do out around the Fen," said Jocelyn.

195

"I'll take Beacon Hill," spoke up a painter whose son and Alex were good friends.

"That's great. Thank you," said Graham.

Martina and her husband offered to do the South End, and Muriel Kopp volunteered for the Harvard Square area. Section by section the others accounted for the whole map. They agreed that if nothing happened in the next two weeks, they would meet again to deploy the new color poster.

It was stifling hot out in Saugus that third week in June. Al Menetti had been late getting home from work again tonight and had had to eat a plate of stiff food Pat had kept for him in the oven. In this heat she wasn't going to cook dinner twice.

"Look at you," she said when he laid down his fork. "Your clothes are hanging on you. You must have lost ten pounds!"

"Good," he said. "I needed to." That was true, but still his cheeks were sunken. Losing weight had left him drawn-looking.

Now he was upstairs in the bedroom going over reports on the Selky case. There were more than seven hundred of them—phone conversations, interviews, polygraph tests, and so on. He'd spent so many hours reading them, he should have had them memorized. Pat said as much. "I have," he said, pressing his lips together. He went over and over them anyway.

As soon as Pat had the three youngest kids tucked in their beds, she invited Al to come out onto the patio with her for some coffee and cake.

The night was warm, moist, and starry. Pat handed him a cup of instant Sanka and a plate of pound cake with toasted coconut. He really didn't want it, but he knew that if there was one thing his placid wife disliked, it was feeling fat by herself.

"So," he said after a long drink of the night's sweet quiet. He hadn't taken an hour to relax with Pat for a good long time. "How've you been?"

"Oh, pretty good, thanks. Want to hear about Eugene wetting his bed?"

"He's wetting his bed again? Is something wrong with him?"

196

"Who knows? The doctor said just to be very patient and wait for him to grow out of it."

"Yeah, well, let's hope so, because that kind of thing can embarrass a guy at college."

Al drank his coffee and looked at the stars, and in seconds was back on Fremont Street. He could see that morning as if he had been there. He could see that little boy wave to his mother and turn the corner. He could see him walk down the street, giving a little skip now and then, the way Eugene did.

"So, Al," said Pat, "did it hurt you much when the rumor went around that the Selky case had been solved?"

"Yeah, it did. I don't think Susan realized how much it hurt. But the last day or two, the more I go over those reports, the more I have a creeping suspicion I've been on the wrong track since the beginning."

"Really? Have you come up with something?"

"As I told you, I made a dumb move the first day, looking for a custody fight. I didn't call for bloodhounds right away. . . ."

"But you did what would have been right ninety percent of the time."

He waved her remark away. "It was a mistake. So I went the other way after that. I said, 'Okay, it's a stranger. It's no one these people know. It's a psycho killer, it's a child molester, it's a poor deranged woman who wants a kid.' I've even found myself very seriously listening to these psychics. It's interesting. Just about all of them believe the boy is alive."

"But last week you were dragging the South Bay for him."

"Yeah, we were. Thank God Susan never heard about that. We dragged for two days. Of course he wasn't there."

"So do you have a new theory?"

"Susan is convinced that the boy is alive somewhere and that the media are her hope. She feels that if she keeps the faith and keeps looking for Alex and waiting for him to come home, sooner or later someone will recognize him, and it will happen."

"Does she really believe that?"

Al said, "I don't know. She's one very determined lady. It's like

197

asking the Pope if he believes in God. Anyway, I've been going right down the line with her. I've checked records, I've combed the books, I've checked into every possible thing you can trace about perverts and child molesters and pornography rings and kidnappers. Lately I've begun to suspect I've led myself down the garden path."

"Oh, yes?" Pat had just realized that another very small slice of cake wasn't going to kill her.

"I don't know that I'm looking for a stranger, and I don't know that I'm looking for a live boy. Most murders are committed by people who know the victim. This was a bright kid, and his mother had talked to him about going with strangers. That's the warning bell I kept ignoring. Why would he go with someone he didn't know? If he was forced, how come nobody saw him struggle or heard him scream? The street was full of people."

"Are you saying you think it was done by someone he knew?"

Al shrugged. "It's possible. I *want* to believe what the mother believes, but the other thing is very, very possible. I can't do my job right if I don't check it out."

"Do you suspect someone in particular?" asked Pat.

Menetti didn't answer. He looked at his fingernails. She knew she wouldn't hear any more tonight.

ON THE Monday of the first week of July the producer of "A.M. Boston" called Susan. He said, "Mrs. Selky, we've just received word that another child, a little five-year-old girl, has disappeared in South Boston. The little girl's mother has agreed to appear on our show tomorrow morning, and we'll have a psychologist with us to talk about what happens to a family when a child disappears. I wondered if you'd be willing to join us."

"If you will show Alex's picture on the air," Susan replied. "And if you'll make it very clear that the case is active and we want the viewers to keep looking for him."

"Fine," he said. "Makeup call is at six thirty, and we're on the air live from eight to nine. We won't know until tomorrow which segment you'll be on, so plan to be with us for the whole show."

SUSAN and the other mother sat side by side in the makeup room. The makeup artists were husband and wife, their identical black kits set up on a counter. Susan watched in the mirror as the woman worked on her, nodding when Susan said she would like as little as possible, please. On went the mascara and scarlet lipstick anyway. This was a soft-news show, or more truthfully, an entertainment show, and the viewers were not entertained by guests who looked chronically ill under the lights.

The makeup man was chattering to the missing girl's mother, a light-skinned black woman named Jannette. Her round face was yellow with worry, but she was excited about being on a TV show. "Do you usually wear eye shadow, darling?" babbled the makeup man. "Now we are going to give you highlighter on the cheekbones, here and here."

Susan felt like shouting, Hey, buster, this woman has just lost a child! But Jannette seemed distracted in spite of herself. "Here?" she asked, pointing to her cheek.

"*No, here,*" said the makeup man. "Then you put the cheek color here." He brushed on powdered rouge of a purple tone to create the impression of hollows. "And *voilà!* Cheekbones!"

Jannette looked at herself intently. She seemed reluctant to yield her chair to the Chinese actor who was going to demonstrate his recipe for omelets on the segment after theirs.

The producer's assistant showed them to the greenroom, where they were to wait. "Of course it isn't really green," said the assistant. "That's just a show-business term." Susan already knew that, but Jannette did not, and she seemed quite interested. "I heard them say that on Johnny Carson," she remarked.

Five minutes before the show was to begin, two policemen were shown into the greenroom. "Mrs. Smith?" one asked. Jannette identified herself. Susan realized later that she was surprised that they didn't even ask to see her privately. "We've found your little girl, Mrs. Smith," said the officer. "She's dead. The hatch was partly open on your neighbor's cistern. She fell in and drowned." Jannette simply looked up at them with a puzzled expression until she was led away, and Susan was left to stare at the Chinese actor in stunned silence.

A few minutes before her segment the producer's assistant came in and bent over Susan. She talked to her as a nurse speaks to a sick child. "You going to be all right, dear? Would you like a glass of water? . . . Okay, what we're going to do is send you on with the psychologist by yourself. Do you feel up to it? . . . Good girl!" Susan wanted very badly to slap her face.

In the studio, Susan and the psychologist were introduced. Dr. Mandelbaum was a painfully thin young man with friendly eyes. They stood in the relative darkness behind the lights and cameras, watching the show's host finish a segment with a state senator. When it was over, the assistant rushed Susan and the psychologist into the blue-white bath of light on the set. "We have sixty seconds to get you both miked and settled," she said.

A sound man was clipping a tiny microphone onto Susan's blouse. The assistant was burbling, "We've given you eleven minutes, because we thought there were going to be three of you. Eleven minutes can be a long time under these hot lights, but don't be nervous. Valerie Scott will be interviewing you. Oh, here's our Valerie. Valerie, this is Mrs. Selky, and this is Dr. Mandelbaum. Okay, ready?" The assistant favored them with her widest smile and skipped off the set.

They sat in low armchairs around a plastic-topped coffee table, and the segment began. Valerie Scott explained that Mrs. Smith, whose presence on the show had been announced, was not with them because her little girl had, tragically, been found. She retold the story of Alex's disappearance more than six weeks before, and while she talked, Susan saw in the monitor that they were broadcasting Alex's picture. For a moment she got lost in that laughing face. There was Alex, in a freeze-action frame. In a moment he would start moving, finish his laugh.

"Mrs. Selky, you were in the greenroom with Mrs. Smith just

a few minutes ago when police came to tell her that her little girl had been found, dead. Can you tell us what your feelings were at that moment?"

"Why, yes," said Susan. "I thought, When you have a baby, you look forward to protecting him and guiding him in gentle stages through all the hard things about growing up. And now suddenly her little girl has gone on ahead of her into the experience that we all fear the most."

Valerie Scott seemed to expect more. "It must have been a very *sad* moment," she prompted.

Susan looked as if she were not sure what the word meant. "Well . . . yes," she agreed. Valerie turned to Dr. Mandelbaum, who delivered what was expected of him. Death of a child, deeply disorienting, psychologists feel, deepest grief known. It flowed over Susan like a stream flowing over a rock.

"Mrs. Selky's position is different from Mrs. Smith's," Valerie resumed, "in that her little boy has disappeared and she has no way of knowing if he's dead or not. Tell me, Mrs. Selky, are there any new leads?"

Obediently Susan described the situation. No new leads, but every reason to hope that someone had Alex and was taking good care of him. Essential for viewers to memorize his face, to watch for him, and report anything they saw.

"Your confidence is inspiring, but there must be times when you fear that knock on the door, bringing you the same news that Mrs. Smith heard this morning?" Susan looked at the sleek, polished face that asked her the question. Tell us you're afraid, Mrs. Selky. Break down and cry. Give it to us, Mrs. Selky.

Susan wondered if Menetti were watching. She said, "Yes, of course, but fears are different from faith. I have faith that my son is alive. I believe that if he were gone from the earth, I would know it. Faith is a power in itself, and it happens to be the only one I have left. If we care about missing children like Alex, if we all remember them and look for them, then there is hope that they will be recognized and returned. If we don't, then, alive or not, there's no hope."

201

"Are you saying that if you give up hope, the police will stop searching for Alex?"

"Not only the police. Your viewers. Everyone. If Alex is alive, sooner or later someone may see him. If I keep faith that he's alive, if I keep asking for help to look for him, there's a chance that he will be brought home. If I don't, there isn't. Therefore, I believe he is alive."

"Isn't that a non sequitur, Mrs. Selky?"

"No."

Dr. Mandelbaum spoke up, to Valerie's obvious relief. "Mrs. Selky is in a very unusual situation from a psychologist's point of view, because in a normal mourning situation, there comes a point when the mourner must pick up the pieces of his life and go on. But in the case of an unknown fate, the person is prevented from going on to the healing stage of grief. The mourner is frozen in the most painful moment of human experience. We saw this phenomenon during the Vietnam War, with the families of soldiers missing in action."

Susan listened gratefully as Dr. Mandelbaum droned on until the end of the segment. Valerie broke in when she got a thirty-second sign from a technician, and cued the picture of Alex again, and that was all Susan wanted.

IN THE next few days Susan began to receive phone calls from all over the country from other parents who had lost children. Their stories were heartbreaking, and Susan began to feel that she had a responsibility to help all of these parents alone in their nightmares, if her situation could help anybody else. It was one of the thoughts that kept her facing the media over and over again in the weeks to come. Every time she thought of stopping, she would hear one more story of parents who had almost given up when some local newspaper ran one last squib and their child was recognized and brought home.

Susan fell into the habit of beginning her days by sitting at the window from eight to nine, drinking a cup of tea and watching the sidewalk below. She gazed down at the steaming hot neighborhood street, nearly immobile except for her watchful eyes. By eight thirty almost every morning she would see Menetti's car pull up. He would get out and start from her doorstep to walk down the street exactly as Alex had. When he got to the corner, he stopped and looked back up the street, as Alex had. Then he turned the corner and disappeared, as Alex had.

Any morning Menetti didn't come, Susan got depressed.

In mid-July Susan relented and agreed to let her father and stepmother come east from Ohio for the weekend. They would be careful not to be any bother. They would stay at a hotel. Susan dreaded the visit. For years the safest and happiest topic of conversation they shared had been Alex.

They made it very easy for her. Her father was a tall, thin, quiet man in his mid-seventies. At home he kept to himself and played a lot of golf. Susan's stepmother, Connie, looked twenty years younger than her husband, having been plucked and dyed and face-lifted within an inch of her life. She was not a silly woman, but silence made her anxious and this led her often to chatter when she had nothing to say.

The first night for a special extravagance they took Susan to dinner at Locke-Ober's. She was touched to note that her father as well as Connie worked hard at maintaining a flow of conversation. They talked about the flavor of everything; neither remarked that Susan was eating none of her lobster soufflé.

The next evening they took her to see the road company of *Annie*. "We're so lucky it's here. It's the one play your father really wanted to see," Connie confided. There was no way they could have known that Alex had asked for the sound track of *Annie* for Christmas and played it noon and night till he could sing every song. (Alex in the tub, draped with suds from his bubble bath, belting, *"Lucky me! Lucky me! Look at what I'm dripping with . . . little girls."*)

After the theater Susan's father said, "Why don't you come back to the hotel for a nightcap, since we won't see you in the morning?" She wanted so much to go home and be alone, but she made herself say she'd love to.

Her father had a brandy, which Connie and Susan declined. Susan sat uncomfortably in a chair while they sat on their beds.

"Susan," said her father, looking down at his fingernails. "I'm very proud of the way you're handling this." Susan froze in her chair. If he said any more, she would cry. But he didn't.

"Well," he said, standing up. "It was lovely to see you, honey. Thank you for—"

"Thank you for a lovely time, Daddy."

"And here's a little something . . . Just in case . . ." He took from the dresser a large gaily wrapped package and handed it to her. The card said, *To my grandson on his birthday.*

LATE on a Monday afternoon, about a week after her father's visit, Susan's phone rang. It was Menetti. He hadn't been near the neighborhood all day, and she'd been feeling very low.

"Susan. I just wanted to see if you were home."

"I'm home. You didn't come by this morning."

"I'm afraid I was waiting on some news. I'm still expecting a call any minute, but in case it doesn't come in soon, I wanted to know where to reach you this evening."

"What's happened?" She knew from his voice it wasn't good.

"Well, I got a call from Philadelphia PD today. Some kids early this morning found a plastic bag with a body in the woods down there."

She felt a deep wallop of pain, as if everything inside her had just cracked up the middle.

"You think it's Alex."

"Susan, it's a small body. They didn't know when they called me if it was male or female. We're waiting for the coroner's report. It's taking a while."

"Okay," she said. "I'll be here."

She sat a moment by herself in the afternoon light and then called Graham. He wasn't home. She told Naomi, and Naomi said she'd find him right away. Graham arrived in less than an hour. "Did he call back yet?" was all he said as he burst in the door. She shook her head.

"Is it evil for me to pray it's not Alex?" she asked. Graham shook his head, and they sat down together on the couch.

"We always knew it might be this," he said.

"I know," she whispered.

The call came at eight o'clock. By that time dusk had fallen in the room, but they hadn't turned on the lights. Graham leaped to answer it.

"It's a female," said Menetti. "The body was incomplete; that's why it took so long. They make her four or five inches taller than Alex, probably nine years old." As he listened, Graham's face telegraphed the news to Susan, an expression of awesome relief.

"The details don't correlate with any kid who's been reported missing," Menetti was saying.

"You mean a nine-year-old girl could disappear and no one would report it?"

"Yeah. Hey, Graham, tell Susan good night for me. Tell her I'm glad."

"I will, Al. Thank you."

Graham went back and took Susan in his arms. "What are these, tears?" he said, holding her.

"I'm so relieved. . . ." Her voice was trembling. "It's disgusting, but I thank God. I feel like celebrating."

"Me, too! Let's go eat something spicy and drink champagne."

"Let's call TJ and Annie!"

"No, let's just be together."

"Okay. Let's go!"

But halfway through dinner the mood was spoiled. Susan couldn't eat. She felt choked at the thought of happiness, as if that alone was a betrayal of Alex.

"Susan," said Graham, "you know it could have been Alex."

"I know that. Don't you think I know that?"

"I think you know it in your head, but I don't see you doing anything to prepare yourself for it."

"What do you mean?"

"Honey, if that call tonight had gone the other way, or if we just don't ever hear anything again . . ."

"Yes?" she said coldly.

"What I'm trying to say is, there may come a time when you will have to consider accepting . . ."

"Accepting what? That it's too painful to go on hoping, so I should give up on him? That I should cut him off to save myself the inconvenience of missing him?"

"Not of missing him, Susan. We'll miss him for the rest of our lives. Of trying to save him if he can't be saved. Susan, for your own good . . ."

"For *my* own good! What about *our* own good? Am I in this by myself now? Isn't he your son, too?"

Graham looked down at the table and sighed. Her eyes gleamed with an anger he dreaded because it seemed to come from somebody else who now and then woke up inside her.

"Of course he's my son, too," he said. "I just wanted to talk about you because you worry me."

"So I'm in trouble over this, but you're perfectly fine, eh? Crazy Susan, can't cope? Well, I'm coping, Graham. And don't tell me I haven't had plenty to cope with."

"Please, Susan. I didn't mean anything like that, and in your heart you know I didn't. Of course I'm having trouble; I'm having more trouble than I ever thought I could bear."

She glared at him. "Well, maybe you're bearing up so well because you didn't care so much in the first place. You didn't care enough to resist breaking up his home, did you?"

Graham's face fell and he looked awful, but his voice was still soft as he said, "Susan, when you get like this, you say things that are very hard to forgive."

She knew it was true. She knew it was precisely her ruthless rage when she was hurt that had contributed to the crash of the marriage. "I want to go home," she said. And the two people inside her, the sane one and the hurt one, fought all the way home, trying to say to Graham that she knew how wrong she was. But her eyes and throat were still dry with anger—at what, she wasn't even sure—when they parted in silence. It wasn't until the door closed behind him that she started to cry.

She didn't hear from Graham for almost a week. In fact she didn't hear from anybody not connected with the case. *Boston* magazine sent a reporter to do a story with her. Susan found it a relief to talk to someone who listened with intelligence, who wouldn't then go away in pain and never call again.

Susan knew now that some people she'd known for years were crossing the street when they saw her, so they wouldn't have to chat. She didn't blame them, but she could have used the contact, a daily smile and a "Hello, how are you?"

But, then, what could she answer?

She felt sure that Graham would at least come back on Alex's birthday. He wouldn't let her spend that day alone.

The phones were especially busy all that muggy rainy day of Alex Selky's seventh birthday. The Boston papers ran his picture and a recap of his disappearance for the occasion, and Susan appeared on a talk show called "Live at Noon." Sometimes now, when she spoke to strangers about Alex, she was dry and matter-of-fact, even to the point of being slightly ironic, as people are when they are deeply immersed in a topic and explaining it for the hundredth time to novices. Her control surprised her, since sometimes she seemed to weep all day. After her segment she heard two of the light-crew men talking in the hall.

"I've been covering news for twenty years," one said, "but that's one of the toughest cookies I've ever seen."

"Yeah, very tough lady. . . ." They went on down the hall.

Compared to what? thought Susan. How many mothers have you known whose sons have been missing for seventy-three days?

Martina called in the middle of that afternoon.

"Hi, Susan," she said in a worried voice. "How are you?"

"I've had better days, actually. This is Alex's birthday."

"Oh, I know," said Martina. She seemed embarrassed.

"Thank you," Susan said softly. "I'm glad you remembered."

After a while Susan tried to call Jocelyn. She thought she would like to have Jocelyn and Justine come for tea. She'd go out and get some little cakes. She would like to do something happy for Alex today. . . . There was no answer at Jocelyn's.

It wasn't until nearly suppertime that it occurred to her that Graham might not come. He couldn't really be meaning to stay away today. By nightfall, when he had still not phoned, she was paralyzed with leaden depression.

At nine o'clock she heard steps on the stairs. Graham? No, not his step.

TJ called, "Susan? Susan? Are you here?" Then he let himself in and walked into the living room. He turned on a lamp and went over to where she sat by the window, scooped her up, and sat down, cradling her against his chest.

"Happy birthday," he whispered, and she nodded against his chest and began to cry, and went on for a long time.

When she felt emptied of tears at last, Susan got up and made some tea. They sat together by the fireplace, and she asked TJ politely, "Where's Annie?"

"She had a concert tonight. She sent you her love and said to tell you she's going to sing the lullaby for Alex." Susan nodded. Annie was a cellist, and Alex loved to listen to her play and sing. Last year on his birthday, TJ and Annie had come at bedtime as a surprise and serenaded Alex under his window.

> "Hushaby . . . Don't you cry
> Go to sleep, Little Baby.
> When you wake, you will find
> All the pretty little horses."

"Where's Graham?" TJ asked softly.

Susan shrugged and shook her head. TJ didn't press it.

"Today," said TJ, "I thought about the day Alex was born. I got to see him through the nursery window in the evening. He had a little straight nose that looked just like Graham's. Graham and I could see one of his little fists outside the blanket. You were asleep, but I sneaked in and left you flowers, remember? You looked like you were having the sweetest dream."

"I was." There had been no Alex, and then all in one day he was in their lives. And now there was no Alex again. Who could have dreamed the time between that day and this one would be so short?

"Remember the day he was christened? He yelled when the minister put the water on his head. He looked furious to wake up like that, and we all had trouble not to laugh. I was afraid I'd drop him when you handed him to me."

TJ reached into his pocket and took out a jeweler's box, which he handed to Susan. She opened it, and in it found a small Swiss wristwatch on a child's band; it was engraved on the back. To AGS FROM TJF, JULY 27, 1980.

"I had it done in the spring," whispered TJ.

Susan realized it was the first time in all the years she had known him she'd seen TJ crying. "He gave us so much joy," she said. "We didn't know we weren't going to have time to give him all the things he deserved."

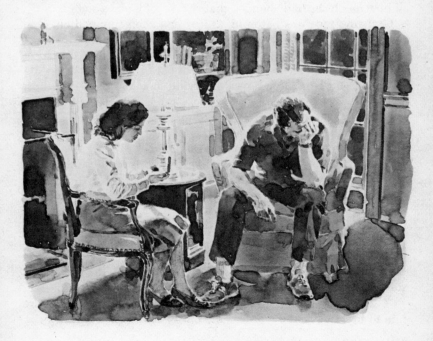

Out of words, joined in one warmth but in their heads each alone with his grief, they sat in silence for a long half hour.

Then through the living-room window they saw a bright light from a car driving slowly down the street. TJ went to the window and leaned out. The light careened around the walls.

"Police car," he said. The light went out and the motor sound died. Susan froze as she heard him say, "They've got Graham. They're holding him up." TJ and Susan looked at each other in bewilderment. Then TJ leaped down the stairs.

It seemed to Susan to take forever for them to get Graham up one step at a time. She could hear one of the policemen saying, "Easy. Easy. *Don't rush.*"

Then TJ said, "You're okay." And a voice that might have been Graham's, if he had rags in his mouth, said something. When she saw him come through the door, she knew it was a measure of how much she had changed that she didn't make a sound.

Graham's face was battered, as if it had been stamped on. One eye was swollen shut. It was a mottled purplish blue. His lips, too, were swollen and bloody from where they'd been sliced through by his own teeth. He held one arm stiffly at his side, but when she looked at it fearfully, he said, trying not to move his lips, "'S bruised. Not broken."

TJ helped him to a chair as one of the policemen said, "He wouldn't let us take him to a hospital, missus. He said he had to get here. He oughta have that arm x-rayed."

"He oughta have everything x-rayed," said the other one.

"I'll go tomorrow," Graham enunciated with great care.

"What happened? Where did you find him?" asked Susan.

"North Cambridge. From what we gather, he got what he thought was a ransom call. And instead of calling the police, he decided to walk into an alley by himself at ten o'clock at night carrying ten thousand dollars in cash."

Susan's heart nearly stopped. "Good God!" said TJ. They both stared at Graham.

"I . . . got this call from some woman," Graham said. It hurt him to breathe, so the words came out of his swollen lips in brief

210

gasps. "She said she had . . . Alex. She said he . . . got sick. So she was scared. She didn't dare call . . . a doctor for him. She said she'd sell him back . . . to me . . . for ten thousand dollars."

"Didn't you ask to speak to him?" Susan asked in a tiny voice. Graham nodded. "I heard . . . this little voice say, 'Hi, Daddy.'" Here Susan saw his one open eye fill with tears. "I told her . . . it wasn't enough. . . . I couldn't tell if it was Alex. She said he had a fever and . . . and had . . . to go back to bed."

"But why didn't you call the police?" asked TJ.

"She said . . . if I did . . . she'd leave him alone and he might die. She said she had a boy friend on . . . the police, and she would know if . . . I called . . . them."

"But where did you get the money?" asked Susan. It was more than she and Graham had ever had at one time, except for the down payment on the house.

"Borrowed it . . . two thousand from Dad . . . eight thousand from Robert."

"We gotta be getting back," said the first policeman.

Susan nodded. "Thank you for bringing him home."

"I'd rather have taken him to a hospital," said the second policeman. "You be sure he goes first thing in the morning."

The first policeman looked at Susan and said, "I wish he'd of called us first, Mrs. Selky." She nodded as if to say, I know, and then he asked, "Do you want us to help get him into bed?"

"Yes, thank you."

The two gently hoisted Graham to his feet, and he put his good arm around one pair of blue shoulders. Susan went up the stairs before them, turning on the lights, while the two officers half pushed, half lifted Graham up to the bedroom. Then they said their good-nights.

"I'll go out with them and lock up," said TJ, who had followed them. He put his arms gently around Graham and held him briefly. "You dumb jerk," he whispered. Graham tapped TJ's shoulder with his palm and nodded.

When they were alone, Susan helped Graham undress and painstakingly inched his body into bed. "Light out?" she whispered. He nodded. In the darkness she felt him reach his hand toward her. She knelt beside the bed. With his good arm he drew her against him and held her hard; through the tears and the swollen mouth she could hardly hear what he whispered.

"I wanted . . . so much . . . to bring him home to you."

Later she slipped into bed beside him in the dark, trying not to make the mattress bobble, and spent the night, half awake, half sitting, with his mauled face supported against her shoulder. The breath in his mangled nose made a thin rasping sound, as if wheezing and fluttering through something torn deep inside him.

GRAHAM had cracked ribs and multiple bruises. The doctors strapped the ribs in place, and gave him a wide cloth belt with many buckles for support. The first evening when Susan went to see him in the hospital, he seemed very low. He looked over at the door when she came in, as if he'd been waiting for her, and held out his hand. She stood by his bed holding it until it was time to go. The second evening his color was better and he was breathing more easily. "I can leave tomorrow," he told her.

"I know. I just saw the doctor. You'll have to be still, though."

Graham nodded. "I'd like to come home," he said.

She looked at him as if she were seeing something behind his eyes. "Okay," she said. He gave her his hand again, and again she stood quietly, holding it.

"Do you want me to come back for you?" she asked.

He shook his head. "TJ will bring me. He'll go get my stuff from Naomi."

"Okay. I'll see you tomorrow, then."

"Okay." He pressed her hand before he let it go.

On the way to the elevator she met Naomi. Neither smiled as they approached each other. Susan said, "Hello," and Naomi nodded. They were poised face to face for a moment, each holding an orange visitor's card. Then they passed each other.

Al Menetti had been to see Graham in the hospital twice, and now he came in every day to hear the story over and over, hoping for something that would tell him where to start looking. But it was useless. The ransom call could have come from anywhere, and the two men who beat Graham had worn ski masks. Graham couldn't even say how tall they were. Menetti kept asking why Graham hadn't called him the minute he got the ransom demand. No matter how often he heard the explanation, it didn't seem to satisfy him.

Philippe was delighted to find Graham home again when he came to clean. He sat on the edge of the bed and demanded to hear all about each injury. Then he told Graham in generous detail about the time he had broken his leg in two places while skiing. When he'd finished his cleaning, he laid a tea tray for himself, Graham, and Susan and carried it up to Graham's room.

He took a sip of his tea. "Susan, did Jocelyn tell you I have a new client? He's a channel."

"A channel?" asked Susan and Graham together.

"Like a medium. You know, a channel from the other side. He showed me a videotape of one of his sessions."

"What was it like?"

"Oh, it was weird. He rolled his eyes, then he began to talk in this odd sort of chipmunk voice." Philippe began reciting nonsense syllables in a high, electronic-type whine.

"Don't make me laugh, Philippe," said Graham with his hand against his sore ribs.

"Oh, sorry. Shall I go on?"

"Yes, please. Just don't be funny."

"Well, it works like this. He's a channel for this spirit called Yasha, and he said I could come to a session and ask Yasha a question. I'm going Friday to ask him about Alex."

"Thank you, Philippe."

"You're welcome. I doubt if he can tell me any more than the cards, but there's no point not trying."

Graham was watching Susan. He saw in her face that beginning query: Could this be it? Could this help? Wanting to distract

213

her, he said, "Do the cards for me, Philippe. Find out how long it will be before I can turn over in bed without yelling."

"You can't just ask the cards a question like that," said Philippe seriously. "They'll only answer what they want to, you know."

"That's okay, Philippe. I'll take my chances." Philippe went to get a deck of cards from the living room. Graham smiled at Susan. "See," he said softly, "a few swift kicks in the head, and even I believe in fortune-tellers."

Philippe returned and smoothed the bed sheet beside Graham to make a place for cards. "I'll shuffle them," he said to Graham, "and you cut. Good. Okay, now watch. I lay them out in this pattern." He set out the cards as they came from the top of the deck. "And then I interpret the way they lie in relation to one another. For instance, this one can mean house, or home, and now . . . oh, the black man . . . that could be the devil or the hangman or a dark, handsome stranger, depending . . ." He let the sentence hang, then he sat looking at the cards with a puzzled expression that gradually deepened to a look of distress.

"Okay, Philippe," said Graham. "Let's have it. There's the house and the black man, and there's the queen of hearts right beside it, which is Susan, of course. The devil is going to break into the house and steal the silverware, and then Susan is going to run away with him."

"Well, you may think it's funny," said Philippe, "but if that card is the hangman, then someone in this house is going to be arrested." He scooped up his cards and left the room.

August in Boston is always a punishment of stifling gritty heat, white and glaring in the daytime, scarlet and noisy at night. Along the riverbank that summer the Esplanade was filled late into the evening with half-naked bodies in shorts, jogging or on roller skates, dipping and spinning along the sidewalks with disco music blaring from their headphone radios.

One Sunday, soon after Graham could get about, he and Susan went to the Esplanade for a picnic with Jocelyn and Justine. When they had finished lunch, they walked along the grassy banks across from the Cambridge boat basin, where flocks of white-winged sailboats swooped along the water. There were people everywhere—couples, young students who jammed into Boston and Cambridge for summer sessions, people laughing, people sleeping, people playing softball and Frisbee with their kids.

Susan watched the throng, momentarily content. It was good to see all the children. There were so many, but how could none of them be Alex?

Jocelyn and Susan had brought Justine and Alex here one Saturday in March, several weeks after Graham had moved out. There had been mounds of melting gray snow on the riverbank, and the children were engrossed in a game that involved racing each other up a small slope and falling over in mud, laughing.

As Susan sat down on a bench, Jocelyn had said, "I asked Alex if he'd like to sleep over tonight, but he said he couldn't. Mommy would be too sad."

"He did?" He was right. The house had seemed so empty without Graham; Susan hadn't been ready to be without Alex, too.

"I told him you'd be fine," said Jocelyn. "I said, 'Mommy has lots of other friends who could keep her company.' He said, 'She'd miss me, though, because I'm her smallest friend.'" Susan had looked across the distance at the children playing.

"I asked him if he misses his father," said Jocelyn, "and he said yes. He said, 'I think about Daddy more than food.'"

Graham now put his arm around Susan's shoulders as they made their way cautiously along the riverbank. She adjusted her stride to match his, and they concentrated on harmonizing their forward motion, together, one damaged beast with a gravely modified horizon. Once they looked at each other at the same moment and smiled; then they turned their attention to clearing a path for a little boy who wobbled rapidly toward them, his face anxious and joyous on a brand-new two-wheeler.

EXCEPT for the rib belt he still wore, Graham was nearly back to normal, at least physically. It was true, however, that he no longer believed Alex was alive. Not that being beaten up proved

216

anything, but in the month's work of healing his body, the gingerly caution and the slowly diminishing ache, he had imperceptibly healed over the source of his hope. Although this had not been stated between him and Susan, she knew it, and it made her edgy, as if he were a cuckoo in her nest.

Nobody ever said, exactly, that the police department was giving up on Alex. In mid-July there had still been five or six detectives who were in fairly constant touch with Susan. But one by one they were unavailable when she called. By the end of August, there was only Menetti and a sergeant named Laughlin who kept her informed of any tips or leads. These were down to a few dozen a week, from hundreds a day in the beginning.

Susan had been to the Fourth District headquarters once that month to ask them in person to increase the manpower in her search. The building, incongruous on desolate Warren Avenue, had a massive gray cut-stone façade.

The detectives' offices lined a narrow hallway that ran the length of the second floor. Susan found Menetti's office at the top of the stairs. It was a corner office with two desks, a lot of scarred wooden chairs, and posters of Alex on every wall. It was empty. Susan walked on down the hall, passing small, cheerless rooms on either side where detectives smoked cigarettes and plied their trade. She recognized many of the officers. One by one they spoke to her or gave a nod of recognition. She waited nearly half an hour before she got to speak to the head of the department, Lieutenant Bennet. He was a tall, gray-haired man. Offering her a chair, he asked what he could do for her.

"Well," she said, "there doesn't seem to be anyone working on my case. I haven't even seen Al Menetti all week."

"Your case is very important to us," he said. "Every man in this department is ready to drop what he's doing and follow any lead we get if there's any chance he can help find that little boy. Believe me, I know how you feel."

"If I shoot the next person who says he knows how I feel, would it be justifiable homicide?"

"Okay, okay," said Bennet. He gazed at her paternally. "But

217

I've been in this business a long time. I do know how you feel."

"Being in the business is not the same thing as losing your son!"

"Maybe not," Bennet said blandly as he shifted in his chair. "But I still know more about this business than you do. We are following every lead we get. If we have anything promising to track down, this whole department will be at your service."

Susan was sitting very straight on her chair. "And who is the judge of what is promising?" Her voice trembled.

Bennet stood and smiled. "I know how you feel," he repeated deliberately, "and we will continue to bend all our efforts to solve this case. It has our very top priority. I'll see that Lieutenant Menetti stays in close touch with you."

Quivering with emotion, Susan left the office.

Menetti called her early in the afternoon.

"He as much as said they have no one looking for Alex because there are no leads at all, so let's give up!" she yelled at him.

"It's not true. I swear to you," said Al. "There are two of us assigned to Alex full time, and six others who spend part of every day on it."

"But I haven't even seen you for a week!"

"I was checking on some things. Believe me, nothing has changed. We're looking for him the best we know how."

"Well, then, Al . . . tell me, what should I be doing to keep up the pressure? Do the talk shows help?"

He paused before answering. "It's hard to say. We get a lot more calls when there's publicity. None of them have been adding up to anything, but you never know."

"I see," she said, and surprised herself with the sneering tone in her voice. "Meaning," she said, correcting her tone, "that it makes more work without actually helping."

"You never know what it will stir up," he said. "Look, don't worry about it. Do whatever you feel you can handle."

For a week after this conversation Menetti was there every morning at eight thirty, walking the street from Susan's door around the corner onto Beacon. He'd look up at her window as he got out of the car. If she was there, he'd nod.

Susan now had her public manner pat. When she saw an acquaintance on the street, she took control of the situation so there was no awkwardness.

"Alma," she'd call. "Hello. I haven't seen you in a couple of weeks. Isn't the weather filthy? Poor Taxi's nearly cooked, aren't you, fur person? Have a good afternoon." And off she'd go with a smile.

She called the English Department and arranged her course schedule for the coming year: a general lecture course in the American novel, an honors seminar on Willa Cather, and another on twentieth-century southern fiction.

She agreed to an interview with Charlotte Mayhew, a writer from *Mother's Day* in New York, for a story that would ask the readers to join the hunt for Alex. She spent several evenings arranging all her photographs of Alex from his birth to the time he disappeared. She hoped the magazine would use a couple of pages of them, arranged to look like the pages of a family album.

She had taken to rising very early. She had trouble sleeping more than four or five hours a night, and besides, they often got crank calls in the early hours of the morning. At seven one morning when Susan came in from a walk she went up to Alex's room, taking care not to creak the stairs and wake Graham. In Alex's room she placed one of his baby chairs at the closet so she could step up and reach the shelf where she had put away his sweaters in the spring. These she brought down. On a back hook she found Alex's favorite jacket, made of blue cotton with black knit ribbing at the waist and cuffs. When she slipped her hand into one of its pockets, she touched a squash ball and a little nest of rubber bands. She stood tingling with the most intense recall of her son she had felt in months. It was like holding his hand.

"Are you putting his clothes away?" Graham stood sleepily in the doorway. She started when he spoke.

"No," she said, "getting out his fall things."

"Oh," said Graham after a long pause. He went into the bathroom and shut the door.

ROBERT HAD RENTED A HOUSE IN Nantucket for August, and he invited his parents and Susan and Graham to come for Labor Day. Graham wanted them to go.

"It's the big party weekend. Robert will want us to go to a yacht club dance dressed as chickens," said Susan.

"Well, we won't," said Graham, putting his arms around her. "We'll go sailing by ourselves, and we'll eat a lot of steamers, and we'll sleep in the sun."

"Do you really want to go?" she asked.

"I think Mother and Dad would like to see us."

"I know. They would."

"And I hate to turn Robert down. He sounded lonely."

"Well," she said.

"And I'm lonely, too." She immediately felt this remark as from his whole body, warm against her, and she felt a twinge of panic that turned to resentment as it reached her consciousness.

"Okay," she said, turning from him. "I guess it will be okay."

The evening before they were to leave, the phone rang while Susan was packing. Graham answered it in the kitchen.

"Who is this?" she heard him say. She put down the clothes she was folding and went to the top of the stairs.

"Where in Toronto? . . . Why didn't you call us before?" She went quickly into the bedroom and picked up the extension.

"I'm on the upstairs phone, Graham. This is Mrs. Selky."

The voice on the other end, young, husky, and nervous, said, "Oh, hello," and started again.

It was a woman in Toronto; her sister, she said, lived down the hall from a young couple who'd been trying for years to adopt a baby. This June they had suddenly turned up with a nice bright six-year-old boy who bore a powerful resemblance to Alex.

"Did you call the Toronto police?" Graham asked.

No, she hadn't. She'd only seen the boy three times, and her sister said, "Don't be ridiculous. They got tired of waiting for an infant and adopted an older child. They're a lovely couple." But if he's such a nice bright child, why wouldn't he have been adopted before? Healthy white children were in great demand.

220

"How do you know he's so healthy and bright?" asked Susan.

The woman had talked to him. She stopped him in the hall one day last week and had a long talk with him. "He said his name was Ronny. I asked him if he'd ever lived in Boston, but he said he didn't think so. Then the mother came along and she didn't look at all pleased. She rushed him off into the apartment."

"But why did you wait so long?" Graham asked again. "Why didn't you call us the first time you saw him?"

"My sister mentioned on the phone tonight that the family is moving to California. I didn't tell my sister I was going to call you." Would she give her name and address? She would rather not. She gave the name and address of the couple with the little boy; then she said she was sorry and she hung up.

Susan ran down the stairs. Graham was sitting with his chin on his hand, staring at the phone.

"What do you think?" she asked.

He didn't look up. "I don't know. What do you think?"

"I think I ought to call Al."

"That's what I thought you were going to say."

She looked at Graham sharply, but he wasn't looking at her.

PAT and the children were already in the car when the phone rang. Al only heard it because he'd gone back for some clothesline with which to tie his suitcase to the roof of the car. When he came out without the clothesline and walked around to Pat's window on the passenger side, she said, "Let me guess. That was Susan Selky, and we're not going to the Cape."

"I'm sorry," he said. "Listen, you go ahead. I'll join you as soon as I can. Maybe I can get there for tomorrow night."

In the back seat the kids had stopped chattering and shoving each other, and now Eugene wailed, "Daddy!"

"Pat, I'm sorry. Something came up, and that's life, okay? I'll get there as soon as I can."

Pat slid over to the driver's side. She started the car. "Al? I would like this to be the last time this happens for a while. This has not been a lovely summer."

"One way or the other, I don't think this case will go on much longer."

"Okay," she said to the back seat, "who gets to ride up here with me? I'm thinking of a number from one to ten. . . ."

He watched how she backed out of the driveway, and hoped she'd slow down once she was out of sight.

WHEN Susan hung up from calling Al, Graham was still not looking at her. "Well?" he said.

"Al agreed that we couldn't not check it out, and he said he'd get right to work."

"And what about us?" asked Graham. "You didn't give him Robert's number in Nantucket. Does that mean we're not going?"

"Well, Graham, what if they need us to identify him? What if we were fogged in and it took us days to get back?"

"Susan, what did Al think the odds were that this would be Alex? How many leads like this have they tracked down so far?"

She looked at him stubbornly.

"I think we should go to Nantucket," he said.

"And do what? Sit by the phone all weekend out there?"

"I think we should go to Nantucket, Susan, and go sailing and eat steamers. I think we should decide to live."

"As in live it up? Goodness, Graham, don't let me keep you. Maybe Robert has party streamers and funny hats."

He looked at her hard. "If not now, then when? If you don't come this time, will you next time?"

"I don't know."

"How long will we let it go on, Susan? The rest of our lives?"

"*I don't know!*"

"Well, I'm going to Nantucket tomorrow morning. I'd like you to go with me."

"And if I don't?"

They looked at each other with long, steady stares.

"I don't know," he said finally.

"Well, I guess we'll see," she said.

So he went to Nantucket by himself, and Susan spent a long,

222

nearly silent weekend in the deserted city. She sat quietly in the house, dark by contrast to the light outside, waiting for the phone to ring. It wasn't until twilight Saturday that Al called. "I'm sorry," he said. "It looks legit. The couple haven't been out of Canada since last summer, and they have the boy's birth certificate and all the adoption papers in order. The boy does look like Alex. But does Alex speak any French?"

"No."

"This boy is bilingual."

Something beneath her rib cage leaped and tore. These slams of pain were so physical, Susan wondered if it were possible to go on taking them without the inner fibers beginning to shiver apart, like a wooden boat breaking up in a storm.

"Oh," she said. "Well, I suppose I should be getting used to this." But not only was she not getting used to it, it was getting worse instead of better. She tried to reach Graham in Nantucket, but the phone in Robert's house rang and rang and rang with that particular tinny summer-house sound.

On Sunday afternoon she dialed Philippe's number. He answered after the third ring, and he sounded very absent.

"I'm sorry, did I wake you? It's Susan."

"Susan. Oh, no, that's all right. Is anything the matter?"

"No, not at all. I'm sorry if I disturbed you. It just occurred to me you never said if you went to that channel person to ask the spirit about Alex."

"Oh," Philippe said. "Yes, I went. It was peculiar."

"Do you have a minute to tell me about it?"

"Sure, Susan. Just hold on a second." After a brief silence he was back. "Well, it was in this big apartment over in the Fenway. We all sat on cushions on the floor, and after we meditated for a while, people started to ask questions. So I asked if Yasha knew what had happened to Alex, and he thought about it and then he said, 'The earth weeps.' That's all he would say."

"Oh," said Susan.

"But don't be depressed. Yasha says that all the time. He isn't interested in human affairs. He's mainly interested in what a mess

223

we're making of the planet, so when you ask him a question that he thinks is too specific, he just says, 'The earth weeps.' "

"I see," said Susan. "Well, I just remembered you hadn't told me how that came out. I'm sorry if I bothered you."

"No, that's all right. I'll see you on Tuesday."

She did not, however, see him on Tuesday. On Monday evening of Labor Day weekend Philippe was arrested for soliciting a minor.

It was an evening that had a hint of fall coolness in it, and before Philippe had left his apartment, he put on a jacket he had not worn since spring. He was wearing it when the Vice Squad picked him up on Boylston Street. In the jacket pocket the police found a slashed and bloodstained pair of boy's underpants. In the waistband was a name tape that said ALEX SELKY.

THE phone on the nightstand by Susan's bed was an instrument, not a tool as a chisel is the tool of a sculptor, but as a prophet is an instrument of God. When she opened her heart to hope or pray, she often stared at the telephone, as if her grain of faith could press through the wires to expand outward and make itself felt. Bring my boy back. Bring my boy back.

On the morning of Tuesday, September 2, a little after dawn, the telephone elected to bring her the information that Henry Sullivan, known to her as Philippe Lucienne, had been arrested and formally charged with the crime of kidnapping in the first degree, for the theft and presumably the murder of her son, Alexander Graham Selky, Jr. The afternoon paper carried the full story. POLICE BREAK SELKY CASE, ran the headline.

The story read:

Police announced this morning that they have arrested a suspect in the case that has baffled the city, the disappearance of six-year-old Alexander Selky a block from his home in Back Bay on May 15 of this year. Arrested today is Henry Sullivan, 42, a self-confessed homosexual and a convicted child molester who has worked as a houseboy in the Selky home for over two years. Police say that although Sullivan, who calls himself Philippe Lucienne, passed a lie-detector test in the days just after the boy's disappearance, he has been under close observation for several weeks.

Detective Albert Menetti, whose dedication to the solving of this mystery is likely to win him high commendation from the department, explained this morning, "I suspected from the beginning that the kidnapper had to be someone the boy knew. Everything pointed to that, but it was only after weeks of checking police records from all over the country that we discovered Sullivan's true identity and previous record. At that time we began to recheck his alibi for the day of May 15 and those following, and when we found a number of serious discrepancies, the decision was made to put him under surveillance."

The trail that led to Sullivan's arrest began with the discovery that he had served eighteen months in prison in Salt Lake City, Utah, in 1959 for impairing the morals of a minor.

Evidence began to mount when police discovered that a neighbor of John Murchison's, a wealthy art dealer who used Sullivan's services as a housecleaner, saw Sullivan repeatedly enter Murchison's lavish duplex apartment on Beacon Hill during the days immediately following the Selky boy's disappearance. She was aware that Murchison was away in Europe for the week.

The neighbor, whose information has been corroborated by others on the block, said that at one point Sullivan arrived carrying groceries and that during the nights in question there were sometimes loud noises coming from the apartment that could have been part of a scuffle or struggle.

On the night before Murchison was to return, the neighbor, whom police have not identified, apparently heard screams and loud noises coming from the master bathroom area. Late that evening Sullivan was seen leaving the apartment carrying two large plastic garbage bags.

Police admit that up until last night their case against Sullivan seemed to be at a stalemate. Detective Menetti explained, "I have two witnesses who put Sullivan at the scene of the abduction the morning Alex disappeared, although he has sworn he was somewhere else. It would have been a simple matter for Sullivan to persuade the boy to accompany him, since Alex knew and trusted him. The Murchison apartment provided a perfect hideout, but at the end of the weekend, when Murchison was due to return, I believe that the suspect realized that he could neither release the boy nor continue to hold him. At that time I believe that he murdered him and then divided his body between two plastic bags so that neither bag would break when he carried it down the stairs."

The district attorney's office says that it plans to proceed directly to the grand jury, asking for an indictment on the charge of first-degree kidnapping. Under the state penal code, kidnapping in the first degree includes a case in which the person abducted dies during the abduction or before he is able to return to safety. The penalties for this crime are the same as for first-degree murder.

AFTER the first death, there is no other. But Graham and Susan had lost their child so many times. Graham's mourning was ferocious, like a man who walks deliberately into the heart of a storm and opens his coat to it. Susan's grieving instead seemed to be held inside her, as slow-burning hardwood holds the heat. She had lost her son; she had lost her own youth. Within her was something that would never cease to ache. That anguish was all that remained of her son's life.

And God gave His only begotten Son. Yes. Because if the world could not understand God's love as love, it could at least understand the loss of a child, which even to God is the worst the heart can suffer.

The first night after Philippe's arrest Susan dreamed of Alex, the first time in a long time. She had been trying to remember exactly the way his hair fell across his forehead the last night they were together as he sat on the floor of his bedroom in pajamas while she read to him. She could not, but in the dream he was there, walking between her and Graham, holding both their hands. It was spring, and they walked through a park that was mounded high with pink and white azaleas blooming on high green bushes. Susan felt Alex's hand in hers, and her heart glowed as if it were full of sunlight.

Sometime during the second day, Graham looked up at her with an expression close to surprise and said, "This is going to go on forever, isn't it?"

Susan nodded.

She and Graham were silent and dry-eyed almost the whole time through those first three nights and days.

TJ and Annie came, Susan's father and stepmother came, Robert and Graham's parents came. Then, once they got there, nobody knew what to do. The press was encamped on the front steps, so that neither Graham nor Susan could leave the house. Margaret Mayo went in and out to buy food for them all. She brought in the newspapers, and on the fourth day she insisted that Susan read them. By then Philippe had been indicted and arraigned and was being held at the Charles Street jail.

Everyone sat around and tried not to talk about what they were thinking. There were no set mealtimes, just platters of cold food on the dining-room table that Margaret refilled from time to time. The gathering had the air of a wake without a funeral.

Graham's father grew restless and kept getting up and walking around the room as if he were looking for something. Finally he strode over and turned the TV set on. He watched a rerun of "Hollywood Squares," and then came the noon newscast.

"Good afternoon," said the announcer. "Cleanup efforts continue around the metropolitan area in the wake of high winds and record-breaking rains. Damage has been estimated in the millions of dollars, with heavy flooding in many parts of the state."

"The earth weeps," Susan said bleakly to Graham. Then she remembered that he didn't know the joke. Who did? Philippe.

Philippe appeared on the screen, walking between two huge uniformed policemen. His hands were handcuffed in front of him. He made no attempt to duck or hide his head from the cameras; rather, at one point Susan had the impression that he had looked straight through the camera at her. As he appeared,

227

a swarm of reporters surged toward him like bugs on a cake crumb, and you could hear them shouting questions at him. "Mr. Sullivan, Mr. Sullivan! How do you feel?" "We understand that you pleaded innocent." "What are you going to say to Mrs. Selky?"

Without uttering a word, Philippe made his way through them and got into the waiting police car.

The announcer's voice was saying, "This was the scene a few minutes ago on the steps of the Suffolk County courthouse, where Henry Sullivan, the alleged murderer of little Alexander Selky, has just been arraigned on a charge of first-degree kidnapping. As you can see, Mr. Sullivan would not speak to the reporters who have been waiting here hoping to get a word with him. There was a near riot after his departure, as angry demonstrators attacked a small group of gay activists."

At that moment the picture took several zags and pointed toward the sky as the announcer explained that the cameraman had been knocked down in the melee. The shot changed to a view of Susan's front door, apparently being taken live about twenty feet from where the family sat.

The announcer was saying, "And at the house where little Alex Selky lived, the family is still in seclusion. The only statement so far has come from a family friend, Margaret Mayo." The door on the screen opened, and they watched a rerun of Margaret stepping out and stopping on the front step. Her straight iron-colored hair sat on her head like a helmet, and she faced lights and waited calmly for the questions to stop being flung at her. "Mrs. Mayo, how is the family?" "Have they spoken to Henry Sullivan?" "Did you have any idea he was under suspicion?" "Did Mrs. Selky?" "Are they going to give a statement?"

"Well," she said when there was a lull, "I have something to share with you, but I have no intention of shouting." There was relative quiet, although no pause in the flashing of camera bulbs. She said, "Two hundred years ago, when a family suffered as this one has, straw would be put down in front of the house to deaden the sound of wheels, and horses' hoofs would be muffled before they entered the streets. No one expects such a show of civility now, but this family has lost enough. It would be good of you to allow them to mourn in private." There was a brief silence, during which Margaret made her way down the steps.

"Wish I'd done that," said Susan's father.

SUSAN had to go out sometime, but she physically shrank from it. At last she made herself walk out the door behaving as Margaret had. She tried to hold herself like Margaret, and to wear Margaret's imperturbable expression. When she opened the door, there was a howl of questions from the waiting reporters. She started down the steps, and one reporter actually caught her by the arm as he shouted something at her. She looked at him with patient eyes. She looked down at the hand on her arm; she looked back at him. The hand dropped. She walked on down the steps and gained the sidewalk. Then she walked away. After two days of this the group finally disappeared.

SUSAN deeply dreaded her first day of teaching again. Every step she took in the direction of a normal life was a step away from her lost child. In the early morning of the first day of classes she had a dream that when she started her lecture, she couldn't hear her own voice. Instead she heard Alex crying.

Graham's first lecture of the term was the same morning as hers. She knew he hadn't slept well, either. But when he had had his coffee, he said, "I'm glad it's here. I'm glad to have something to do." He kissed her on the cheek and wished her luck.

She was looking over her notes from the opening lecture for last year when TJ walked in the door.

"Oh," she said. "Graham's already left."

"I know. This is the neighborhood escort service."

"Ah." She went through the notes one more time while TJ sat down at the edge of a chair and waited. He kept his car keys dangling in his hand.

"TJ, I really don't want to do this."

"But you're going to," he said.

"At least you can't say I should do it because Alex would have wanted me to. Alex would have wanted me to stay at home."

"You're going to do it for yourself," he said.

"Oh, TJ, imagine having no reason but myself to do anything."

He saw the panic beginning. "Come on," he said. "Move."

ONE afternoon about a week after classes had begun, Susan found a tall man with an astonishingly round head waiting for her in the hall outside the room where she held her seminar. "Mrs. Selky," he said, walking beside her as she started down the hall. "I'm Lesley George. I'm Henry's attorney."

"Henry?" She stopped.

"Philippe," he said.

"Oh." She felt a quake of loathing grip her insides, followed by a real fear that she might throw up. This passed quickly. The man's eyes swam behind round wire-rimmed glasses.

"Can I buy you some coffee?" he asked.

"I guess," she said.

"The point is," said the attorney when they were seated in a booth in a nearby restaurant and Susan had ordered tea, "Henry wants to see you."

"Why?"

"To tell you he's not guilty." The round eyes were remarkably ingenuous. "You're the only one he *will* see. He wouldn't talk to the court's psychiatrist. He tried to fire me the first day I met him because I mentioned the idea of an insanity plea."

"I take it you think he did it." She was astounded at the impact of this phrase. "Killed my son" was what "did it" meant.

Lesley George looked thoughtfully at his hands. "I believe he's entitled to the best possible defense. And I believe he stands a good chance of being acquitted. In spite of all the papers are making of it, the prosecution's case is very weak."

Susan's mouth was dry with fear. Her insides felt as if the acid of her tea had tanned them. She simply did not believe she could endure any more ambiguity than she had already. The worst had happened. At least the worst was over.

"If I can keep Henry's Utah conviction out of the record—and

230

I ought to be able to—what have you got left? There are witnesses who put him on Beacon Street the morning your boy disappeared, and that's bad, because he lied to the police about that. The odd thing is, he passed the lie-detector test they gave him in the beginning. He's failed two in a row since he was arrested, but I can keep all that out of the record. Frightened subject. Prejudiced interpretation of the test. That sort of thing."

"What about motive?" Susan whispered.

The lawyer waved his hand. "Don't need a motive in a sex case. Sex is a universal motive. Of course, in Henry's case, his . . . um, particular predilections will weigh heavily with a jury."

"And what about the . . . Alex's . . . in his pocket?"

This time Lesley George looked directly at her. "Henry can explain that," he said. "The blood type on the pants is O-positive. Very common. It's your son's type, and it's also Henry's. He can explain a lot of things. Well enough to create reasonable doubt."

Susan felt a creeping horror as the ambiguity made itself part of her. Was he telling her that Alex was alive and an innocent man was going to be tried for doing something that might not have happened at all? Or was he saying that the man who murdered her son stood a very good chance of going free?

"I'll see him," she said.

"Well, good. I'll arrange it."

THE room in which Susan waited for Henry Sullivan was walled with large turquoise tiles, like a school cafeteria. There were high windows covered with heavy wire, through which slanted bright bars of light jailed behind crisscrossed shadows. A guard sat at a big bare desk with a telephone on it.

Philippe was led in between two guards wearing blue shirts and pistols on their hips. He sat down at a table across from Susan. They looked into each other's eyes for what seemed a long time. Hypocrite is what came into her head. His eyes were bald blue, with gray radial glints around the pupil like spokes on a wheel. Do you not flinch because you are innocent? she asked the eyes, or because you are so guilty?

"Shall I call you Philippe or Henry?" She spoke first.

"Henry."

That surprised her. She also caught, a beat later, that he hadn't pulled the vowel the way Philippe would have. Heeenry. "You wanted to see me?" she asked.

He nodded. "Susan," he said, "I am guilty of a great many things. I am, as my stepfather would say, a screaming queer. But I have never in my life knowingly hurt another person, and I did not, ever, in any way hurt Alex."

Their faces were matched in blankness as they faced each other across the table, like Man and Death playing chess.

"You lied about being on Beacon Street the morning Alex disappeared."

"No," he said. "I didn't."

"You failed a lie-detector test about it. Twice."

"Susan, I was scared."

"How do you explain two people who say they saw you there?"

"I can't. Error. Mistaken identity. Take your pick."

"What were you doing at Murchison's that weekend if you didn't have Alex hidden there?"

"If you met somebody you liked and you lived in a fourth-floor walk-up but you had the keys to a duplex apartment with an owner in Europe, what would you do?"

She looked at him levelly. "What about what you had in your pocket?" She didn't want to hear the answer. She was afraid she would not believe him and afraid that she would. Resisting, she felt the old hope stir painfully within her.

He held up his right hand with his palm facing her. There was a scar an inch long from what must have been a deep cut. "At your house. Last spring. I reached into a sinkful of sudsy water and cut my hand on a broken glass. I keep rags for dusting under the sink, and I grabbed one. An old pair of Alex's underpants. I cut them with the kitchen shears and tied the cloth around my hand. I was bleeding all over the place. I started home with the pair of underpants on my hand, but by the time I got to the subway I realized that the bleeding had stopped, so I took the bandage off and put it in my pocket. Then I went on home."

She stared at him. "Did you go somewhere for stitches?"

"I told you, the bleeding stopped."

"I see," she said, though she saw nothing. She was feeling.

WITHOUT a plan, in a suspension of belief and disbelief, Susan found herself again on Warren Avenue, on her way to Menetti's office. She walked up the stairs to the second floor slowly. Before she turned into his office, she had a sudden intuition of what she would see, and she was right.

Inside, the posters of Alex were all gone. On the bulletin board facing the door was a new poster with a police sketch of a young man who had raped two young girls. WANTED, said the poster. HAVE YOU SEEN THIS MAN?

It was the first time Susan had seen Menetti since Philippe's arrest. He met her with a look of very great sorrow in his eyes. "Come in," he said, and led her into his office. He sat down at his desk, and she sat on a straight-backed chair facing him.

"How are you?" he asked sympathetically.

"I've been to see Philippe," she said.

Menetti sighed. "Never in my life," he said, "have I hoped so much that I was wrong about a case."

"I think you are," said Susan.

"Excuse me?" Menetti had a pretty good idea that he was about to be promoted. He'd been on the news every day for a week. He'd gotten in the rhythm of modestly dismissing his contribution to solving the mystery.

"I think you made a mistake, Al. I don't think he did it."

"Well," he said gently, "I guess I can understand that. He is very persuasive. That's part of the DA's case against him."

"Al, have you talked to him?"

"Of course I've talked to him."

"Did you give him a chance to explain?"

"Look, the case is out of my hands now. My department only handles a case up till the time that we discover for certain that a crime has been committed. Philippe was arrested by Vice, and

233

the case against him, that's handled by Homicide. Of course they keep me informed."

"Have you heard his explanation?"

"Wait here a minute," said Al. "I'll be right back." He got up and strode out, looking annoyed. In a minute he returned and sat back down in his chair. He dropped some papers on the desk. "I want you to follow me carefully," he said. "We've got a very strong case against Sullivan, believe me, and it is not going to be tried in the newspapers before a jury is impaneled, so—"

"What evidence do you have? Besides the underpants?"

Menetti looked exasperated. "I'm sorry," he said, "but that's just none of your business."

"Oh, really."

"Excuse me. I'm sorry. What I meant to say was, the prisoner has a right to a fair trial, and the people have a right to a fair trial against him. There's a gag order on the department, and I'm not going to tell you or the press any more. But look, now. This is a copy of the psychiatrist's record from the court in Utah. I'll read you the conclusion. 'It is the examiner's opinion that the prisoner is a psychopathic personality. He has clear homosexual drives and a predisposition to commit sexual crimes that make him a menace to society. It is recommended that he be confined in an institution suitable for the care and treatment of his disorder.'"

Menetti laid down the papers and looked at Susan. Her eyes were fixed on his as if they were boring tools.

"Now *listen*," he said, losing his temper. "*I have done all I can for you*. It's over. You'll just have to accept that."

"If you're wrong, and I'm right, then my son's still missing."

He stood up. "You'll have to talk to Homicide, and I've already told you that they can't tell you any more than I have."

"Who are the witnesses who saw Philippe the morning Alex disappeared? Why didn't I ever hear about them?"

"I'm sorry. There is nothing more I can do for you."

Susan gazed at him steadily for a long moment. When he looked so uncomfortable that she thought the moment would stay with him, she rose slowly and left.

IN THE LIVING ROOM THE CLOCK ON the mantel over the fireplace ticked softly. Graham sat at his desk in the corner, working quietly on his Milton book. Susan noticed how he sat. No twitching, no twisting a lock of hair, no tapping a pencil. His grief seemed to have coursed through him in one galling dose, leaving behind only this fiercely determined stillness. Somewhere upstairs, at the evening bathtime, storytime, an idle creak reminded her that there was nothing human moving up there.

"Graham," she said. He held up a hand to indicate that he wanted a moment more before being interrupted. Oh, the stillness. No more drilling clamor of the telephone. No meandering friendly chat between them. As much of the future as they cared to contemplate was tomorrow, and they had more than enough reason to avoid the past. The present, without inflection or implication, was all, and they floated in it quietly, side by side.

"Okay," said Graham. He turned his head to her without turning in his chair.

"I went to see Philippe today. His lawyer asked me to."

Now he put down his pen and turned to face her. "Well," he said. He wasn't asking, but he was going to have to hear.

"He wanted to tell me that he didn't kill Alex."

"Yes, I'm sure he wanted to tell you that." Graham looked at her stolidly.

"I think it's true," said Susan.

Graham just looked at her. She could see his eyes flick over her, out at the night, and back to her.

He said, "No."

"What do you mean, no?"

He stood up from his desk and carefully pushed in his chair. Towering over her, he said, much louder, "No . . . no . . . no! No more." He left the room and went upstairs, and she sat looking after him, stunned.

She sat for some time listening to him move around. What was he doing? Not getting ready for bed. Looking for something? What? Finally she recognized the rhythm of his footsteps. He was packing. There he went into the bathroom for his shaving things; there he was checking the dresser drawers to see what he forgot; there he was closing the suitcase. There he was walking into Alex's room and standing in the darkness for a long time.

She heard the suitcase bump against the banister as he came down the stairs. He set it down in the kitchen and came into the living room. He looked at her once, with an unreadable expression; then he went over to his desk, opened his briefcase, and began packing his papers. What was he challenging her to say? Yes, I believe it's over; yes, I want to forget I had a son? Have a son? Yes, I surrender Alex so I can love you?

No.

At last he closed the briefcase and turned to look at her. His eyes were filled with a dense, beaten, challenging stare.

She said only, "Where would I reach you, if I needed to?"

He said harshly, "At Naomi's."

He was out the door when she suddenly ran to the top of the stairs and called down after him, "Wait a minute. Don't you even have to call her to tell her you're coming?" He shook his head, glaring, and she could see him holding his downcurved lips together to keep in the tears.

SUSAN put in a call to Charlotte Mayhew at *Mother's Day* in New York.

"She's in a meeting," said her secretary. "Can I tell her what this is in reference to?" Charlotte Mayhew had spent some ten hours in Susan's house less than a month ago, taping interviews and preparing an article on Alex to be entitled "Have You Seen This Child?" She had the scrapbook Susan had made up, containing almost all of her photographs of Alex.

"It's in reference to an article she's writing," said Susan. She had to keep calling for three days before Charlotte called back.

"Susan," said the arch, maternal voice. "I haven't had a minute to return your call, but you've been on my mind. How *are* you?"

"Fine," said Susan.

"I'm sure you're wanting the photographs back. I'll send them airmail special. Give me the address again."

"Charlotte, I wanted to talk to you about the article. Could we meet? I'd be glad to take the shuttle down."

"Oh, *yes*. Let's do lunch; just let me check my calendar. . . . Oh, isn't this disgusting. Do you know, I don't have a lunch open for the next two weeks?"

"But, Charlotte, I don't care about lunch. I'd just like to talk to you soon about the article."

"Well, honey, I'm afraid the thrust of the article was the inspirational approach, your faith and your courage . . . plus the appeal to the readers themselves, the idea that they could *help*. That's how I sold it to the editorial board."

Susan thought of the phone calls from this woman last July to the effect that the editors of *Mother's Day* felt that Susan's story was the story of the decade.

"But, Charlotte, I don't feel that the nature of the story has changed. I'm convinced that the police have made a mistake." She paused to hear Charlotte's reaction to this bombshell, but there was judicious silence at the other end of the line.

"Yes," Susan said. "I've talked to Henry Sullivan, and I believe that in all good faith the police have made a mistake. A tragic mistake," she added, suddenly seeing the headline as *Mother's Day* would write it. "Don't you see? Nothing has changed. Alex may still be out there, missing me, but because the police have made this terrible mistake, not only is an innocent man in grave danger, but so is Alex and so am I and so are all our hopes. Charlotte, if I'm right, don't you see what it means?"

Susan finally stopped talking. A silent beat or two.

"I *do* see," said Charlotte emphatically. "I see exactly. But to be honest, this just isn't a *Mother's Day* story. We actually have a list of no-noes, and I'm afraid anything about homosexuals . . . you understand, as far as we're concerned we don't know they exist. Pathetic, isn't it? But that's what I'm up against. There just isn't any way I could write the story that would make it right for

Mother's Day. I'm sure somebody will do a bang-up job of it, and I'm sorry it won't be us. Now, lambie ..."

"Good-by, Charlotte," said Susan.

Susan continued to teach her classes, working mechanically from last year's notes. But there were times, more and more often, when she thought of giving up out of sheer loneliness. One night a new faculty couple on a one-year fellowship from Israel invited her on the spur of the moment to join them and a few friends for dinner. The talk over drinks was lively and trivial, and Susan was keenly aware of how long it had been since she'd been with people who were just enjoying themselves. The evening was an escape back into the lost world of the ordinary, until just before supper was served, when the hostess brought in her little six-month-old daughter in her pink terry-cloth stretch suit to be kissed good night.

The women each took a turn holding her, and for Susan the warm fragrant weight of the baby against her breast brought back a deeply held memory that gave her profound pleasure.

"She's a real dream," Susan said to the young mother when she came back from putting her baby in the crib.

The mother nodded shyly. "I worry about her all day long. So many things can happen to babies, crib death, accidents . . . I won't leave her outside in the sun in her carriage; I'm afraid someone will steal her."

Here her husband joined in, laughing. "There are thousands of babies in Boston, but ours is so perfect that gangs of criminals are plotting to steal her away from us."

The mother said softly and earnestly, "But things do happen to babies. If something did, I know I would kill myself."

"Why do you say that?" asked Susan sharply. "Is that what you think you *should* do?"

The young woman looked at her in surprise.

"Do you have children?" one of the other guests asked Susan.

"Yes," she replied vehemently, and then, realizing that she could not answer any specific questions about her child without spoiling the evening, she contradicted herself and said, "No."

By that time it was clear to everyone that Susan was reacting to a rather ordinary situation with uncommon emotion. When conversation resumed, it had lost its spontaneous drift, so Susan apologized and excused herself early.

That night for the first time she understood why some parents who have lost children move and start a new life among strangers. But how could she go away? How could she, ever? This was where Alex knew to find her. This was where he would try to come home.

In the long, still hours of her days Susan established new rules and rhythms to replace the events of her former life. She made herself cook at least one recognizable meal a day and not eat it standing up at the sink. Every evening at eleven she took a mug of hot mint tea up to bed with her. If she could keep her entire attention confined to the pages of her book as she lay in bed and sipped the tea, she could usually go to sleep by midnight.

In her inner life, there were two things she had rules about. One was If Only. If Only I had walked with him that morning. If Only he'd left a minute earlier, or later. If Only I'd called him back for his jacket. . . . She could bear to imagine almost any of the possible fates that Alex had met. She could not bear It Might Not Have Happened.

The other thing was imagining how he would come back. At first she had thought the phone would ring. She would pick it up and there would be his voice. "Hello, Mommy?" Perhaps she still believed that, for a millisecond, each time the phone rang, even now. But the phone rang so often, and dreams replayed too many times lose their power to move.

After that she'd decided that the way it would happen would be through Menetti. He'd call to say they were checking out a lead. They'd received a call from a schoolteacher in Florida who'd recognized the new little boy in first grade. Then there would be wrenching hours of waiting and pacing, and then Menetti would call to say that Alex was on a plane home. The scene at the airport. The press. Graham. The explosion of joy in her heart.

240

And the look in Menetti's eyes as he gave her back her son. Well . . . that one was gone now.

But there were still ways it would happen. She allowed herself to develop only one at a time, and she allowed herself to think of it only in the hour before sleep, when she turned out the light. For instance, someone would see a picture in an old magazine at the hairdresser's and recognize the little "grandchild" of the people down the block. Or, a couple from the neighborhood would pass a schoolyard one day and see a little boy playing alone. They would recognize the face on the poster, even though his hair would be dyed and his missing tooth grown in, because no one, no one, could mistake that brilliant smile. They would call the police, or they would simply drive up to her door one day and ring the bell. . . .

Lord, I believe; help thou mine unbelief.

THE posters of Alex, the ones that said STILL MISSING, had nearly all been taken down. Susan had new ones printed up using a different photograph, another way of seeing his face, and in the evenings and on weekends she would walk around the neighborhood asking permission to post them. She preferred to put them in storefronts, where they could be seen through the glass but not harmed by the weather or defaced. Recently on the subway she had seen one of the old posters with Alex's face drawn over with a felt-tip pen to look like a minstrel show pickaninny.

Often now when she showed a store owner the new poster, he would look at her oddly and say, "I heard they solved that; the kid was murdered by some queer."

"No, it was a mistake," she'd say.

"Oh. I guess, go ahead and put it up," he would say.

But the owner of a deli in Kenmore Square, thinking Susan was another of the volunteers, said, "Hey, honey, give me a break. People want to come in here and eat without feeling like they should lose their appetite from sympathy. Somebody should tell the parents, enough is enough."

"Thank you so much," said Susan.

ONE CHILLY SUNDAY MORNING IN mid-October Jocelyn appeared at Susan's door carrying a bag of bagels and a copy of the *Globe*. "Justine's at a friend's, and I said to myself, This is *too* nice a morning to be having breakfast alone. So here I am."

"I'm delighted," said Susan. She put on a pot of fresh coffee and, from the refrigerator, produced orange juice and butter. On a shelf, in the back, she found a jar of jam. "Oh-oh. Here's some antique jam. It seems to have fur on it."

"Looks to have been there since Alex," said Jocelyn.

Susan looked at her warily. "Yes, probably," she agreed.

When the coffee was ready, they sat at the dining table in the sunlight and read the paper. It was like old times, except that in old times the children would have been playing upstairs.

"Feel like taking a walk?" asked Susan, folding her paper.

"No, thanks," said Jocelyn. "You know you don't take walks, honey; you go on hunts."

"Now, exactly what do you mean by that?"

"Just what I said," answered Jocelyn. "You never go out any-more without studying every little child to see if it's Alex. You look down every alley and peek into people's windows. . . . I can't sit by any longer and watch you do this to yourself."

Susan got up and carried the breakfast dishes into the kitchen; then she returned to the table and with a deep breath said, "Okay, Jocelyn. Get it off your chest."

"All right, honey." Jocelyn reached across the table and touched Susan's arm. "You're a brave lady," she said. "You've been through a whole lot of pain and you've carried it like a warrior. But it's time to let go. You're only hurting yourself. I know it's none of my business, but your friends are worried about you."

"Really?" said Susan dryly. "Where are they?"

"Look, Susan. There was a time in my life when I was just so unhappy I was making myself and everyone else miserable, and it took someone I loved, getting real tough with me, to help me pull out of it. So, I have to say this because I love you. It's time for you to face facts. Alex is gone, and he's not coming back, and the way you're taking it makes me afraid for you."

"I'm sorry if it's inconvenienced you," said Susan.

"That's all right," said Jocelyn. "Be angry at me. It's a start. That's probably one reason you haven't begun to heal yourself; you're carrying all that anger about what Philippe did inside of you. Susan, you must want to *kill* him."

"I not only don't want to kill him, I want to clear him. I don't think he did anything."

"See, that's what I'm talking about. It scares me to say this, but you're out of touch with reality. If you don't face what's really happened to you, there's going to be no pulling you back."

"If I don't believe what you believe, I'm out of touch with reality?"

"Now, listen. I know you're angry, but I'm trying to help. I just wish you would see my therapist. She's *brilliant.*"

"Jocelyn, there is a difference between neurotic pain and real pain. There's a difference between stress over the bags under your eyes and what you feel when your only child is stolen."

After Jocelyn left, Susan threw the jar of moldy jam against the kitchen wall and cried hot tears of annoyance and loneliness as the red clotted mess dripped down the wall.

On November 3 a small story appeared in the Boston *Globe*. A man named Albert Lipscomb was found living in a cabin in a small town in West Virginia with two young boys he had abducted. One was nine and one was twelve. The one who was twelve had never even been reported missing. The other one had disappeared from a park near his home in Philadelphia over a year ago and had been written off as a runaway. According to the news report, the boys had been calling the man Dad, and even attended school. What had led the police to investigate the "family" was the curiosity of a country schoolteacher who was puzzled by the fact that the boys claimed to be brothers, although one of them was black.

Albert Lipscomb, the paper noted, was a convicted sex offender. He was known to have been in the Boston area in the spring and had been questioned about the disappearance of Alex Selky, which was the principal reason the story now made the Boston papers.

To Susan, it was a sign. The local media woke up and remembered her name. One news show wanted to know if they could film her phoning the mother in Philadelphia whose little boy had been found, giving congratulations. Would they run pictures of Alex? Susan asked. Would they let her explain that she still believed he, too, would be found? They agreed that they would.

It was as if the clock had been turned back. The phone rang, the reporters called, and the news shows asked her to come on and talk about how it feels to hope that somewhere in the world your lost son is alive. She didn't care that they thought she was deranged. Hope coursed through her like a cleansing fire, and she was full of energy and fierce conviction.

She called Menetti. Yes, he said, he'd seen the story. No, it didn't make any difference. They had already questioned Lipscomb at the time; there was no point in doing it again.

Menetti saw her on the news show. He was in a bar up the street from police headquarters. On the black-and-white TV set above the bar she seemed a little thinner than the last time he saw her. He sipped his draft and watched the deep, steady look in her eyes as she called the woman whose child had come home. The smile on her face, so like the little boy's on the poster, nearly broke his heart. Where was her courage coming from? How long was she going to keep it up?

The traffic was heavy on the expressway when he started for Saugus. It was nearly at a standstill by the time he reached the Mystic River Bridge. He could turn on the radio and listen to one of those helicopter guys who told you where the tie-ups were, but tonight he didn't want the distraction. He was scanning the traffic. His eyes moved ceaselessly. Presently he recognized what he was doing: he was looking for the blue car. Blue 1963 or 1964 Oldsmobile sedan; rust spots on the doors; whitewall tire on the right-front wheel. Systematically, he scanned the slowly moving lanes and asked himself for the thousandth time, How could it happen that that car was never seen again?

IN THE second week of November Philippe tried to kill himself. He was cut down from a bar in his cell from which he had hung himself with a torn bed sheet. Nobody knew how long he'd been there, and the hospital had not yet determined whether or not there had been brain damage. Susan tried to see him at the hospital, but she was refused.

Late one evening she called Graham. "He's not here," said Naomi.

"Naomi," said Susan through tears, "I need to talk to him. I don't know what it means, Philippe trying to die. Does it mean he lied to me? What can't he live with—his guilt? Or his innocence? I don't know who else to talk to. No one else has lost Alex except Graham."

There was a long silence. Finally Naomi said, "All right, Susan. I'll give him the message. But we're trying hard to make a life together here, and I resent you using this situation all the time to get to Graham."

Graham called her back the next morning, but by that time the urge to speak to him had passed.

As THE DAYS GREW SHORTER and the chill in the autumn air deepened, the panes of glass in the living-room windows were covered with thin frost when Susan went with her coffee cup in the early mornings to sit looking down at the street. From the lush gold and blue of the last morning on earth that she had seen her son, the light had changed to the flat gray brightness of impending winter.

He would be so cold now if, by some prayer-answering overlay of time, she could see him once more on this street as she saw him that last morning. If she looked down as she did every morning, and there he simply was, striding out into the new spring day. She could see him so clearly. The lilt of his walk, his sturdy neck and arms, and the flash of sunlight on his dark hair. And every morning, every morning of her life, she saw him reach the corner, turn, and, smiling, wave good-by.

These long, empty days she rarely felt anger or fear or sadness. What she felt was a brimming love for him and no way to give it. There was a dim sensory memory that haunted her—the smell of his skin, the sight of his head pressed against her cheek so close that its outline became the curve of the earth, and the angular feel of limbs, all knees and elbows—that gave a pleasure too complex to recover or yet ever to give up, the deep, unremarkable joy of hugging her child.

It WAS a slushy gray-bright morning the week after Thanksgiving. When Menetti arrived at the office, he happened to overhear Sergeant Pollard saying into the phone, "I see . . . I see. Yes, well, as I told you, we've closed the file on that case. Yes. It was in all the papers, Mrs. Robbins." He glanced at Menetti, who mouthed at him silently, "Which case?"

"Selky," Pollard mouthed back.

Menetti reached for the phone. "This is Lieutenant Menetti," he said. "Can I help you?"

"I'm calling to help you," said the woman. "I know where that little Selky child is, and I've called twice now to tell you about it. If I were a Massachusetts resident, I'd be pretty concerned about what the police are doing all day. You can't bring home one sad little child."

"Yes, I understand," said Menetti. "Could you give me your name and address, please?"

"I told you already. Malvina Robbins, 4429 Baily Street, Willimantic, Connecticut." As he wrote this down, Menetti saw Sergeant Pollard roll his eyes up at the ceiling. Mrs. Robbins was saying, "I can see the child out my window now marching around in that mush by himself. Why isn't he in school? Tell me that."

"I can't, Mrs. Robbins. You tell me."

"Because he's that stolen child. I did tell you. I knew it when they moved in. The man didn't have no toys for him like a real daddy would."

"How do you know he doesn't have any toys?" Menetti asked.

"I watched them move in! They only got the one suitcase. When I used to go someplace with my kids, it would take a wheelbarrow to bring the toys in."

"Maybe they can't afford toys. Maybe they're poor."

"Poor! He's no more a daddy than the man in the moon."

"And how do you know that, Mrs. Robbins?"

"I know it because I know this is that little stolen child. I got the picture of him from the paper, and also I saw his mother on TV and she showed us another picture. What happened was, when I was reading the paper about this little Boston boy that disappeared, I looked up and there was Jesus, and He said to me, 'Malvina, you better clip that picture. My Father moves in mysterious ways, and it may be that you, Malvina, will be the instrument that will bring the lost little lamb home to his grieving mommy.' And I said to Jesus . . .'"

At this point Menetti picked up an eraser from the desk and threw it at Sergeant Pollard. "I see, Mrs. Robbins," he was saying as Pollard, laughing soundlessly, went on about his work.

Now that Malvina Robbins had Menetti's name, she telephoned him on an average of twice a week. He sometimes wondered how she found time to work him in between conversations with Jesus.

In the week after Christmas he'd had to listen to a complete rendition of what the Lord had said to Malvina when He came to share her holiday turkey. (Would you believe that the dear Christ baby had never tasted turkey before in all His life?)

This morning it had taken close to three minutes by the clock for her to pause long enough for Menetti to say into the phone, "Happy New Year to you, too, Malvina."

"I want to know when you'll be coming down here," she was saying, "because after you pick up that little lost child, I want you to bring him by here for milk and cookies. I offered him a plate of my Christmas cookies just the other day, but that man just looked at me with the one straight eye he's got and took that child off by the arm like I was the devil. Won't let him talk to me at all. . . ."

"Malvina," said Menetti, "thank you for calling. I have to go now and make arrangements to come down there. Yes, I'll be in touch very soon about when we're coming, and I'll let you know. It takes time to line up all the squad cars and so on. . . . Yes, Malvina. Thank you. I'll pray for you, too."

Menetti hung up and sank his head in his hands. I'll pray, all right, he thought. I'll pray that the phone company takes your phone out by the roots, you poor nut case.

And in Willimantic, Connecticut, Malvina Robbins hung up her phone and went back to the kitchen window to look out into the next-door yard again. No way she was going to rest until somebody came to rescue that child.

There he was, poor little boy. He was sitting on the concrete step by himself, just staring into the empty yard. There was a layer of gray snow on the ground. In one corner of the yard a broken canvas chair lay against the fence. The little boy wore no mittens. He had laid out a row of little squares of bread, white against the dirty snow, in a neat line. Malvina watched him stare at them until at last a mangy sparrow dropped down, ate one of the chunks, hopped around for a while, then flew off again. After a long pause the boy got up and replaced the sparrow's bread with another little piece; then he sat back down again.

248

It was the Friday evening of the long Washington's Birthday weekend, and Menetti had arrived home late. Dinner was already over. Pat was angrily washing dishes. Eugene had just rushed upstairs crying and slammed the bedroom door. Before Al could find out what was going on, the phone rang. He grabbed it.

"Hello, Al?"

"Yes, Susan," he said. Pat took her hands out of the soapy water and whirled around and glared at him. Menetti pulled a chair out from the kitchen table and sat down in his overcoat. "How are you?" he said into the phone. He had felt an odd quiver when he heard her voice again after so many weeks.

"Fine. Al, I just got a phone call from this woman in Connecticut. She's called me twice, actually."

Damn it, Menetti said to himself. Malvina. This was where he stopped feeling sorry for the loons out there and started wishing he could just have them rounded up and fitted with straitjackets. It was annoying enough having Malvina on his back, but now she was going to cause real pain.

"She lives in Willimantic," Susan was saying. "She said she's been in touch with you."

"Malvina Robbins, right?"

"Yes."

"Now, Susan—"

"Al." Something in her voice seemed to flood him with awful sadness.

"Susan," he said wearily, "did she tell you about Jesus coming to Christmas dinner? Or how He takes His tea every afternoon? Did she tell you how He used to take two lumps, but now He just takes cream?"

There was a long silence, and Menetti tried to remember how it was he got into the position of adding to Susan's hurt. He knew from her pause that she had heard enough from Malvina to doubt her.

249

Susan started again. "But that doesn't prove there's no boy there. Why isn't a child that age in school, Al?"

Menetti stretched and shook his head. "He could be retarded; he could have a handicap. . . ."

"Or he could be Alex."

Menetti sighed, trying to think of what to say.

"Couldn't he, Al?" she persisted. "Are you so sure that there is not *one* chance left under heaven that it is Alex that you can't even check it out? Can't you just have the police in Willimantic drive by and *look?*"

"No," he said. "I can't. This case is closed, and there is no way I could justify an action like that. I am under very specific orders not to spend any more time on this matter, for the very good reason that we have Henry Sullivan's trial coming up. If it comes out that any member of my department, let alone me, is muddying the waters by looking for the child Henry Sullivan killed, I'd be very surprised if we didn't see the indictment thrown out, and I'd be lucky if I wound up directing traffic. Got it?" He was shouting, and the volume of his voice made him understand how torn he was with pity for her, and guilt.

Susan was silent for another long moment, during which he dreaded her reaction. When it came, her voice sounded a little frightened, but firm.

"I guess I could go to Willimantic myself," she said.

Menetti pictured her going to Malvina's door and felt a spasm of fear. He knew so much better than she how many different kinds of weird a person like Malvina might be. "Look, don't do that, all right?"

"What else can I do?"

"Think it over a little while. Sort out what you want to believe from what's happening. It's a long weekend anyway. Just give yourself the time off, and we'll talk about it Tuesday."

"Give myself time off from what?"

"Susan, I'll talk to you Tuesday."

He hung up the phone and turned wearily to share his sorrow with Pat, only to see from the way she was staring at him that

250

she clearly had a few things she intended to share with him first.

"Susan Selky?" she said coldly.

He shrugged and nodded.

"Not only did you miss dinner again for the fifth time in two weeks, we're going to start with Susan Selky again? We're going to have a replay of last summer, when the kids forgot what you looked like?"

"I haven't talked to her in two months," said Al.

"Did you happen to notice your youngest son, that's the one called Eugene, bawling up the stairs as you graced us with your presence this evening?"

"Yes."

"Did it cross your mind to wonder what was going on before you dived for the telephone? You've spent more time in the last year worrying about a kid who's been dead since May than you have about your own children, you know that?"

Menetti just stared at her. She was in full cry, all right.

"For your information," stormed Pat, "Eugene is crying because I said he could sleep over at Willy's house this weekend, and now he can't because he wet his bed again."

"I see. And I made him do it."

"Very funny. Did you bother to read that article I gave you?"

Al dimly remembered her giving him one of those women's magazines to read, but he hated those magazines. They were all about Jell-O molds and breast cancer.

"If you had read it, you might be able to figure out that when a kid with no medical problem continues to wet his bed, he's probably trying to get attention. Like, for instance, the attention of his father. You haven't spent one whole day alone with Eugene since I brought him home from the hospital. Just because he's the youngest and you've already been through this six times before doesn't mean Eugene has. Remember when Angela was Eugene's age? You used to spend all day Saturday with her."

Al knew it was true. He hardly ever spent time with Eugene, the way he had with the first kids.

"And don't think I want to keep him home. Maryann and the

twins are coming in the morning, and now I don't have anywhere for the babies to sleep."

"Your sister's coming? Why?"

"Because it's the long weekend, that's why!"

"Good," said Al. "Then you won't need me. I'll take Eugene and we'll go off for the day, and you and Maryann can spend the whole day complaining about your mother." He got up and marched up the stairs to hammer on Eugene's door.

"Eugene! Eugene!"

Eugene, who expected to be spanked for wetting his bed, didn't answer.

"Eugene," yelled Al through the door, "how'd you like to spend the day with me tomorrow, buddy? We'll go off somewhere and leave the ladies and the babies to themselves, okay?"

Eugene opened his door and came out, his face still puffy from crying. "Gee, Dad," he said. "Okay."

THEY drove out right after breakfast. Eugene was glowing with pleasure, and it was a while before he asked, "Where we going, Dad?"

It was a bitterly cold day, and though the roads were clear, the yards and sidewalks were piled with snow.

"Gee, I don't know. How about the aquarium?"

"We went there with Mom last week."

Menetti thought awhile. "Well, what do you want to do?"

"I'd like to see your office. I've never been there."

Menetti thought about it. "But, Eugene, your mother would kill me if I went to the office today. Even to show you."

"She would?"

"Yes. She's very mad at me for spending too much time there."

"You're right," said Eugene philosophically. "It's okay, though, Dad," he added. "I just like driving with you."

"Well, fine. I'll tell you what. You can be my deputy, and we'll pretend we're going on a mission."

"Hey, great! Can I have a gun?"

"Sure," said Menetti. "Here." He cocked his thumb and stuck

out his index finger to make a pistol. Eugene solemnly pretended to take it and tuck it into his belt.

They drove for several miles in silence, both feeling highly satisfied. Suddenly Menetti thought, Maybe I can kill two birds with one stone here. After all, I do have to go somewhere. I could let him know what police work is really like.

"Say, Deputy . . ."

"Sir," said Eugene.

"I've got a mission you can help me out with. But it's a very delicate one, and it must be an absolute secret. No talking about it down at headquarters."

"Honestly, Dad?" asked Eugene.

"Absolutely. Do you accept?"

"Yes, sir."

"Okay. First, open the glove compartment and find me the road map marked Southern New England." Eugene did this. "Now open it up." Eugene unfolded the large creased sheet. "Good. See the legend on the side of the map. Try to find a town called Willimantic, under Connecticut."

There was a long silence while the deputy held the map close to his face. "Found it!" he cried finally. He showed his father the map, pointing to Willimantic.

"Route 6, that's what I thought," said Menetti. "Good man!"

Eugene refolded the map with some difficulty. "What do I do next, sir?" he asked.

"You sit."

"How much longer?"

"At least another hour."

"Why do we have to go so far?"

"We are doing one of the jobs that we do often, and that is checking out a crank call. Sometimes we ask for information, and a lot of cuckoos call us up and tell us wild stories. We have to check them out, because a person can be crazy but still know a little piece of the truth."

"Do you think it will be dangerous, Dad?"

Menetti sighed. "No, I don't. I think it will just be sad."

After a long hour that included a stop at Howard Johnson's for milk shakes, they reached Willimantic. Menetti gave his deputy his orders. "First, no one must know we're here or that we ever came here; and second, you must not talk to me while I try to find Baily Street, because being talked to while I'm getting lost in a strange city makes me very jumpy. Understood?"

The deputy nodded.

Willimantic is a small city east of Hartford. From the highway one can see a cluster of turn-of-the-century brick manufacturing buildings, like the abandoned textile mills of eastern Massachusetts. Once down into the warren of streets of the town, Menetti found his way to a grimy neighborhood of frame houses, the sort of neighborhood with a launderette on every second block and a tavern on every corner. On a street of sooty two-family houses he asked a man in khakis and a lumber jacket for Baily Street, and got a blank stare.

Menetti pushed on. After four or five blocks he stopped a woman coming in from her yard with a basket of wash. She was pretty sure Baily Street was somewhere on the north side.

As Menetti felt his way from one street to the next, a sad black ball of embarrassment began to grow inside him. This was a truly dumb thing to be doing. If the DA's office ever found out, if the press got one whiff of it . . . For that matter, if Eugene told Pat how they spent the day and she figured out what he'd been up to . . . Menetti glanced over at his deputy, who was sitting erect, studying the passing neighborhood, with his pistol at the ready. Well, he could do this much for Susan, keep the ripest nuts off her back. Afterward he and Eugene could have lunch; then the drive back would take two more hours, and by then they could go to a movie and kill the rest of the day. What do people do with kids all day?

He drove slowly through a small section of shops, and found his way into another residential neighborhood. Point Street. Canal Street. Baily Street. Well, I found it.

"Baily Street, sir!"

"Yes, I see, Deputy." Here they were. At least it wouldn't take long. He was glad he'd have Eugene for company on the way back. Then he wouldn't have to spend two hours driving alone with that sour restless feeling. Which way do the numbers go? Try on the right first.

The first numbers on the block were in the 3300s, and they were going down. He pulled into a driveway to turn around.

"Are we almost there, Dad?" Eugene whispered.

"Almost there, pal." He paused, peering to find a house number as he drove slowly down the street. Found one; 3812. Good. "Now, when we get there, Deputy, your job will be to guard the car. I won't be inside long, and I'll give you a full report when I'm done. You cover me from outside, okay?"

"Okay, sir. What number are we looking for, sir?"

"It's 4429. Sorry, Deputy. I should have told you sooner."

"Okay. We just passed 4018."

More dreary blocks to reach the 4400s. Okay, Malvina, thought Menetti. Here's your big chance to show me where Jesus sits and drinks tea with you; 4421, 4423, 4429. There you are, Malvina.

The car drifted to a stop. Menetti had switched off the ignition and turned to unlock his door before he saw it. Eugene watched his father freeze. The boy waited patiently, but nothing happened. Why wasn't his father getting out of the car? Eugene glanced up at him and was astonished to see that his eyes were glazed with tears. Eugene followed his father's gaze. He wasn't looking at 4429. He was looking at the house next door, a gray house with peeling paint and a torn screen on the door. In front of the house was parked an old blue car with rust spots all over the doors, and on the front-right wheel, a whitewall tire.

"Daddy?" whispered Eugene after a minute.

"Oh, my God," said his father. "Susan . . ." He put up both hands to cover his face, and for a second or two, he really cried.

MENETTI dried his eyes and nose with his big handkerchief. He told Eugene to stay in the car, head low, and watch the house next to 4429. If anyone came out, Eugene was to lean on the horn. "I'll be right back," he said.

Menetti walked up to 4429 and rang the bell. He was still not very far from tears. He hoped he'd have a grip on himself when he had to speak again.

The door was opened by a tiny black woman with cloud-white hair. She was wearing glasses and an apron, and she greeted Menetti with a look of annoyance. "Well, you certainly took your time, Lieutenant," she said with perfect mad confidence after he had introduced himself. "Come in here before he sees you." She tipped her head in the direction of the house next door.

Menetti stepped into her living room, which was dark and tidy. "Thank you," he said. "May I use your phone?"

"Right there," said Malvina, pointing. He dialed O and said to the operator, "Get me the police, please. This is an emergency."

Malvina was looking out the window. "I don't see no squad cars," she said suspiciously. "You don't have much time; he goes to work in the hospital afternoons, you know."

Menetti said into the phone, "This is Detective Albert Menetti, Boston PD. . . . Yes. I'm at 4429 Baily Street. It looks like a long shot just paid off for me here, but I'm without any backup. . . . Yes, a missing child. Alex Selky. I haven't actually seen him, but I'm pretty sure. Could I have two unmarked cars, please, as fast as you can. No sirens. I'll wait for you in my car across the street. A gray Plymouth."

Ten minutes later, while four policemen with drawn guns covered them from the street, Menetti stood with two plainclothes detectives on the porch of 4431. He rang the bell. Silence. An eternal wait. And then the door was opened by Alex Selky.

Menetti felt the breath lock in his lungs as it collided once again with a painful urge toward tears—this small, very thin boy with the perfect round head, and eyes that blinked in the bright winter sunlight. His hair was cut ragged and short, dyed a flat corn color. The nails on his small hands were gnawed to the quick. As he stood in the cold holding the door open, Menetti could see a lavender bruise on the inside of his left forearm.

A man came to the door behind Alex. He was dressed in a white polyester pantsuit and white canvas shoes, the uniform of

256

a male nurse. He had a plump pink face, and one brown eye looked off to the right into space. In the living room behind him, Menetti could see the fluorescent blue flicker of the television.

"Yes?" said the man, putting a fleshy hand on Alex's head. "What is it?"

Menetti heard the echo of a thousand rehearsals of the words he had ceased to believe he would ever say. "You are under arrest for the kidnapping of Alexander Selky. You have the right to remain silent. . . ." The man never moved as he was given his rights. He just stared mildly at the men on his porch, as if he half wondered what had taken them so long.

When the handcuffs appeared, Alex, looking bewildered, shrank back and began to whimper, but the man with the wall-eye said only, "Allen, would you please turn off the TV?" And Alex immediately turned back into the living room to do so, and thus missed seeing the man with the walleye being taken away.

Menetti, fighting an urge to scoop the boy up and hold him, followed Alex inside. Alex whirled around when Menetti entered the room, and edged away from him. Menetti went into the kitchen, where, against a counter littered with open boxes of cereal, jars of jelly, and a container of milk, he found a phone and dialed Susan's number. It rang ten times. He hung up and asked an operator to dial it for him. Again, no answer. He went back out onto the porch, where the remaining policemen were waiting for him, openmouthed with excitement.

"Alex Selky! No kidding!" one of them said. "Didn't you arrest a guy for killing him?"

Menetti nodded. His throat ached with joy . . . rage. It had been all he could do, in the moment his gaze met the mild, skewed one in the plump, babyish face, to keep from lunging at the man and battering his head against the doorframe.

"Look," Menetti said now. "I can't reach the mother. What I want to do is just take this boy home the fastest way I can. Can I get an escort?"

"I'll call headquarters," said one of the officers. He went to his car and, leaning in the driver's side, made a call on the radio. He was back in a moment. "You got it," he said. "They just arrived with our man, and the place is going nuts."

"Okay, good," said Menetti. He went back in to Alex and knelt to talk to him eye to eye.

"Alex, my name is Detective Menetti, and I'm going to take you home to your mommy."

Alex just stared at him, his face blank and wary. Menetti held out his hand, and Alex looked at it, then drew back.

Menetti stood up. "Just come on now, Alex," he commanded, and he walked outside. Alex put on a cheap blue parka and followed him onto the porch.

"A team is on its way over to search the house," said one of the waiting policemen. "We can go as soon as they get here."

"Good," said Menetti. The policemen stared at Alex and smiled at him. Alex stared back at them. Menetti suddenly wondered if his pupils were unnaturally constricted. Drugged? His heart groaned. He thought of the nurse's uniform. That gutless creep. It must have been so easy for him.

ALEX stood on the porch, utterly alone. Walter was gone. He was supposed to keep the door locked all the time whenever Walter was gone. He knew what happened if Walter came home and found it open. What he didn't know was what happened if Walter didn't come home. He had wondered about that every time Walter locked him in and drove away. He had a pretty good idea that Walter wasn't coming back this time.

And now there was this one. My-name-is-Detective-Miniddy-I'm-going-to-take-you-to-your-mommy. Uh-huh. Walter wasn't a detective. Why should this one be? Walter hadn't taken him to his daddy. Why should this one take him to Mommy all of a sudden, after all this time? She changed her mind again?

Here comes another car up the street, and it stops at our house. Out get four more men. Here they all come up the steps. If they take me somewhere else, what will happen to my birds?

I hope where they take me next there's a TV. There was no TV in the last place.

258

This Detective Miniddy is squatting down again talking to me. Come, Alex. Well, he has a better car than ours. . . . Gee, he even already has a boy. Maybe this one will be with me at the next place. It would be good to have another kid.

Menetti, holding the front door of his car open, didn't know if he wanted to give all his attention to Alex or if he wanted to never have to look at that blank stare again in his life. He had an overwhelming desire to stop everything for a minute and sit down and pray.

Eugene was agog. "Dad . . ." he breathed. "We found Alex, didn't we? How did you know? Are we going to be famous?"

"Alex," said Menetti, "this is my son Eugene. Eugene, this is Alex. Do you want to ride up here with us, Alex?"

Alex said nothing. Eugene gestured excitedly for Alex to get in beside him. Alex climbed obediently into the car and sat down, facing straight ahead.

When Menetti pulled out into the street, one of the police cars fell in behind them. From the radio came crackling instructions. "Left at the second light. Okay, stay in the right lane."

"That's a police radio," Eugene whispered to Alex. Alex was studying it. He glanced up and eyed Eugene.

"Dad," said Eugene quickly, "could I show him how our microphone works?"

Menetti said, "Good idea. Tell our escort we read them."

Eugene knew how it was done. "We copy," he said sternly into the microphone. "Do you read me?"

"Loud and clear," said the following car. "Take your next right on Barrow Street. You'll pick up the signs for Route 6."

"Here, you do it."

Eugene handed Alex the mike, and after a moment Alex said into it, "We copy," and then handed it quickly back to Eugene.

"Ten four," said the car behind them.

When they reached the highway, Menetti clamped his foot down on the gas and picked up to eighty. The police car behind them stayed on their tail, and Menetti knew the police would be alerting Connecticut Highway Patrol of their approach.

"Unmarked gray Plymouth with police escort proceeding east on Route 6, on urgent police business. . . . Yeah, that's right. We found the Selky kid. . . . Yes, alive. . . . No, thank you, no assistance needed. Just keep the lanes clear and pass the word."

Eugene nudged Alex and pointed to the speedometer. The needle quivered above eighty. Alex looked at it, then back at Eugene. They both looked up at Menetti.

"Are we going to go this fast all the way to Boston, Dad?" asked Eugene.

"Yes, unless it scares you."

"No way!" cried Eugene.

"Are we going too fast for you, Alex?" Alex shook his head.

"Does his mom know we're coming, Dad?" asked Eugene.

"No, she doesn't. I tried to call her, but she must be out."

"She's always out," said Alex suddenly.

"What do you mean?" Menetti turned to him, but Alex had clamped his lips shut.

"Boy, is your mom going to be excited," Eugene whispered to Alex. Alex glanced over, a look that said that Eugene knew nothing about other people's family affairs.

"I've seen your mom on television about fifty times, telling everyone to keep looking for you. And my dad's been looking for you for almost a year. Didn't you see it on the news?"

Alex shook his head.

"They had these posters with pictures of you all over the place. Didn't you see those?" Eugene went on. "And my dad was in charge of looking for you. Weren't you, Dad?"

"Yes," said Menetti softly. "I was."

Alex looked from one to the other. He wasn't surprised. Walter had told him the police would be looking for him.

Their car sped through the countryside. "Hey," Eugene whispered after a while. He guessed that his father had some reason for not asking Alex questions, but Eugene couldn't contain himself. "Did he keep you tied up?"

"What?"

"The guy who kidnapped you."

260

Menetti gave no sign that he was listening. The two small bodies on the passenger side seemed to him to take less room on the seat than one full-size adult. He had always marveled at how kids could slip into a child world where they seemed to assume that the adult driving the car had been struck deaf.

Alex looked perturbed. "My daddy hired Walter to pick me up. It was a secret from Mommy. She wanted me to go to school instead of seeing Daddy."

"You mean you were with your daddy all that time?"

"No," said Alex impatiently. "We went to this room and waited for a few days, but Daddy never came. He forgot."

Eugene was horrified. "I bet you cried a lot."

"I did." Alex's impassivity slipped a little. For a moment his face was congested with the memory of those first days.

"Well, then, why didn't you go back home?"

"Mommy told Walter not to bother. She was mad at me for going with Walter, and she couldn't afford me anymore anyway because I eat a lot. Walter called her around Christmas because I thought she might want me for Christmas, but she told him that was all right, she got another little boy now."

Menetti couldn't keep silent for more of this. "Alex, he just told you those things. They're not true. Your father didn't hire him, and your mother has been looking for you every minute since you disappeared. She missed you very much and she never gave up wanting you back."

Alex studied him with a face that was shrewd and thoughtful. He said nothing.

They sped to the end of the Massachusetts Turnpike, then went north to the Mass Pike Extension and started into Boston. There, city traffic hemmed them in, and the police car behind them had trouble staying with them.

"Will his mommy be there when we get to his house?"

"I don't know, Eugene. They've probably found her by now." Alex was perched forward on the seat, studying the passing city sights, deep in concentration. "Is it getting familiar, Alex?" Menetti asked.

No answer.

They reached the Copley Square exit, where the Willimantic police car caught up with them at the traffic light. Together the two cars drove across Dartmouth Street. Alex was watchful and silent, Eugene was beginning to tense with excitement, and Menetti was numb, wondering what he was heading for.

"She's going to be so *excited*," Eugene whispered to Alex with dramatic earnestness. "She's gonna be *so* excited. We're almost there, Dad, right? Aren't we almost there?"

Alex's gaze flicked warily from one of them to the other. It *was* his neighborhood. Maybe they could be taking him to his mommy. But probably they were taking him to jail.

They stopped at the corner of Marlborough. Alex could almost see Justine's house from here. He sat up straighter and craned his neck, as if he might see someone he knew. What an odd feeling. The feeling of something familiar. He let something flicker inside him, like the shadow of a high-flying bird flashing across a patch of sunlight. Was it possible that he could be allowed to go home?

"Look," yelled Eugene, "there's a poster of you, Alex! See it?" Alex looked, and there in the window of a secretarial school was a poster. STILL MISSING. And under the words, the smiling face. Alex looked at it. Missing. They were missing him? He almost let himself smile, but then he caught on to the trick. Missing. Wanted. He'd seen Wanted posters of other bad people in a post office once. Walter pointed them out. "And they know all about you, too," Walter had said. So Alex never made a peep when he went anywhere with Walter. He kept his head down.

Menetti stepped on the gas hard. He wanted to get to Susan. Behind him the Willimantic police car turned on its siren. The sudden urgent howl of it seemed to echo and reecho from the walls, a sound that filled Alex with cold certainty.

Susan had taken Taxi with her to lunch in the South End with two of her Harvard colleagues, and afterward she walked him the long way home. She was just coming up Marlborough Street when she heard the siren. Pushing her hands deep into her pockets and breathing a cloud into the bitter February air, she thought, Another accident or another crime. Ah, poor souls.

It was only when the noise kept growing louder and louder, as if it were coming for her, that she began to feel afraid. It was more instinctive than specific. She was here, Taxi was here, they'd never again bring Graham home to her. What else did she have to lose?

The siren died as she turned the corner into Fremont Street. She saw so many cars and trucks and people crowded into the street that her heart lurched. She felt herself go cold with dread and forced herself to keep walking.

There were so many people milling up and down her steps, pointing to her, pointing to the street, pointing to each other, that she didn't know where to look first. There were police and news vans, but no fire trucks that she could see. Surprise and fear seemed to freeze the scene before her, so she took it in slow motion. It seemed to be happening in a silent bubble world out of time and feeling. There was a car pulling up that looked just like Menetti's. The two front doors of the car opened at the same time, and Menetti emerged from the driver's side and stood there in the street looking at her, an intense, beseeching look, as if he were trying to say something to her but couldn't open his mouth. His presence made no sense to her at all.

As he scurried through the crowd to the sidewalk, she saw that he had some of his kids with him. The shorter one was probably Eugene, but the other kid, in a blue parka, looked a little older. Judging every small boy as she always did, she dismissed this one as taller than Alex, with dull, short dun-colored hair. She moved forward. Now she knew: her father was dead. No, she'd left the iron on; the house was burning. . . . Margaret. Margaret was hurt, or trapped. . . .

It wasn't until Taxi bolted away from her down the sidewalk, barking with lunatic joy, that she stopped cold and looked at the two children again. Taxi leaped at the blue parka. She looked again and this time really saw the face.

He was there, a dozen paces away from her. Right there. Her brain seemed to disconnect from her vision, as if she could see, but not understand what she saw.

Menetti was with the boys now, and she looked at him with mildness and wonder. It was all so incredibly strange. She was a lake of puzzled feeling dammed up behind the thinnest membrane. How could this be so confusing? How could there be so much to absorb? This was the simplest moment of her life.

It all broke open inside her as she looked back to Alex and just opened her arms to him, and in that moment got past the Alex of the missing months to her own boy. She saw him smile. And then he cried, "Mommy!" And she was on her knees on the frozen sidewalk blind with tears when her son flung himself into her arms.

Beth Gutcheon

It comes as a delightful surprise to see that the creator of a novel as emotionally wrenching as *Still Missing* is a fresh-faced young woman who thoroughly enjoys the varied aspects of her busy life. In conversation Beth Gutcheon is warmly responsive, her remarks tempered by humour and keen intelligence, and she seems not at all impressed with herself, although at thirty-five she has achieved great success in two different areas. In addition to being an accomplished novelist, Beth Gutcheon is an expert quilt maker and author of *The Perfect Patchwork Primer*.

It is impossible to read *Still Missing* without wondering whether Beth Gutcheon has had some close association with a kidnapping. She has not. Her interest in the subject stems from the fact that she learned firsthand what losing a child could mean. She is one of six children in a close and loving family, and her mother never fully recovered from the loss of a six-year-old daughter who died in the course of a routine tonsillectomy.

When asked about the after-effects of an experience like Alex Selky's, Beth replied that she feels a child from a loving home would probably recover in time. She points out that children often perceive events quite differently from adults, so an episode that might seem permanently scarring to an adult could in fact be recalled by a child as merely unpleasant. If an adult can keep from displaying his own shock and horror, a child's innocence might keep him from having those feelings.

Beth grew up in Sewickley, Pennsylvania, and now lives with her architect husband, Jeffrey, and their ten-year-old son in Manhattan. Beth's next book should be a distinct change of pace, for it is a children's fantasy entitled *The Voyages of Edgar Rice Pudding*.

THIS WAS THE NORTH
Anton Money with Ben East

THIS WAS
THE NORTH

A CONDENSATION OF THE BOOK BY

Anton Money WITH **Ben East**

PUBLISHED BY CROWN PUBLISHERS NEW YORK

Anton Money was a young tenderfoot, straight from a good English home, when he first stepped onto Alaskan soil in the spring of 1923. In those days the farthest reaches of the North American continent were still a wilderness, a land of hissing snow and bone-cracking cold, pierced by the howls of wolves and teeming with wildlife. Anton Money went out there looking for adventure, for the freedom he had lacked at home. Sight unseen he had fallen in love with that vast, untamed country.

This is the story of his years on one of the world's last frontiers—his search for gold, his marriage to a beautiful and courageous young woman, his brushes with death when the land he loved turned hostile. A true saga of the North, and of an extraordinary man who met and mastered its every challenge.

1. The Cheechako

At noon on a sunny day in late May of 1923, when the northern earth was vibrant with awakening life, the *Hazel B*, a shallow-draft riverboat, nosed into the bank at Telegraph Creek, British Columbia, a hundred and sixty-five miles up the Stikine River from salt water at Wrangell, Alaska.

Deaf Dan, our pilot, and Dar Smith, the deckhand, jumped ashore and made the bow and stern lines fast to two big cottonwoods where a roadway led down to the beach. There was no dock at Telegraph Creek. Captain Syd Barrington, our skipper, called for a gangplank, and Jack, the cook, stepped to the rail and started tossing scraps to a dozen gaunt and hungry sled dogs on the beach. It had taken us three long days to come up the river against the tumbling snow-fed current of the Stikine. The *Hazel B* would make the return downstream in ten hours.

Of the twenty-odd passengers aboard, Indian and white, I was the only one to whom the country was entirely new, and I thrilled in the excitement and color of the scene before me. Telegraph Creek, which occupied both banks of the creek of the same name, was the jumping-off place for Canada's vast Cassiar mining district, covering an area of more than seventy thousand square miles. The town got its name many years before, when the telegraph line going north crossed the river at that point. Now it sheltered twenty white residents and some two hundred Indians. Two rows of houses faced the river; there were also a schoolhouse, a government office, and the Hudson's Bay Company post.

Ours was the first boat to come up from tidewater since the previous October. There was no radio at that time, and all through the winter the remote little outpost had been cut off from the outside world. Our arrival meant the beginning of the summer rush. Once a week from now until freeze-up a boat would come churning up the Stikine, bringing passengers, supplies, and equipment. Prospectors and hunting parties would outfit here, packtrains would leave for trading posts in the interior.

All of Telegraph Creek had turned out to welcome us. Young and old alike, they lined the edge of the main street overlooking the river from the top of the bank thirty feet above. The few white women were dressed in spring cottons, the men mostly in khaki overalls. Some of the Indian men wore colored head scarves, and beaded jackets and moccasins; the women, purple, yellow, and blue blouses or dresses. Shouts of warm but derisive greetings were bandied back and forth as we carried our gear down the gangplank and up the steep bank to the street.

This, I told myself, is the North, a land of abysmal loneliness, vast and untamed and beautiful, stretching away into endless distances of mountain and valley, river and lake, with places of solitude where no human being has walked. This sprawling land was the country of dreams to which I had come from a third of the way around the world. It was also the frontier, raw and harsh, seductive and brutal by turn. It was here, in this wilderness of miners and trappers, Indians and whites, that I intended to make a place for myself. For without ever having seen it, I was in love with this immense, beautiful, siren land called the North.

THE SUPERSTITIOUS would say I began life under a lucky star. I was born on September 16, 1900, on a country estate near the village of Albury in Surrey, not far from London. I was one of eleven children and the seventh son of a seventh son; you can hardly inherit more potent magic than that.

Ours was a fine old home that dated back to the tenth century,

272

and I still recall the happy days of childhood with my brothers and a younger sister. I remember the tennis and croquet parties, the great old tulip tree beneath which tea was served in fine weather, the sedate walks with our nurse through the beechwoods on the huge estate of our neighbor, the Duke of Northumberland. Later there was Cranleigh, a typical English boarding school.

Then came World War I, and the happy days were over. Before the war ended, it had claimed all of my brothers. I lost one each year from 1914 through 1918, another in Persia soon after as a result of the war. In the end I was the only son left.

I enlisted in 1917, a bit underage, and served two years. I drew a billet as an instructor and escaped the horror of the trenches; still, when the war was over, I was a different man. I had joined up fighting mad and burning to take revenge on the enemies of England. Now I found myself disillusioned and bitter, wondering at the stupidities, the greed, and most of all at the waste of young men like my brothers. It was in part that reaction that would drive me, at twenty-two, to a new home in the North.

My father had been a government mining engineer and, although he had retired early in the war, engineers and explorers from the farthest corners of the earth continued to visit our home. I would listen openmouthed to the marvelous tales they had to tell, and slowly an unquenchable desire began to take shape in my mind. The North was starting to lure me like a Lorelei. I read the books of Jack London and the poems of Robert Service—anything I could find on that faraway, romantic land.

After my release from the army I crammed at mining engineering with a private tutor, but my heart was not in it. I had good offers from uncles and cousins to plant rubber in Ceylon or tea in Darjeeling, but these were not the places I wanted to go to. I ached for the challenges and solitude of a land where I could stand on my own with no influence and no help from family, a place where values were honest and genuine, where the laws that ruled were inexorable, because they were natural laws.

Finally I got a job with the Hudson's Bay Company, the romance-freighted "Company of Adventurers" that had traded in the North

273

since 1670. I arranged to serve at one of the northwest posts, where I hoped to learn something of the fur trade.

I reached Vancouver in early May of 1923, and booked passage to Wrangell on the SS *Princess Alice*. For three days we wended our way north along the coast of British Columbia through the breathtaking beauty of the Inside Passage. Then, bursting with enthusiasm, I stepped ashore onto Alaskan soil. With a dozen or so fellow passengers I headed for Wrangell's only hotel. It was primitive but clean, and I was assigned to a room with another guest, a grizzled, weathered gold miner who thrust out a hand as hard as a steel vise.

"My name's Amos Godfrey," he said. "Guess we'll be sharin' this room until the first boat goes upriver."

I was completely fascinated by Wrangell, with its totem poles, Indians living it up in noisy cafés, the mountains that frowned down on it, the fishing boats, the smell of the sea. The lobby of the hotel bustled all day long with reminders of the wilderness that shut Wrangell in. The first day I was there two trappers came in from their winter trapping grounds on the British Columbia–Alaska border, unloaded their canoe, and piled their catch of beaver pelts high on the lobby floor. I watched wide-eyed as a local fur buyer sorted and graded the round dry skins. Soon the lobby was buzzing with talk of fur prices and catches.

I struck up a conversation with a trapper named Jim Lovett. "Them two'll clean up about forty-five hundred dollars," he said, nodding toward the trapper team.

I whistled. So this was how men made fortunes in the North. Forty-five hundred dollars for two months of hard and lonely work. I was more sure than ever that I had chosen the right life.

I SPENT A HECTIC WEEK in Wrangell until the day finally came when the *Hazel B* was ready for the year's first run up the Stikine. A chill wind was blasting as we eased away from the dock, and, enchanted though I was with every yard of the trip, I sought shelter in the small lounge below the pilothouse.

Amos, my roommate from the hotel, was there, arguing with

274

another miner about claims, while some of the other passengers compared notes or swapped lies about their gold digging. Many had no claims but were going into the wilderness to prospect, spurred by the eternal will-o'-the-wisp of making a rich stake.

While we were at supper that first evening the river entered the mountains, and suddenly we were cut off, imprisoned in a world of our own, unlike any I had ever seen. The mountains tumbled steeply to the water's edge and the river ran between those confining walls in a narrow smooth ribbon.

Ahead, beyond the nearer mountains, snow peaks shone in the westering sun, and in the high valleys glaciers lay like frozen rivers with ruffled surfaces. Waterfalls cascaded hundreds of feet down cliffs of bare rock, to be lost in the timber and brush of the valley floor. The late sun cast lights and shadows of every possible hue over the whole wild scene, and in the valleys the young green of poplar and willow stood in bright contrast to the somber darkness of fir and spruce.

Before darkness settled over the river, we tied up for the night at the Customs and Immigration house on the boundary between Alaska and British Columbia. In the purple velvet dusk of the valley, with the peaks still gilded by the last rays of the sun, the cook came out on deck and began playing soft airs on a concertina. One by one the men came from their staterooms or the lounge, squatting on the deck or standing in a silent circle. Then, hesitantly at first, the singing began.

They were a rough, hard-cursing crew, those miners and trappers, but for a moment, held in a gentle bondage by the music and by the peace and silence that lay over the wild Stikine, each one of them seemed touched with longing for some faraway home that he would not likely see again. That was one evening of my life that I shall remember to the last day.

The next morning, just below the mouth of the Scud River, we came to the swiftest current we had yet encountered. Captain Barrington fought a long battle with the tumbling water, but finally he put the bow of the boat aground on a gravel bar and called for volunteers. Deaf Dan, the pilot, with half a dozen passengers including me, jumped ashore. We grabbed one end of a steel cable and dragged it up the beach to the head of the rushing water, where we made it fast to two big trees. Deaf Dan signaled the skipper, and the boat backed off the gravel bar, swung out into the current, and winched by the power of the capstan, began to move slowly upstream. Above the rapids Captain Barrington headed into shore and picked us up.

For the first twenty or thirty miles above Wrangell, we'd had a great deal of slack water. But now the Stikine was fast and wild, twisting and coiling down its rocky channel like a living thing, running at millrace speed even between rapids—riffles, the rivermen called them, but that seemed an inadequate word for those plunging reaches, where time after time the current was too much for the powerful engines of the *Hazel B* and we had to resort to "lining" again. I made it a point to help at every opportunity, because it was fun and because I counted it part of my education in the North.

The highlight of the trip for me came on the third morning, as we approached a stretch known as the canyon, where the river plunged a full mile between sheer granite walls. Captain Barrington called to me from the pilothouse, "Come on up for a spell." An invitation to the pilothouse, the holy of holies on any boat! My help at lining was paying off.

"You seem to be doing all right for a young cheechako," the skipper greeted me.

He had used the word of Alaska and all the Northwest for a greenhorn, and I welcomed it. A cheechako I was, a tenderfoot fresh out from England, but the friendly tone with which the term was used told me that I had taken the first step toward being accepted by the breed of rough men who made up the fraternity of this wild land.

The captain and I shared the pilothouse windows for a while, watching the swirls of water go careering past. Every now and then I wondered what the feel of steering the boat against the current would be like. And then, totally unexpectedly, the captain offered, "Hold her while I light a smoke."

276

I wrapped my hands around the spokes and felt the stabbing rush of the river come up through the wheel. It was a thrilling sensation and I felt enormously proud.

When the canyon came in sight, the captain shouldered me aside and took the wheel again. The *Hazel B* drove in between the granite cliffs, bucking a current so swift that the river was piled higher in midstream than along the sides. To best it Captain Barrington fell back on a strange technique. He'd let the current catch the bow of the boat, and as it swung he'd use the full power of the engines to claw diagonally toward one rock wall. At the last instant he'd swing toward the opposite side, as though tacking under sail, with the current taking the place of the wind. It called for keen judgment and split-second timing, but each time we tacked we gained a few feet upstream.

Finally we broke out of the head of the canyon; it was as if we had entered another country. Up to now the mountains that had hemmed us in had been steep towering ramparts with snow peaks, and ice in the high valleys; ahead they were low and rounded, timbered or grass-grown.

Here in these gentler mountains a miner's log cabin stood at the mouth of almost every creek. Beside each cabin a small cache on poles provided storage for food, safe from bears, wolves, or wolverines. At a few of these cabins we pulled in to the bank and tied up briefly to leave mail or supplies. It was noon on the fourth day when we came in sight of Telegraph Creek. The most exciting journey of my life up to that time was finished.

As soon as I stepped ashore I headed for the Hudson's Bay Company store and introduced myself to John Boyd, the factor, or chief trader. Boyd passed me over to Jimmy Lowe, a young apprentice my own age, a year out from Scotland. Jimmy led me to his dingy hotel room. Then he showed me the town.

I was beginning, that May afternoon more than fifty years ago, an odyssey that would take me into the outermost corners of this huge northern wilderness. And long before those adventure-filled years were up, the cheechako would be a full-fledged sourdough, ready for any challenge the North held out.

2. Into the Interior

I entered into my new job with the zest of a pilgrim who has arrived at the holy city.

Jimmy Lowe turned out to be a good companion. I had been hired at a better salary than his, and was more fortunate in my housing. Boyd, the factor, had a small bungalow, but because he preferred living in rooms over the trading post, he put me up in the bungalow. The quarters were pleasant, and on weekends Jimmy and I hiked out and saw as much of the surrounding country as we could, camping overnight wherever we fancied, catching fish, mastering the fundamentals of wilderness living.

The most fascinating part of my work was trading with the Indians. Their trapping season wound up in May with the annual spring beaver hunt, and by the beginning of June they were showing up at the Telegraph Creek trading post, pitching their tents along the high bank across the river from the town. By the time the short Arctic summer set in, with its long days of sunshine and nights of no real darkness, there were some three hundred Indians camped in the area.

For them this was the fun season. Since the previous October they had worked hard on their far-flung traplines, usually one family in a place. Now they came to the trading post to barter their pelts for supplies and the few knick-knacks that appealed to them, and to enjoy the year's only social life.

Always they tried to get rid of their poorest skins first, making long faces, telling of the great hardships they had endured during the winter. When these skins had been unloaded and the bare necessities bought, the finer pelts came out, the silky dark mink, the soft voluptuous marten, the otter and fisher and silver fox. With these the Indians bought fancy things—scarves and dresses for their women, beads and needles, colorful bandannas. Now and then one would indulge himself in a ten-gallon hat.

At night they sat around their campfires, watching the moose and caribou and wild-sheep meat simmering gently in their big

278

smoke-blackened kettles and singing their peculiar, monotonous melodies. Finally the leader of the circle would spear a sizable chunk of meat with his knife, grasp it in one hand, and bite into a corner of it. Holding it so, he cut a piece off with a swift slashing stroke of the knife. The chunk was then passed to the next man in the circle, who repeated the process, which continued until all had eaten their fill.

In the Indian camp, children with ragged clothing and dirty faces ran in and out of the tents at will, and were never scolded. Tied to nearby trees, out of one another's reach, were the sled dogs that were then a part of every Indian camp in the North. They were always hungry, for the Indians did not believe in feeding a dog unless he was earning his keep. Of necessity the dogs became expert thieves. I have seen one snitch a can of evaporated milk, puncture it with his teeth, tilt it up in almost human fashion and drink the contents. Even as puppies they learned to pull boxes or chairs into place and stand on them to reach bacon or a ham hanging from the ceiling on a wire. Many of these dogs had some wolf blood in them and they were almost as wild and fierce as wolves.

I learned a lot about Indians and their way of life that first summer at Telegraph Creek, but I soon realized I was not learning anything about the fur trade. I had been hired as a bookkeeper but John Boyd would not allow me anywhere near the books. For three months I worked at one servile job after another, cleaning out a dirty warehouse, scrubbing floors, scraping mold off spoiled bacon. It soon became plain to me that Boyd did not want a bookkeeper, that he could not or would not teach me or any other subordinate anything about the fur trade. So I gave thirty days' notice.

Then my big chance came.

A mining engineer named Arthur Brindle, who had been at the Telegraph Creek post several times and whom I had gotten to know quite well, offered me a job as his assistant for the balance of the season, at better wages than I had been getting. He worked for a Vancouver mining company, and he wanted me to go with him on a long backpack trip into the interior, looking at mining properties. We would go first to Dease Lake, seventy-five miles over the mountains, and then follow the lake down its entire length to explore mineral formations along the shore.

Nothing could have delighted me more than the prospect of those weeks of late summer and autumn in the wilderness. I would come out far wiser in the ways of survival, of hunting for food, living on the trail, making overnight camps—the things I had come to the North in the hope of doing. I'd even learn something about prospecting, and maybe that would prove even more valuable than learning the fur trade. On top of all this, I thoroughly liked Brindle, a slightly built, wiry man of about forty-five who glowed with health and was tough as rawhide. He would be a good trail companion.

The two of us hiked from Telegraph Creek in late August, 1923, carrying sixty-pound packs and following the packhorse trail to Dease Lake. We traveled steadily, cooling our swollen feet in ice-cold creeks when we stopped for lunch, shooting a duck or a rabbit for supper, rolling into our sleeping bags before dark, bone-tired, up at five, and on the trail again by six. I carried a fishline around my hat, and sometimes we varied our evening meal with trout or grayling. Every stream had them, and the countryside teemed with grouse, moose, and bear, as well as ducks and rabbits.

We reached a small Indian settlement at the upper end of Dease Lake in less than a week. We were now at the jumping-off place for the interior of the Yukon country. From here a man could go down the Dease River to the Liard, down the Liard to its junction with the mighty Mackenzie at Fort Simpson, and down north on the Mackenzie all the way to the Arctic Ocean.

An old-time Indian known as Packer Tom was camped at Dease Lake. He had lived there for years and knew the district well. More important to us, he had a rowboat, which we rented for our trip to the foot of the lake.

That afternoon, to the great amusement of the local Indians, I went for a swim, something they would not have dreamed of doing. Instead, they would take an occasional sauna-type bath, building a low tent frame shaped like an inverted bowl, covering it with canvas or moose hide, putting heated rocks inside, and dashing cold water over the rocks to make clouds of steam. The thing that puzzled me

280

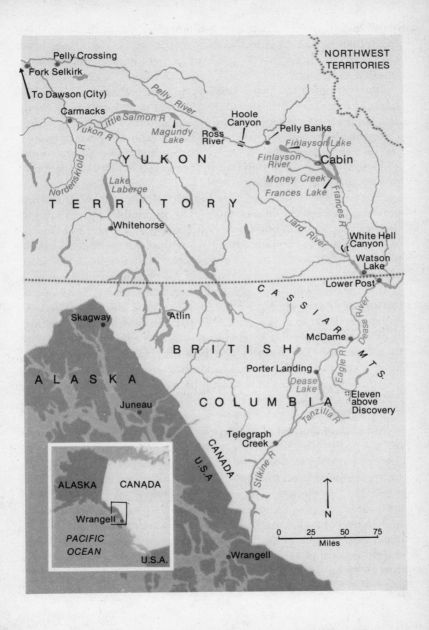

about this custom was that after ten minutes or so in the steam bath the Indian would dress in the same sweaty, greasy clothing, often infested with lice, that he had worn before, and he promptly smelled as strong as ever.

Our trip down to Porter Landing at the northern end of Dease Lake was an uneventful twenty-eight-mile stretch of hard rowing. The landing was a fascinating place, dominated by the Hudson's Bay Company post, with a cluster of scattered cabins belonging to local trappers or prospectors. We were warmly entertained for a couple of days, and then we rented four big pack dogs to carry our gear on a prospecting trip up Thibert Creek.

The dogs were sled animals, big and strong and weighing one hundred and ten pounds or more. The packsaddle was much like that used on horses, but smaller. It consisted of a piece of canvas, carefully fitted to the individual dog, with two cinches to hold it in place and a big pocket, or pannier, on each side to contain the load. The foremost rule was not to overload the dog. Big pack dogs, such as the ones we were renting, could comfortably carry thirty-five or forty pounds day after day, but if overloaded they soon became swaybacked and worthless either for packing or winter sled-pulling.

I can remember few times in my life that I have enjoyed more than that trip. The country was beautiful, laced with creeks and hung with waterfalls. It was also gold country. We saw many abandoned workings, and here and there a lone prospector scooping dirt into a gold pan.

A few days after leaving Porter Landing we made camp at a small lake near the mouth of Mosquito Creek and settled down to do some serious prospecting ourselves. A belt of serpentine rock crossed the country for many miles in this area. To the prospector, serpentine is a favorable formation to follow, as it is usually associated with other minerals. We climbed the steep grassy slope from our lakeside camp until we plodded over the summit. As we cleared the top a broken wall of rock scarred the mountainside beside us, sloping to a huge valley miles below. The going got rougher as we followed closely against the creviced wall, searching for minerals. The smooth green serpentine rock appeared again, its slick shiny surface

282

oily to the touch. Here and there we broke off chunks with the prospector's pick. The serpentine gave way to a sheer wall of schist rock about twenty feet high that followed down the hill toward two tiny lakes. A little farther along we found outcroppings of chrome ore. We took pictures of them and many samples, which we loaded in my packsack.

The next day proved even luckier for us. We noticed that where it met the schist, the serpentine contained veinlets of chrysotile or asbestos. I peeled the fibers from the green rock with my fingernail as we tested the find for a hundred yards down the slope. Although transportation seemed years away from this isolated corner of the wilderness, this could be an important discovery.

So the days went by as we roamed the hills as freely as the wind, following favorable geological formations uphill and downdale, chipping off rock samples from mineral outcroppings, and some-times sampling gravels in creek bottoms for gold. We hunted our grub with a rifle or fished the creeks at night camp, pitching a little mosquito tent beside whatever creek or lake we were near at sundown. Then one morning we awoke to find an inch of snow on the ground and the chill of approaching winter in the air. It was time to leave.

We packed our dogs, mostly with rock samples now instead of food, and started down our back trail for Porter Landing. There we were lucky enough to catch a good breeze, and we sailed our rowboat to the head of Dease Lake in one morning. At the head of the lake luck was with us again: we happened to connect with a hunting packtrain returning to Telegraph Creek. We loaded our outfit on the horses and rode back to town in style.

We arrived four days later and found the town in an uproar, preparing for the year's last run of the *Hazel B*. Hunting parties had come in from the mountains, loaded with trophies. The traders and outfitters were making the skins ready for shipment, the Indians were decked out in their finest, and an air of celebration before the long isolation of winter hung over the place. Some of the whites would be going outside, some would remain and wait for spring in Telegraph Creek.

I had decided to stay and see what the winter would bring. I did not regret my decision, but there was something very final about watching that last boat pull out from shore and head downstream, for there would be no contact with the world outside until the *Hazel B* came back in May. Just before she vanished from sight, the captain sent a long lonesome blast of the whistle echoing back from the hills. I suspect it echoed in the hearts of most of those who were left behind, too. I know it echoed in mine.

WITH THE DEPARTURE of the last riverboat of the season, Telegraph Creek settled down to its winter routine. The packhorses were driven out to winter pasture, where the snowfall would be light and they could survive until spring on wild hay. The trappers got ready to leave for their traplines as soon as the snow was deep enough for dogsled travel, and everybody else began stacking up rows and rows of firewood.

I made a deal with a wood hauler to buy wood from me. A road of sorts led out from town four miles to a stand of timber which could be cut for the asking, and for the next two months I kept busy cutting wood and getting used to my first pair of snowshoes. I also bought a grown husky bitch with three pups and started to break the pups to harness.

Then, about a week before Christmas, the telegraph operator at Telegraph Creek offered me a job.

At that time the Yukon telegraph line was a single wire that stretched from Hazelton, in central British Columbia, through hundreds of miles of roadless wilderness over the mountains to Telegraph Creek, then north through Atlin, and on to Whitehorse. From there it went down the valley of the Yukon to Dawson City. That wire was Telegraph Creek's only means of communication with the outside world during the winter months, except for a once-a-month dogsled mail service at Atlin.

Telegraph stations on the line were eighty to a hundred miles apart. An operator and a lineman wintered at each station, and between were refuge cabins ten or twelve miles apart, a day's travel for a man on snowshoes. Once a year packtrains supplied the main stations. The refuge cabins had only wood and kindling, a bunk, table, and stove. If a tree fell across the line, the linemen went out from each side of the break and repaired it, often meeting and working together. But in rough weather the wire was likely to stay down for as long as three weeks at a time.

My job was to backpack fifty pounds of mail to Raspberry Creek, a station forty miles south, where the lineman from Iskut station, still farther south, would meet me. I'd use the refuge cabins for my overnight stops.

I hiked away from Telegraph Creek on a crisp December morning with the mail, an eiderdown sleeping bag, half a slab of bacon, a little flour, salt, and tea in my pack. I was carrying a .22 and counted on supplementing my meager rations with grouse or rabbits. For the first two miles I followed a well-broken trail, but after that I had to break my own. The snow was soft, the going hard, and it wasn't easy to follow under the telegraph wire that was my only guide. It was getting dark when I took shelter for the night at Sheep Creek cabin, the first refuge stop.

I was on the trail before daybreak the next morning. By early afternoon the temperature, which had stood at twenty below zero during the night, had moderated, and by late afternoon the softening snow was sticking to the webbing of my snowshoes and giving me a bad time. I slogged into the next refuge cabin, at Deep Creek, just before dark, completely worn out.

The next day I ran into serious trouble. A heavy wet snow began to fall and the rawhide on my snowshoes began to stretch, so that they no longer supported my moccasins. My feet were actually dropping through the webbing with every step I took. I tried to repair the lacing, but the knots blistered my feet. Then the wind came up, driving the snow into my face until I could no longer keep track of the wire overhead. That afternoon, in desperation, I tied a length of rawhide to the toe of each shoe and pulled them up out of the wet snow, one after another, as I staggered along.

I should have stopped and made camp in heavy timber, where I would have been sheltered from the storm. But I had romantic notions about the mail getting through on time, and I was sure that the station at Raspberry Creek was just over the next ridge, so I kept going. At dark I realized with stark terror that I had strayed from the telegraph line. I was lost.

I came into a big burn where windfalls tripped me time after time. My watch said ten o'clock. I had been fifteen hours on the trail, in the worst possible kind of going. I do not know how long it was after that—but I think not long—when I fell unconscious in the snow.

To sleep under such conditions is supposed to be certain death. In the darkness of early morning I awoke, dazed and hardly knowing where I was; when I pinched my arm and felt nothing, I concluded I was dead. Then, pushing up my head, I saw stars above and heard a dead tree fall. I was alive.

I raised up one elbow and looked around me. There had been a heavy snowfall during the night, and I was buried under nearly a foot of it. Almost certainly it was that covering that had saved me from freezing to death, for I learned later that between dusk and dawn the temperature had dropped to thirty-five below.

I had left a rutted track the night before, and despite the new snow that had fallen I could still follow it. I backtracked for two miles before I came on the telegraph line. Then I turned and followed it south, making better time now because the cold had dried the snow.

In an hour or so I topped a high knoll and saw a tent standing in the middle of a little flat. I had reached the Iskut Summit refuge camp, fifteen miles beyond my destination at Raspberry Creek!

There were dry wood and matches in the tent, and a stove. I melted snow for water, made a crude flour-paste bannock, and baked it on top of the stove. While I was eating I remembered that this was Christmas Day, my first Christmas in the North.

I fell into the bunk and slept ten hours, made another bannock, and repaired my snowshoes as best I could. I hung the mail sack from the ridgepole of the tent so the Iskut lineman could pick it up, and set out on my back trail for Telegraph Creek. Fifteen miles along, I found where I had passed the Raspberry Creek station in the darkness the night before. I had tramped by within a hundred feet of it.

Two days later I was back in Telegraph Creek, where they were getting ready to send men out to look for me.

I MOVED TO A vacant cabin six miles downriver and began to train my dog team. My pups—Rogue, Rascal, and Runt—came of a good bloodline, and training them was a joy. I soon had them and their mother—Whitey—hauling firewood to the cabin, and when I killed a moose they brought it home in two-hundred-pound loads.

The standard dogsled then was eight feet long, with steel-shod runners and a platform or bed supported on short hardwood posts. Handles at the back enabled the driver to steer. A jerk line—a twenty-foot length of rope—was allowed to trail behind, so a driver could grab it if his team suddenly bolted.

The teams were driven entirely by voice. The dog that did not learn to go at "Mush!" and stop at "Whoa!" and to turn right at "Gee!" and left at "Haw!" was soon replaced. The drivers I knew, white and Indian alike, did not even carry a whip.

I lived alone in the cabin for four months, and only once did I go to town for supplies. The cheechako was on the road to becoming a sourdough.

THE SUMMER OF 1924 I worked for a mining company that was punching what was called, with considerable license, a road through the mountains from Telegraph Creek to Dease Lake, following the packhorse trail uphill and down. There were stretches of that road that were better suited to canoe travel than tractor, and it was as hard a summer as I have ever put in. For instance, it often fell to me to hike the seventy-five miles back to Telegraph Creek and pack out replacements of heavy tractor parts.

In September I made what I intended would be my last trip to Dease Lake. I had my four dogs with me, all of us packing heavy loads, and I was making camp at the Tanzilla River one evening, bone-tired, when I saw two bearded prospectors reeling toward me under huge packs.

They were Hugh Ford and Bill Grady, whom I had seen often in Telegraph Creek. They had been out all summer, prospecting on the headwaters of the Eagle River twenty miles beyond Dease Lake, and they had made a strike. On a little creek almost small enough to jump across they had seen color in their pan, and when they dug down four feet to bedrock they hit coarse nuggets. They had staked their discovery claims and were on the way to Telegraph Creek now to record them with the gold commissioner.

As we talked over hot tea, squatted beside my fire, Grady reached into his packsack and took out a poke of tanned moose hide. He opened it and spilled nuggets of gold out onto a canvas groundsheet. It was dusk, and the light of the campfire made the nuggets flash and sparkle. When I weighed the bigger ones in my hand, a shock went through me like an electric current.

It has been over fifty years since that autumn evening, and I still find myself wondering at the lure of gold and the magic it works. Surely it must have some mystical quality apart from its worth. It kindles a fire in the blood of men who find it; it whispers, "Make me your god and I will give you your heart's desire." The promise is seldom kept, but there are few who can resist that seductive whisper. Men have responded to it since the dawn of civilization, staking their every possession and even life itself in mad races to be first to reach the glittering yellow metal. I know how it is. Holding those nuggets in my hand there beside my flickering fire, I yielded completely to gold fever.

Ford and Grady had already shown their gold to a handful of prospectors at Dease Lake. By now the word would have reached Porter Landing and spread down the Dease River. A real gold stampede would be on, as miners from every creek in the area reacted to the magic cry of "Strike!"

I knew what I must do. I rose at first light next morning, built a small cache close to the trail, and put most of my outfit in it. I would come back for it after my claim was staked. I hiked away from the Tanzilla, carrying only my axe, gun, and bedroll, with my dogs under light pack. Everything depended on reaching that little creek ahead of the miners from down the Dease.

It was twenty-five miles from my camp to the turnoff for the Eagle River trail. When I got there, tracks of boots and moccasins in the mud told me that some stampeders were ahead of me. That first day I halted only long enough to eat and give the dogs a rest, and when I made camp that night I consoled myself with the knowledge that others behind me would have to stop, too.

By late the next afternoon I was at the mouth of the creek where Ford and Grady had made their strike. They had found an old rusted gold pan in the fork of a gnarled spruce tree there and had given the little stream the name of Gold Pan Creek, a name that has stuck to this day. Turning upstream, I saw half a dozen campfires. The miners were all from around Dease Lake, and ten claims had been staked above Discovery, but at least I had won my race with the Dease River contingent.

At first light I cut stakes, paced off the required two-hundred-and-fifty-foot length along the creek and the one-thousand-foot width for a placer claim, and wrote my name and the date on the corner post. Last of all, I added the name of the claim. Eleven above Discovery. That was one of the happiest minutes of my life. I owned my own gold claim! When spring came I could start digging gold. But first I had to go back to Telegraph Creek and record my claim. By the time I started out two days later, there were stakes to Twenty-two above Discovery.

The last boat of the year was tied at the bank when I got back to Telegraph Creek, but I hardly looked in its direction. The outside held no attraction for me now. I went directly to the office of Harry Dodd, the gold commissioner, paid the modest fee, and became the legal owner of Eleven above Discovery.

I met no man in the North whom I came to respect more than Harry Dodd. He had been gold commissioner of the Cassiar mining district for more than twenty-five years, his beginnings going back to the Klondike stampede of 1898. It was years before any other authority came to the district, and Dodd stood alone for law and order in what could well have been a lawless land. The district was vast, but it had a population of fewer than a hundred whites and perhaps a thousand Indians. They brought their troubles to Dodd, and he served as friend, father confessor, and adviser. He also served as a stern but just judge, and his authority was never questioned.

One spring a report came in that an Indian on the Liard River, three hundred miles from Telegraph Creek, had stolen furs from another Indian's traps during the winter. Quietly, Dodd sent word for the accused man to come and see him. The message went by word of mouth—by the marvelous moccasin telegraph, whose workings often seemed incredible. It was five weeks after Dodd sent out the order before it reached the offender in his fishing camp. Two days later he started for Telegraph Creek.

He did not dare ignore the summons, for he knew that Dodd could have his credit cut off at the posts and end his trading furs for salt, tea, and traps. With no written order and no escort, he walked that three hundred miles through the mountains and across the rivers to face whatever might be in store for him.

Half a dozen of us were talking in front of one of the trading posts when he trudged into town and headed for the commissioner's office. A few minutes later Dodd stepped out on his porch and called to us. When we were seated around the office, he announced, "This is a trial. Court is open."

He recited the charge, explained it to the Indian through a trapper interpreter, and asked a few questions. Confession came quickly. The Indian admitted that he had traded furs not caught in his own traps, and Dodd handed down the sentence without any fuss. "Two months at hard labor," he announced.

We had what passed for a jail, a twelve-by-twelve tent with a lumber floor, at the end of Dodd's garden. The prisoner was lodged there and supplied with food, which he cooked himself. Cordwood was brought in and he was equipped with an axe and a crosscut saw. For two months he cut four-foot logs into stovewood length and split and stacked them. He was not confined in any way, but he had no thought of running off. He was released in time to go back for his winter's trapping.

Once I had recorded my claim, I started in on all that had to be done before I could begin working it. I knew that when spring came

290

A pair of brown bears
on a lake shore

The huge moose is frequently
seen in the North

The Cassiar mountains,
the range north
of Dease Lake

Sled dogs are a part
of every camp

I would need lumber for a flume—a long, sloping chute to bring water down where I wanted it—and sluice boxes, where the actual washing of the gravel would be done. I could carry the wood in by dogsled toward the end of winter, once the snow was packed and travel conditions became good, so I acquired two more big dogs— Scotch and Brandy—and started storing and drying lumber from a local sawmill.

As soon as the snow crusted in March I began my hauling. It was a hundred miles from Telegraph Creek to my claim, and I made five round trips, the last one just before the south slopes turned bare under the spring sun. At the claim I found a snow-filled crevice in a rock wall, where meat would keep through most of the summer. I killed a moose and a caribou and stashed the quarters there. To avoid having to feed my dogs, I drove them to Telegraph Creek and boarded them with the owner of the old Stikine Hotel. Then I hiked back and got ready to mine.

Many things had happened at Gold Pan Creek that winter. News of the gold strike had spread to the outside and wild rumors sprang up. Old-timers had come in by dog team over the snows from Dawson City, Fairbanks and other towns. One enterprising arrival, not willing to trust to the luck of mining, had built a crude roadhouse at the mouth of the creek; now he was doing a thriving business. I still recall the sign he put up: EGGS, $1 EACH. MEAL WITH EGGS, $2. For one dollar you got a whole egg of uncertain age. Those that had been cracked or broken went into the meals with eggs, along with moose or caribou meat, a potato, and a canned vegetable. Another dollar paid for a bunk overnight, but the traveler had to supply his own bedroll.

Through the short Arctic spring I dug and grubbed, built a dam, cut trenches down to bedrock, washed gravel, and looked for gold. Every pan I tested showed traces of dust, but never enough to qualify as pay dirt; only once or twice did I find a nugget big enough to ring when dropped into the pan. For a mile up the creek other men were working just as hard, but with a few lucky exceptions they were doing no better than I.

It was almost full summer when a stranger, a tall Scot, walked in

292

one evening and asked to camp on my claim while he looked around. I made him welcome, and he stayed on for a week, helping me dig and test. At the end of that time I had had enough; my total take of gold so far was less than two ounces. But the Scot thought the claim still stood a chance and he wanted to buy it.

I had raced other stampeders for that claim, traveled a thousand miles by dog team packing in lumber for it, and slaved through an entire winter and spring. In the end I sold it for a pound of tea and a half-pound plug of pipe tobacco. In that brief, bitter experience is told much of the story of gold stampedes.

At Dease Lake, on the way back to Telegraph Creek, I saw the tents of stampeders strung along the shore. Most of them were cheechakos from outside, fired with the dream of gold, working at the unaccustomed job of loading pack dogs or lurching off over the muddy trail with backbreaking loads on packboards.

The dream dies hard—as many of them were to prove.

3. The Terrible Canyons

I was at Dease Lake in June of 1925 when the second Hudson's Bay tractor train of the year came in. Who should be on it but Amos Godfrey, the old-timer with whom I had shared a room at Wrangell two years before and whom I now counted among my good friends.

As soon as he saw me he hurried over with exciting news. He had an Indian with him, Little Jimmy, and he explained that the Indian had brought him a sample of high-grade silver-lead ore—galena—earlier that spring. Now Amos had made a deal with a Vancouver mining company to locate the deposit precisely and find out more about its extent. It was somewhere in the Frances Lake area, between three hundred and four hundred miles away across the mountains. Amos could not make the trip alone. Would I go with him? Of course I would.

It would be a boat trip into country totally wild and unknown, still a blank space on government maps. All that was known of the area was rumor, and the rumors were not exactly reassuring. We heard stories of prospectors who had drowned in the rapids, and of unfriendly Indians who wanted no white men trespassing on their hunting grounds. Well, we'd see.

Our route would take us down Dease Lake and the Dease River to the Liard, upstream on the Liard to the Frances, then on up that river to Frances Lake. Our plans called for a poling boat twenty-eight feet long and blunt at both ends. Since there were no boatbuilders at Dease Lake, we'd have to build our own, whipsawing the green lumber for it. The next morning we walked the shore until we found a stand of straight-grained spruce; then we set up camp and went to work.

The first step was to select four heavy, evenly spaced trees that stood in a rectangle, for our sawpit. We cut them about six feet above the ground, and on the stumps we notched and set four logs to make a frame eight feet long and four wide. Next, on one side we spliced in two long poles that sloped down to the ground—skids on which we could roll logs to the top of the frame.

We rolled the first fifteen-foot log up on the sawpit frame and peeled off the bark with an axe. Next we blackened a length of string with a piece of charcoal. By stretching the string taut the full length of the log, lifting the middle and letting it snap back, we got a straight black line for the whipsaw to follow. Then we rolled the log over and repeated the procedure on the opposite side. That gave us two lines that showed where the first slab would be cut off, and by repeating that on all four sides we could square our log. After that we'd use our charcoal line to mark off boards of the thickness we wanted.

Amos had brought a seven-foot whipsaw from Telegraph Creek. It was an instrument of torture, with handles set at right angles to the blade at each end to form a T. To use it one man had to stand on the sawpit frame, the other in the pit below. They pulled the saw up and down like a crosscut, keeping it vertical. The top man guided the blade along the black line on his side, while the man in the pit did the same on the underside of the log.

To say that the whipsawing was hard and disagreeable work is a total understatement. It called for watchfulness and care, and

294

neither man could take his eyes off that black mark. Added to the
backbreaking labor was the agony inflicted by the hungry, relentless
hordes of mosquitoes. Every once in a while, when the insects, the
sawdust, and the heat became too much to endure, Amos and I
would take a break and walk into the lake, clothes and all.

Amos was about fifty years old at that time, but he worked as hard
as I did, and with fifteen years in the North behind him, he showed
far more understanding than I of what lay ahead and of the
requirements of our boat and equipment. At his direction we cut
our boards of varying lengths, so that the joints would not all fall in
one place; we were going into dangerous water and wanted all the
strength we could give the boat. We cut knees and built a frame,
fastening the boards to it with long screws. Next we hewed out a big
sweep for steering, shaped like an oar but ten feet long, and set two
posts in the stern for it to rest between. At last the boat was caulked
and ready.

We made two oars and cut two long poles of dry spruce. Then we
rigged a mast through the forward seat, sewed canvas to a line for a
sail, and we were finished. Fourteen days after we cut the first
board our boat went into the water. We named it the *Come What
May*, and that was to prove a very appropriate choice.

DAYBREAK MIST was still drifting across Dease Lake in ghostly
streamers as we hoisted our sail and shoved off. We ran the length of
the lake, twenty-eight miles, in five hours, passed Porter Landing
without stopping, and headed into the Dease River.

It was a beautiful stream, with heavy spruce forests coming to the
water's edge, high mountains in the background, and small creeks
running in every few miles. There were ducks and moose in the
sloughs, black bears on the gravel bars, eagles and ravens overhead,
and none of them showed much fear of the boat drifting swiftly
downstream. I told myself again, as I had so often in the past two
years, that this untamed land, where fear was unknown, was what
the Garden of Eden must have been like.

If the Dease was beautiful, it was also dangerous in places. We
made camp the first night a short distance from Cottonwood Rapids,

which we'd confront the first thing next morning. They had a bad name and deserved it, for they had taken their fair toll of miners, traders, and trappers.

After dinner we walked down the bank a short distance for a look at the rapids. The danger lay in a string of big boulders that stretched diagonally across the river from shore to shore. About halfway across, one huge rock stood up above the foaming current. A boat driven against that rock would be smashed or swamped, and avoiding it would call for tricky work at the oars and sweep. The alternative was to portage boat and outfit around the rapids. But our boat had not been built for carrying.

The next day, as soon as we had eaten breakfast, we let the current carry us down into the caldron of white water. I rowed as I had never rowed in my life and Amos worked the sweep with every ounce of his strength. Just above the big rock we almost turned sidewise, something we both knew meant disaster. But we strained at our work, righted the boat, and swept past that great boulder so close we all but scraped it. A minute later we were floating in smooth water below the rapids.

We camped that night at the McDame Creek post of the Hudson's Bay Company. Amos had not been down the Dease below McDame Creek, so from here on, all the way to our destination in the Frances Lake country, the rivers and their rapids would be totally new to both of us. All we knew was that we could expect plenty of bad water and dangerous canyons.

We left the McDame Creek post the following afternoon, intending to make a few miles downstream before camping. We rounded the first bend and ahead of us sighted a shallow rapid, too rock-broken for our boat, foaming more than halfway across the river. The rest of the current knifed through a crevice between walls of rock. The short, sheer canyon was wide enough for the boat, and although the current ran like a millrace, the water was smooth.

We headed into that crevice, with Amos at the sweep and me at the oars, and as the river took us we saw that at the lower end of the canyon the water dropped in a three-foot fall, enough to spell disaster if our boat should turn sidewise.

We swept down the canyon, slid over the drop and into a whirlpool thirty feet across. As we spun into it I saw that the water was being pulled down at the vortex with a loud, ominous sucking sound. Then suddenly that vortex started to boil upward instead, rising higher and higher, spinning faster and faster, and lifting the boat with it.

Unless we could get clear before the vortex began to suck downward again, we'd be pulled down with it. But the oars seemed to have no effect on the spinning motion of the boat, so I shipped them and grabbed one of our poles; as we whirled close to the rock wall I jammed the pole against it and heaved with all my strength. That push and Amos's furious work with the sweep broke the grip of the whirlpool. We shot clear and went bouncing downstream. In that same instant I heard the terrifying sucking noise again and looked back to see the center of the whirlpool sinking rapidly. It had been a close call.

The Dease let up on us after that. Gravel bars split it into channels, tree-covered islands appeared, bearberry and wild strawberries and lupine made a riot of color in every open glade. We had a few more close calls as we made our way farther and farther north. But we scraped through each one safely, and though battered and bruised, the *Come What May* showed no sign of a crack. At last we arrived at the mouth of the Dease and saw the wide sweep of the great Liard River. Half a mile upstream were the old log buildings of Lower Post.

Lower Post lies almost on the British Columbia–Yukon Territory border, not far from where the Alaska Highway now passes Watson Lake. We camped there for two days, trying to learn more of the rivers that lay ahead of us, the Frances and upper Liard. But no one could help us. We were told only that there was very dangerous water in the latter, and we knew we would have to fight our way through it against the current. As for the Frances, nothing was known of it.

Then, on our second day at the post, a visitor arrived unexpectedly. He was a big, rollicking Swede who had come down the Liard in a wonderful dugout canoe hewed from the trunk of a cottonwood tree. It was thirty-two feet long and only about eighteen inches wide in the center. The Swede could turn that long canoe on a dime and send it skimming across the river like a water beetle. He knew more about the upper Liard than anyone we had encountered, and we invited him to share our evening meal with us.

A bad canyon ten miles long began six miles above the post, he said. In high water it was impassable. Even now, with the river well below flood stage, he did not think we could pole upstream through it. And once we had entered it, there would be no way of getting out. He strongly advised us to abandon our boat at this point and walk overland.

The Swede had never been on the Frances, he told us, but what he had heard about it from the Indians was all bad. There again, he thought, we would be better off on foot. But our outfit was too heavy for that. Win or lose, we'd have to stay on the rivers.

IF I LIVE to be a hundred, I'll never forget the canyons on the Liard and the Frances.

Amos and I left Lower Post at daylight. The Liard was gentle here, except in the riffles, and we poled steadily upstream, keeping to the inside of bends, where the current ran slowest.

Six miles from the post we reached the lower end of the canyon the Swede had told us about. We had to line the boat up through the first barrier of fast water, wading waist-deep close to the bank. Then we turned another bend and ahead of us sheer rock walls narrowed into the canyon itself. We heard the sound of the rapids, a dull roar like distant thunder, born of the surge and ebb of water pounding heavily against rocks. We found a bit of beach, tied our boat, and made lunch. That proved to be the last place we could get ashore for four savage miles.

As we made the first turn above the lunch camp the bare rock walls rose sheer for three hundred to four hundred feet. Between them were scattered huge boulders and chunks of mountain sticking out of the water twenty and thirty feet high. The river boiled around the boulders, throwing waves eight and ten feet high and pouring down between them in cascades impossible for any boat to ascend.

298

It was straight poling now. There was no beach at all and in places the potholes were so deep that frequently we lost bottom with our poles. The power of the water tore at us, trying to sweep us against the rocks. Each time a wave would strike, tearing my pole from its grip on the river bottom, Amos would plunge his pole down firmly to hold the boat until I regained control.

Another slight bend in the river caused the main current to throw the full blast of water against a sheer wall on our side. We could not pole against the power of this deluge; we simply had to cross over and hope for a passage upstream on the other side. Gingerly we pushed to the lee of a huge boulder, being careful not to get sucked into its eddy. Downstream the river looked clear for about five hundred feet, which might enable us to make the far shore.

With a heave on our poles we shot out into the foaming torrent. Instantly the force of the water swung the boat almost halfway round. Plunging our poles down again and again, we found we were safely quartering toward the far bank, but despite our efforts we were being carried swiftly downstream instead of up. We must have been only thirty feet from the far shore when Amos struck a rock with the sweep and was thrown off-balance for just a moment. But that moment was too long. The current sucked us between two enormous boulders and we slid down the chute between them like a toboggan on a steep slope. In five minutes we were back at the lunch camp, having lost five hours of gain!

Yet perhaps we were lucky. We had learned that we could get upstream the way we had come down, except for the twin boulders, and we felt sure that on the next try we could keep to the shoreside of them. Tired and hungry, we camped for the night.

As the sun broke over the rim of the canyon we poled out into the river again. We made it to a point just before the perilous chute and found a narrow channel against the shore that allowed us to proceed until we came to a jutting point that blocked all passage. We had to tie up, unload the boat, and carry everything up and over that point of rock. This was doubly tough, because the rock sloped like a church roof and the spray kept it slippery. With the lightened boat floating high, I scrambled ahead of the point with the bowline in hand. Amos stood on the sharp point of rock and pulled on the stern line to keep the boat out in the stream. The *Come What May* swamped in spite of our guiding, but somehow we lugged it halfway up the upper end of the rocky slope and bailed it out.

We reloaded and crossed to the east side again, not far above our turning point of the day before. We struck hard against the rock wall on the far side, which here had a ten-foot overhang. The water almost immediately deepened so that we lost bottom with our poles. It would be suicide to try to cross again near here. In desperation I laid the pole in the boat and grabbed the overhanging rock wall with my fingers. To my surprise I found I could hang on to it and pull without my fingers slipping. Amos held his pole against the bottom, although his arm was almost underwater, while slowly I literally clawed our way upstream for over an hour. It was gruelling work, and we had to resort to portaging once more before we reached the head of the canyon. It was sundown when we finally came to open water. With a sigh of relief we made camp a mile above the last whitecaps.

Thereafter the Liard became a delight. As we progressed upstream it widened and the current slackened. Wild flowers grew in abundance. Whisky jacks stole bacon from our frypan, and cow moose and their calves became more frequent, standing quietly in the shallow water near shore and watching us undisturbed as we poled past. The world and its worries seemed very far distant.

At noon of the sixth day after leaving Lower Post we came to the mouth of the Frances. A big island split it into two channels. We picked the deeper one and floated into the river itself.

The next day the channel narrowed and the current turned fast. We made slow headway against it, and when we stopped for lunch we could hear a telltale roar coming from upstream; we'd soon know what the canyons of the Frances were like.

At sundown that evening we came upon a steep, rock-strewn hell of white water that stretched ahead of us as far as we could see. We made camp and walked upstream to size things up.

Broken limestone walls rose three hundred feet above the river on both banks. Huge chunks had fallen away and lay in a jumble in the riverbed, creating one ten-foot wave after another. We climbed to the top of the wall and saw what looked like a series of waterfalls, the lowest six feet high, where the river tumbled over successive tiers of bedrock. Between falls it roared with incredible force, smashing against the great limestone boulders. No living man could pole a boat upstream against its power and fury. Unless we could find a way to line, along one bank or the other, our boat journey was ended.

We named the place White Hell Canyon. Our name was never recorded and on maps today it is called Middle Canyon. But I still think ours was a far more appropriate name.

As we drank our tea by the fire that night, Amos suggested for the first time that we give up and turn back. I thought for a minute he was testing me, and I laughed at him.

Standing on the wall above the river earlier, watching the roaring tumult of water, I confess I had been frightened, wondering whether we could challenge this canyon and come out alive. But now I had my confidence back; there had to be a way through. I know now, fifty years later, that I was leaning on a confidence born of youth and inexperience. I simply did not know how to measure the terrible danger those falls and rapids posed.

Suddenly I sensed that Amos was dead serious about turning back. The thought of giving up when we were so close to our goal was almost too much to bear, and I opened my mouth to urge that if we had to quit the river, we should fashion backpacks and go overland as the Indians did. But I thought better of it, knowing that the decision lay with my partner. Tired as I was, I slept fitfully that night, wondering what the decision would be.

The next morning we scouted the opposite side of the canyon and concluded that we could line the boat up to a point where a sloping shelf of rock ran down into the water. The wall here was of broken rock that had some brush and timber, and we could see a chance to drag our boat overland and portage our outfit upstream for a thousand yards. That would take us to a place where we could line once more. It would be an almost unbelievable task.

We left our camp pitched, and our rifles, an axe, and some food behind, in case of mishap. We lined the boat up to the rock shelf, and went at the job of clearing brush and trees and building a roadway. The bigger trees we laid down for rails, the smaller ones we cut into six-foot lengths for rollers. The boat was far too heavy for two men to carry, but we could roll and skid it on those rails. We ran into an unforeseen barrier at the upstream end of our roadway, a sheer-walled ridge that went almost straight up for fifteen feet and then dropped the same distance to the river on the other side. But luckily we had brought along block-and-tackle gear, and we decided we could manage the ridge.

It was slow work, but two days later we had the boat at the foot of the rock ridge. I have no words to describe the torture mosquitoes inflicted on us during those two days. We then went back for our gear and supplies, portaged everything up to that point, rested, and went at the part of the job we dreaded most, skidding the boat up and over the ridge. We hung our two blocks to a stout tree, made a sling around the bow, and got rollers in place. The rest was surprisingly easy.

The next morning we went back to lining. A short distance upstream the beach disappeared in a sheer rock wall a hundred feet high, which then gave way to a steep slope. I was able to walk along the top of the wall and haul on the bowline while Amos stayed in the boat and fended it away from the rock wall.

All went well until I came to a deep gully that cut through the rim. It was only a few feet wide, and I decided I could jump across. But as I gathered up a few extra feet of line and crouched for the jump, my footing gave way beneath me and I went hurtling down into the river. Immediately the current swept me out toward midstream, then carried me swiftly past the boat. I swam desperately, but it did no good.

It was a stroke of luck that saved me. I still had the bowline in one hand, and Amos was holding the boat against the raging current with his pole thrust hard against the bottom. He braced himself and hung on and when I reached the end of my line I was brought up with a terrific jerk and swung in to the bank as if on a long pendulum. It had been a close call.

We rested until I got my breath back and then went on. We lined where we could, poled where there was no shore to walk on. Then, after another mile, the rapids suddenly turned less savage and the current slackened. White Hell Canyon was behind us.

TEN MILES ABOVE the canyon, to our puzzlement, we saw tree stumps on the bank. Then a small cabin came into view, and dark-skinned youngsters came running down to the shore to stare at us. We tied up and were greeted by an old-time trapper named Watson, who was living on this remote and untraveled river with his Indian wife and their children.

He told us he trapped down the Frances and the Liard as far as Fish Lake at the head of the canyon, about fifteen miles above Lower Post. (Later he moved his residence to Fish Lake, and it became known as Watson Lake, the name it still carries. Today it is a major station on the Alaska Highway, and also the site of an important airport.) Watson knew the Frances below his cabin, but he could tell us almost nothing about what lay above it. As for Frances Lake, he could say only that some Indian families lived and trapped there, and that there was an Indian trail leading through the mountains from the lake to Lower Post. With that meager information we headed into the unknown again.

Not long after we shoved off we began to catch glimpses of distant mountains ahead. Far to the northeast the shining snow peaks of the Too-tscho range pierced the sky, and off to the east the lower ramparts of the Tses-i-tu Mountains showed through openings in the timber. Two days' travel above Watson's cabin brought us to a place known now as False Canyon. The river was fast, but the rapids offered no difficulty and we poled through them easily enough. Farther upstream, islands began to appear in the river, and far ahead we could see that a wide valley opened out, hemmed in by mountains. We were sure that Frances Lake lay in that valley.

That night, as we lay in our bedrolls close to the dying embers of our campfire, excitement throbbed through me. Some great event seemed to be waiting for me at this lake in the middle of the most isolated area left in North America.

I woke at four the next morning, ready to go. As we dug our poles into the shallow stream for the last few miles, the wide opening between the mountains took definite shape, and large glacial boulders became visible in the river channels. Toward mid-afternoon the gap in the trees widened and the mountains came fully into view. Suddenly the bright glint of the sun shone on a vast body of water, and the huge expanse of Frances Lake spread out ahead of us. The river emptied the lake at the southwest corner, leaving a wide, flat area to the east, while a high wall of crystalline limestone hemmed in the west beach. Snowcapped mountains rose to nine thousand feet east of the lake. A mile or so away we could see a timber-covered sandspit sticking out into the lake for half a mile, cutting off any view beyond.

We had made it! We had conquered the four-hundred-odd miles of the Dease, the Liard, and the Frances. We had survived the terrifying canyons and rapids. After we'd beached the boat and made camp, I walked alone to the end of the sandspit and gazed at my surroundings.

My first full view of the lake overwhelmed me. The scent of wild roses, spruce, and pine perfumed the air. The jagged glory of the snowcapped mountains was reflected on the mirror waters of the lake. But after the weeks of roar and echo on the rivers, it was the silence of the huge valley that dominated all my senses. An ecstatic peacefulness engulfed me. It was for a moment as if I had walked through a veil into another world where a million years were set aside, enabling me to see and feel something extraordinary not given to everyday man. For that moment I was transported out of this world, so that I was outside of my body *and could see myself standing there*.

4. Gold!

We rowed up Frances Lake at a leisurely pace. A few miles above the head of the river the lake made a sweeping turn to the west. We were to learn later that it forked here into two arms, with a broad peninsula between. But the entrance to the east arm was narrow and obscured by islands, and we passed it without paying it any attention. A dozen miles up the west arm we found the first sign of human habitation. A bundle of tepee poles stood against a tree, and there were the remains of many fires on the ground. Plainly this was the site of a winter camp for the Frances Lake Indians.

Late that afternoon, nearing the head of the lake, we saw the smoke of a campfire rising through the trees. We pulled to the beach and tied up. The fire was tiny, built between two tents, and squatting in front of it was the oldest Indian I had ever seen.

He wore a soiled garment made of caribou skin. His copper-brown face, wrinkled as a prune, was half hidden behind matted white hair. But it was his nails that were the strangest thing about him. His scrawny hands ended in actual claws, about an inch long and curved like an eagle's. His feet were gnarled and misshapen, too, and the nails of his toes were almost as curved and long as those on his fingers.

He was obviously anxious to be friendly, for as I walked up to him with my hand held high in greeting he jabbered excitedly in a language I could not make out. After about a minute, an old gray-haired woman came out of the tent nearest me and stood beside the man; I assumed she was his wife.

I fell back on sign language, first asking the old man where the occupants of the other tent were. He circled a bony arm to indicate a day's travel, making the sunup-to-sundown sign three times. They would be back in three days, I concluded. No doubt they had gone hunting to replenish the camp's food supply.

Amos and I said good-by and rowed away to make our camp beside a tiny creek. We'd wait here until the rest of the band returned and then ask them to help us locate the body of galena, the silver-lead ore we had come to find.

After supper we went back to the old Indian and his wife, gave them half a pound of tea and a plug of tobacco, and showed them a sample of the galena. Instantly the man pointed across the lake to the east and made the sunup-to-sundown sign twice. We'd find the ore there, two days back in the mountains.

305

To fill the time until the other Indians returned, we poled up toward the head of Frances Lake. We came to a mile-wide delta where a big river (we'd learn later it was the Finlayson) flowed in from the west through a canyon. We poled into this new river and up through its delta to the canyon. The water was shallow and easily navigable for two or three miles. There the south wall had broken down in a half-moon flat of gravel beaches and channels that carried water only when the river was at high stage. We could pole no farther, so we beached the boat and went ahead on foot. We had seen big quartz veins in the rock wall on the north side of the river, hinting at gold, and Amos chipped off samples with his prospector's pick. They showed some mineralization but no free gold.

Across from these veins there was a gully slanting down from the rim of the canyon and cutting across the gravel flat to the river. At the bottom of it a tiny stream trickled in, hardly big enough to deserve the name of creek. At the mouth of that trickle, walking on exposed bedrock where the water was only a few inches deep, I saw something glint under my feet as if a small mirror had caught the sun. I was a couple of steps past it before the significance of that flash registered. I stepped back, and the gleam of a gold nugget leaped at me through the water.

"Gold, Amos!" I shouted. "I've found a nugget!"

I dropped to my knees in the shallow water and tried with my knife to dig it out of the crevice where it was wedged. Mud roiled the water and I lost sight of the precious nugget. I hacked the crevice with the pick and waited for the water to clear, but the current had moved the small lump of gold and I could no longer see it.

I ran for the gold pan in the boat. Amos watched skeptically as I cleared the crevice of mud and rock, filled the pan with dirt, and washed the dirt very carefully. My nugget flashed at me again the first time I tilted the pan, and when I finished, a string of small nuggets lay like a shining halo bordering the residue of black sand left in the pan.

I had discovered gold! On a nameless creek, in what seemed a million miles from civilization, the dream of every prospector had come true for me.

An Alaskan tundra pond

Timber wolves can drag down
and kill caribou

The spruce grouse,
so easily caught it is
known as the "fool hen"

Amos and I dug and panned until dusk, possessed by gold madness, forgetful of everything around us save the gravel and mud and the flakes and small nuggets we found. Not once did the pan fail to show color, and when we started back to camp in three hours' time, we had recovered half an ounce of gold with a single pick and pan. Good panning, that!

We tested many places in that half-mile-long crescent of gravel that we were calling the Half-Moon Discovery, and not a day went by that did not yield at least half an ounce of gold. If we could take out that much using a pan, we knew we could do far better with a sluice box, but we had not brought the whipsaw with us and so had no way to make one. But that could wait. We had made a truly rich strike, and it would take many summers to work the Half-Moon clean.

The Indian hunters were waiting for us when we returned to camp on the fourth evening. Little Jimmy, who had shown Amos the galena sample back at Telegraph Creek, was in the group. He had started back to Frances Lake overland as soon as he left us there, and he had made better time afoot than we had by boat. With him were two other Indians, Chief Smith and Caesar.

All three spoke broken English (probably learned from stampeders and traders they encountered at Lower Post on the Liard), and they told us they had had a good hunt. They had cached part of their moose meat and had returned to the camp with sixteen pack dogs, each carrying forty pounds. Nobody would be short of food for the remainder of the summer.

The three cleared up for us the identity of the old Indian with the eagle-claw nails. He was Dentiah, they said—Indian for Old Chief. His age was hard to believe. He and his son had helped construct the trading post at Pelly Banks for the Hudson's Bay Company in 1842. Since Dentiah had a son old enough at that time to be hired for heavy work, it seemed likely that the old man had been born shortly after 1800. That meant he was now about a hundred and twenty-three years old. He died at Frances Lake in 1929, claiming to be a hundred and twenty-seven. He was probably close to right.

The next morning Amos and I made arrangements with Little

Jimmy and Caesar to go and examine the silver-lead ore. While Amos prepared for the trip, I left camp to collect our tools at Half-Moon. When I got back, the whole Indian encampment was paying us a ceremonial visit.

Two more men, Oaltal and Meegan, had shown up with their families, making a total of six men, including the old chief. There were five or six women and between thirty and forty kids of all ages. Not one of the women or youngsters had seen a white man before, and with my hair bleached white by the sun I was a focus of curiosity for the whole group.

To one little girl about six years old, not quite as shy as the rest, I handed a piece of bannock spread with jam. She ran into the trees with it, but word of the treat spread, and in minutes I was surrounded by a dozen laughing youngsters, their straight black hair flying in the wind. I set a can of jam and a whole bannock on the end of our camp table and told them, through Caesar, to share it. When the bannock was gone, there were a lot of sticky faces and some very wide grins.

Caesar told me that there were two more men who belonged with the group, but they were off trading for salt, traps, and tea at Lower Post on the Liard. They had gone overland by way of a long mountain trail that followed the valley at the foot of the high slopes, and they would return the same way. Plainly the Indians of this region did not travel the rivers, which were too savage and dangerous to serve as canoe routes.

At sunrise the next morning Little Jimmy, Caesar, Amos, and I left our camp in the *Come What May* for the trip to the deposit of galena ore. Caesar, who had explained that Frances Lake has two arms, guided us as we rowed down the west arm.

It was afternoon when we came to the narrows where the east arm, fast-currented and island-choked, enters the lake. We camped there that night and started up the east arm the next morning. Around noon we tied up at the mouth of a small creek ten miles short of the head of the arm, ate lunch, and started on foot for the galena veins.

A trail zigzagged up beside the creek, and we had walked only a short distance when Caesar pointed to a place where the carpet of moss had been scraped off the ground. "Find um here," he said.

A vein of solid galena lay exposed, eighteen inches wide, held between walls of black schist. Caesar told us that he had killed a moose on a flat half a mile up the mountain. Having no dogs along to pack out the meat, he had made a sling of the hide, loaded it, and dragged it down the slope. At this place the load had pulled the moss away and he had seen the galena. It was a find of considerable importance.

We camped there for several days, exploring the area. We uncovered ore all the way back to the beach and located an even wider vein farther up the creek. Finally we staked boundary lines for eight claims, all that the company that had financed our trip could want. Now we could go back to our gold panning.

We made a fast trip back to camp, where we fashioned a crude sluice box from the trunk of a dead cottonwood. To bring running water into the box, we built a wing dam of rock, out from the shore into the Finlayson. Next we tore the *Come What May's* canvas sail into strips and sewed them up to form a makeshift hose eight feet long. It provided a good flow of water into the head of the box. Then we went to work with the one shovel we had. When we had washed all the gravel within reach of the box, we floated more down, a yard at a time, in our boat. At the end of two days we had recovered more than fifty dollars' worth of gold. Our discovery was a true bonanza.

My partner and I agreed then and there on complete secrecy. When we returned to civilization we would report on the silverlead veins, but the gold would remain known only to us.

FREEZE-UP TIME was only six weeks away. Frost was whitening the ground night after night, and pebbles at the edge of the river glistened like jewels when the morning sun struck their sheath of ice. Playing our mounting profits against the oncoming winter was risky business, but we agreed to keep on mining as long as we dared.

The rivers were at their low autumn levels now, and the rapids would be far less difficult than they had been when we made our

310

way into the country. On top of that, we'd be going downstream on the Frances and the Liard, and we figured we could make the trip out in twenty-three days if luck was with us. But to be safe we decided to allow a month.

The day finally came when we did not dare tarry longer. On September 16, 1925, my twenty-fifth birthday, we cleaned up the sluice box and stood it against a tree. That night we loaded only the necessary things into the boat, leaving the rest of our outfit behind for me; I was coming back.

Right after daybreak the next morning, with much bantering and many promises to the Indians, we pushed out into the lake. We were heading south with more than six hundred dollars' worth of dust and nuggets, not bad for seventeen days of work.

We raised a blanket for a sail and ran the length of Frances Lake and several miles down the Frances River that first day. Wedges of wild geese flew overhead all day long, driving steadily into the south, reminding us that it was time to go.

We reached False Canyon the second day, managed it with no trouble, and at dusk that night we camped above White Hell Canyon. The river had lost much of its savage power here, but it still had enough to compel us to portage everything except the boat. Soon we came to the place where I had nearly drowned on the way up, and we pulled ashore to look things over.

Every hour counted now. We were at least sixteen or seventeen days from Dease Lake, and the threat of slush ice in the rivers hung over us like a sword blade. The rivers of the North country run heavy with such ice weeks before the lakes lose their summer heat and freeze over. The ice forms first in the small creeks, especially those that rise in the high mountains and are snow fed. The ice flows out into the river, more forms, and soon it becomes very difficult to run a boat downstream and impossible to fight upstream against the current. There is enough hard ice mixed with the slush to cut a boat to ribbons in a few miles.

To save time now, we decided that Amos would pack our outfit to the foot of the rapids and I would run them in the boat. We unloaded our gear. Then I pushed the boat out into the stream, and

311

began rowing like a madman in an endeavor to keep steerageway as the first whitecaps struck.

The force of the water carried the *Come What May* along like a matchbox, flinging it from one bouncing wave to the next. Suddenly, as if held in the clutches of some demon of the river, the tiny boat swept between two boulders and fell into the maelstrom of foam below. Somehow the momentum gained above carried it through the turmoil and out of the spray, and I found myself pulling hard in smooth fast water until I gained the shore below the rapids.

We reloaded the *Come What May*, rode the current of the Frances down to the wide-sweeping Liard, and camped that night at the head of the canyon on that river. Though this canyon was worse than those on the Frances, low water had tamed it, and there was not a single stretch too savage to run with the loaded boat. By midmorning we pulled to shore at Lower Post, stocked up quickly on butter, bacon, and jam, then poled across the Liard and into the mouth of the Dease. The rest of the way to Dease Lake would be upstream. But wherever poling was difficult the summer boat crews of the Hudson's Bay Company had cut a trail along one bank or the other for lining. We took advantage of those trails, and on the eighth day after leaving Frances Lake we were at the McDame Creek post, four days ahead of the best schedule we had hoped for.

Here luck was with us. A mining crew was closing down for the winter. They'd be going up to Dease Lake in two more days, using a small powerboat, and they invited us to join them. From Dease Lake we could ride to Telegraph Creek by tractor train. Our summer of hardship and danger was at an end.

We cached our boat, and the rest of the trip was more fun than work. When we reached Telegraph Creek five days later the *Hazel B* was tied to the bank, ready to leave next morning. Amos and I would go separate ways now. I would return to the gold discovery alone; he was leaving for the outside, where he had a wife and a family.

I bought out Amos's share in the Half-Moon claim, and spent the next few days outfitting myself and exercising my six dogs, to run off some of the fat they had put on while boarding at the Stikine Hotel.

312

The pups I'd bought last year, during my first winter in the North, were fully grown now and one of them, Rogue, was the leader of my team.

To anyone who showed curiosity I displayed samples of the galena ore but kept my gold findings to myself. Last of all I went to Harry Dodd, the gold commissioner, registered my claim, and for safety's sake left my poke of gold with him. Then I loaded forty-pound packs on each of my dogs, shouldered a heavy pack of my own, and faded quietly out of town. I was on my way back to the Half-Moon.

It took four days to make the seventy-five miles to the head of Dease Lake. The Hudson's Bay Company had a new post there now, and it had all the equipment I needed. I bought a toboggan, a lightweight silk tent, and a small stove with a cast-iron top. I also bought picks, gold pans, two more shovels, a seven-foot whipsaw, and a two-inch auger which I'd use to drill holes for wooden pegs that would hold together the logs of the cabin I intended to build.

There was a shelf of ice along the shore of the lake, thick enough for safe travel with the toboggan if we kept close to the beach. The temperature had dropped to fifteen below zero, and when I reached the head of the Dease River the second day, I found the ice firm and safe. The snow was not deep enough to form bad drifts, and by picking my way or falling back on the trail used by boat crews in summer, I had no difficulty.

I traveled from daylight to dusk, and made the hundred and eighty miles to Lower Post on the Liard in eight days. From the Indians there, I bought a supply of babiche—moose rawhide thongs for spare snowshoe webbing. From them I also learned the location of the trail used by the Frances Lake Indians when they came to the post to trade. It followed close to the foothills east of the Frances River, they told me, winding north and northwest almost on a straight line to Frances Lake—a far more direct route than Amos and I had taken.

I put the dogs on the trail and entered as beautiful a winter wonderland as I have ever seen. The clean white snow lay everywhere, broken only by the occasional track of a moose, the packed trails of snowshoe rabbits, or the footprints of wolf and marten, fox and lynx. Except for the swishing of the toboggan and the panting of the dogs the silence surrounded us so forcefully it made me feel we were trespassing into a forbidden paradise.

The winter stillness of the northern wilderness has a hushed quality all its own. On a windless day, when a few flakes of snow eddy softly to the earth, or in the flooding brilliance of a moonlit night, that absence of sound presses down upon the mind and spirit so tangibly that it can be felt. But it brings peace, not loneliness. This was the perfect solitude I had come to the North to find, and I reveled in it.

It was an hour before dusk one evening when the dogs and I came down off a high ridge and saw Frances Lake before us, frozen for half a mile out from the shores, filled with drifting ice in the middle. We crossed to the west shore, and I drove the dogs into a stand of heavy timber and made camp. I was almost home.

I had enjoyed every mile of that trip, and it had also done much to build my self-confidence. I had been two and a half years in the North now, and there was very little resemblance left between the green cheechako who had gone up the Stikine to Telegraph Creek and the trail-hardened, self-reliant sourdough who mushed his dogs across the end of Frances Lake that afternoon.

All the next day we traveled up the lake on the rim ice, and that night we camped at the delta of the Big Sheep Lick River, the Il-es-tooa of the Indians. It was later named for me, and today's maps show it as Money Creek.

Early the next morning I drove the dogs the five miles to the campsite Amos and I had used, where I planned to build my cabin. My Indian neighbors were gone now, scattered on their trapping grounds. I faced a winter of total solitude.

I PITCHED my silk tent in a thick stand of trees, covered the floor with boughs, and installed my little stove. Next I stored my supplies on the high cache Amos and I had built, made brush beds for the dogs, and cut a pile of firewood and kindling.

The next day, snowshoeing across the delta of the Finlayson in search of logs for my cabin, I killed two moose. Within two miles of

314

my tent I had taken enough fresh meat to last the dogs and me well toward spring, provided we alternated it with fish.

Now I could go at the job of building my cabin. I shoveled away the snow from a level area in the lee of a high bank. I'd need forty logs fifteen feet long. I found a fine stand of spruce on the deltas and managed to cut and trim seven or eight trees a day. I hauled them to the site with the dogs and the toboggan, notched them at the ends, and began the walls of my new home.

Thick green moss grew everywhere around the cabin, and when I had a tier of four logs in place, I covered the tier with a four-inch layer of moss for chinking. The tier above pressed this down to form an almost airtight joint. I built the gable ends by pegging each log to the one below it, and was ready for the roof, the most difficult part of the job. I notched a stout ridgepole at both ends and laid it in place. Then I cut small poles ten feet long, laying them from the ridge down to the side walls, allowing a generous overhang and pegging them to the top log. Finally I covered the roof poles with a thick layer of moss and added a few poles to hold it in place. When spring came I would build a better roof, but for now this one was coldproof and, I hoped, watertight.

As I laid up the log walls of the cabin, I had cut openings for two windows and a door. I made the door of two layers of poles with moss tamped tightly between, and hung it on wooden hinges so that it fitted snugly. I had brought a roll of isinglass for the windows. It was not clear, but it let light through.

At last I moved into my new home. That was a great day. There may be things in life more satisfying than building a warm cabin with your own hands hundreds of miles from the nearest source of materials or help—but I have not discovered them. In the warmth of the cabin I could even take a bath, a luxury that had been denied me for weeks in the drafty, often freezing-cold tent. I made a bunk and table, a bench for the stove, and a shelf or two, and the cabin assumed some degree of comfort.

Winter had clamped down in earnest now. The open water of the lake froze, and snow lay deep over the land. The temperature hovered at around forty below, dropping down to sixty now and

315

then. I stretched my gill net under the ice of the lake a hundred feet from shore, anchoring it with poles at each end. I was catching all the whitefish that the dogs and I could use, and now and then a lake trout.

One morning I harnessed the dogs and set out to explore the upper end of Frances Lake, above the delta of the Finlayson. We had traveled about a dozen miles when I saw a band of wild sheep licking at clay banks a short distance ahead. I had found a natural salt lick. Sheep trails were all over the place, and if I had had any doubt about a supply of fresh meat for the remainder of the winter, it was ended now. The salt-hungry sheep would use this place until spring, and of all the wild meat available in that country theirs was the most flavorful.

I shot two of them, loaded the carcasses on the toboggan, and turned the dogs back toward the cabin. That was a jubilant homecoming, in the failing light of a cold winter afternoon.

A FEW DAYS after I had found the sheep lick I saw a band of caribou strung out across the lake three or four miles below the cabin. They had come down the Il-es-tooa River, following the low brush on which they feed in winter. I watched them through my powerful field glasses as they crossed the lake. There must have been three hundred of them romping in the clear thirty-below air. Some of the young ones lunged with their antlers against others in mock battle. Sometimes one would throw another down, then prance around in the joy of victory until the conquered one would leap up and give chase across the lake ice.

Seeing them play like one big family, I was suddenly very lonely. Christmas was only a few days off, and I found myself reflecting on the joyful Christmases of my childhood. Somehow, I thought, if I could touch those carefree caribou and talk to them, it would give me a sense of companionship.

Knowing that a strange scent would stampede the caribou, I made careful plans. Early the next morning I hitched my dogs to the toboggan and, armed with pick and shovel, mushed up to the salt lick. I broke loose a few hundred pounds of the frozen muck and loaded it onto the toboggan. The next day I mushed down the lake to the delta of the Il-es-tooa and spread the salty clay chunks out among the caribou brush. I knew that my scent would cling to the brush where I had touched it, but I hoped the caribou would tolerate the human scent in their eagerness to lick salt.

The next day, through my field glasses, I saw the leader begin to lick. Almost immediately the rest of the herd followed. In threes and fives they stumbled out from the shelter of the trees and began licking, too, nibbling occasionally at the brush. Every once in a while one of them would raise his head and snort as he caught my scent, but then he would settle back and go on licking the salty clay.

Two days later I mushed up the river again, recovered more salt from the lick, and as before, scattered it widely over the delta. It was an all-day job, twenty-four miles round trip, and the stars were bright in the dark sky when I got back to the cabin. Tomorrow would be Christmas Day, and I would try an experiment.

Before daylight I snowshoed down to the Il-es-tooa and settled myself under a big tree. I waited for what seemed hours, getting colder by the minute. Then, quite casually, there they came.

Over the brow of the upper gravel terraces I saw the leader, his magnificent spread of antlers silhouetted against the cloudless blue sky. Following closely behind came his herd. Unhurried, nipping the tops off the brush that stuck up through the two feet of snow and digging the snow occasionally with the shovel-like growth of horn that protrudes down over their foreheads, they walked toward me. The big bull leader must have been twenty yards from me when he jerked up his head and snorted, turning back toward the herd. I feared they would stampede, but the big bull hesitated and in a moment faced me again and cautiously came nearer. He touched the first block of salt and began to lick.

I stood perfectly still, my hands deep in my pockets. I did not want the caribou to be afraid of me. I wanted to be friends, to understand better these carefree, happy animals.

Soon they were licking the salt blocks all around me. One, a small bull, came up close to me, and I ventured to hold out a handful of the table salt I had brought with me. At my arm movement he reared up, and I thought for a moment that he meant to strike me down. But he just shook his head, backed off a few steps, and resumed licking the salty clay, eyeing me the while. I had won. The desire for salt had overcome the fear of human scent and even the sight of me.

Gingerly I stepped out from under my tree and approached the nearest caribou. To my surprise and joy he seemed undisturbed. Slowly I held out a handful of table salt. He leaned his beautiful antlered head down, sniffing from a foot away. Frozen, hardly breathing, I stood stock-still. He leaned his head over and licked the salt from my hand.

What a glorious, triumphant, happy sensation! To feel that cold and wet nose snuffing into my palm, an animal truly of the wilderness, unafraid, licking my hand! I had a terrific sense of accomplishment, of being at one with all of nature.

Gaining courage, I moved slowly into the herd. Shuffling along quietly on my snowshoes and avoiding any quick movement, I was able to *walk* with the caribou as they grazed out to the lake's edge, licking the salt blocks everywhere. To one after another I held out my hand filled with salt—and they would lick it clean. None seemed to fear me; I was accepted as one of them. As I moved out onto the lake ice, they followed.

And even after I left them, snowshoeing over my broken trail toward the cabin three miles away, one or two followed close behind me, looking for more salt. Indeed, God was in His heaven that Christmas Day.

I BEGAN NOW to make preparations for spring. I fashioned a sawpit where I could cut the twelve-foot logs I needed for my flume and sluice box. Then I felled the trees, hauled them into place, and started to whipsaw the boards. I had thought whipsawing a devilish job when Amos and I cut the lumber for the *Come What May.* Doing it alone was more than twice as hard. Luckily, however, I could take my time, for I had the rest of the winter with nothing else to do.

By the end of January I was beginning to feel lonesome, so I

318

decided to go shopping. I badly needed a bigger stove to heat the cabin, and it would be fun to get a few food luxuries, too.

I had learned from the Indians back in the summer that there was a trading post on the Pelly River at Pelly Banks, some seventy-five miles by rough trail northwest of my cabin. It was one of a dozen posts scattered on the side streams of the Yukon basin, belonging to the Taylor & Drury Company, an outfit that had its headquarters in Whitehorse. The trail led up the Finlayson River, the Indians had said, along the northeast side of Finlayson Lake, and then down a creek to the Pelly.

I started my trip with a light load on the toboggan. The dogs and I made thirty miles the first day and reached Finlayson Lake the day after. Late the third day, following a small creek down to the Pelly, we hit a trapper's well-broken toboggan trail. Shortly after the trail topped a rise and I saw a dozen cabins strung along the bank of a good-sized river. We were at Pelly Banks post, the most isolated of any in the upper Yukon country. As late as the 1940s, maps of that area still showed the creeks in dotted lines, indicating that their exact location and source were not known.

The trader in charge of the post was Van Gorder, a powerfully-built six-foot Virginian who had come to the North many years before and stayed because he liked the country and the freedom it afforded. He had an Indian wife and several children. He was also a very good host, and he invited me to dinner and put me up for the night.

I bought a big barrel-type heating stove, a case of raisins, a drum of dried milk, and a few other supplies. Prices were high, for all freight had to be brought from Seattle or Vancouver to Skagway, a distance of one thousand miles. From Skagway the trade goods moved via railroad to Whitehorse—about a hundred miles—and then five hundred miles via steamers to Fort Selkirk and Ross River post. Because of the rapids in Hoole Canyon, on the Pelly River above Ross River post, the last seventy-five miles were by boat, and that final leg included a portage around the canyon. It was no wonder that things were so expensive.

I loaded my supplies and mushed out at daylight the next

morning. We had come as far as the head of Finlayson Lake on the way home when I witnessed the most dramatic display I have ever seen of the hunting methods of wolves.

Near the lake the country flattened out into a swampy area, frozen smooth and solid now, and easy travel for the dogs. As we came to the shore a lone caribou broke from the timber ahead and ran full tilt out onto the ice. Seconds later a huge black wolf leaped down from the low bank in close pursuit. Behind him came a smaller red wolf, a female, and five younger ones, mostly gray. Their long muscular bodies flowed over the snow as if carried on the wind, and they were gaining on the caribou with every stride.

The black leader came even with the hind legs of the caribou and slashed at the left one without slackening pace. Then he swerved away to let the red bitch take his place. She slashed, just as he had done. The caribou stumbled and almost went down. He regained his feet, but his left hind leg dragged, useless; the wolves had cut or injured the hamstring.

Now the pups came racing up on the right side and slashed at their victim. This time the caribou sank down on his haunches, both hind legs disabled. The leader and the bitch were standing about twenty yards off, and they watched the pups close in.

I suppose my sympathies should have been with the inevitable loser in that pitiless attack. For the most part man is inclined to take the side of the underdog. But I didn't feel that way. The wolves were predators—but so was I. They were killing for the same reason I killed, because it meant food. They had as much right to take a caribou as I did. So, spellbound by the teamwork and perfect discipline of that savage pack, I watched.

Slowly the leader and his mate drifted closer and closer to the doomed caribou. Disabled as he was, he was still dangerous. He could no longer run, but he could split the skull of any member of the pack with a single blow of a forehoof.

The wolves now gathered in a semicircle around him, waiting—patient and deadly. Then as if at a signal three of the youngsters feinted toward the head of their victim. The caribou reared to strike, but in that same instant the leader flashed in and struck the

320

caribou behind a shoulder. The blow knocked the bull over on his side, and the pack was on him at once. One wolf slashed through the jugular, and the caribou was dead.

That night, in the stillness of the winter dark, I heard the wolves howling. The wilderness has no sound more beautiful, or more haunting, than the long-drawn-out notes of the wild and lonely wolf song. Beginning in a low key, poignant howls rose in perfect harmony through weird half tones and full-throated notes until they reached a crescendo of high-pitched wailing, then slid slowly down the scale to the lower notes again. It sounded like a song of ghosts from a lost region.

Back at the cabin with my new supplies, I settled once more into my solitary winter routine. I worked at the sawpit, where I cut enough boards for a cabin floor. Then I hauled the lumber I'd cut for the mine across the delta and up the frozen Finlayson River to the Half-Moon claim.

On one such trip I saw a family of otters at play where a low gravel bench sloped down into a gully a few feet back from the river. They had made a slide on the snowbank from the top of the bench down to the river, and as I watched they followed one another in turn, climbing the steep bank on their short legs. Then they just flopped on their bellies and glided down the steep, icy slope, swishing out onto the river ice like a bunch of kids at play on a slide into a swimming pool.

Papa otter was huge, four feet long, with a big flattened head, and whiskers sticking out each side like a seal's. He seemed rather clumsy when running, yet he was the most graceful and the fastest swimmer imaginable. Mama otter was about a foot shorter and maybe a little more plump, but she ran up the steep slope and slid down just as fast and happily as the others. The three youngsters were noticeably smaller, not over two feet long. The young ones tried to pass each other while climbing up the hill, which resulted in collisions and often in two of them sliding down together.

They would sometimes play on that slide for hours on end, then disappear into their den or swim under the ice and into the huge lake, where there was limitless food for them.

321

IN MARCH, when the lengthening days began to signal the end of winter, the Indians came back from their trapping grounds. They arrived one evening at sunset with their families loaded on the toboggans, the dog teams strung out across the lake, an age-old cavalcade of the North country.

Had the Indians found me with a trapline, I might have been in danger. But when they saw that I was holed up in my cabin, with a packed trail leading up the Finlayson toward my gold claim, they knew I had come to mine and they were all smiles.

That spring of 1926 took its own time arriving in the Yukon. First the snow on the lake melted and pools of water covered the ice, freezing at night, thawing by midday. Then the ice began its March booming as it cracked and lifted with the rising water beneath it, an unfailingly reliable harbinger of the coming breakup. The Indians left again for their annual spring beaver hunt. They would not return before early June.

The freezing nights prevented me from starting my gold operation, so I worked on a boat I had decided to build for summer fun and to aid in hunting and fishing. By the time it was completed, the gravel at the Half-Moon was thawed sufficiently for me to break it up with a shovel and I began working on my sluice boxes and flume.

Spring began to hurry along now. Wide cracks opened across the lake, and there were a hundred yards of open water along the beach in front of my cabin. I widened the three-mile trail from the cabin to the mine, for I intended to continue living at the cabin, hiking back and forth each morning and evening. It was comfortable at the cabin, and the mosquitoes would not be as bad on the lakeshore as in the brushy canyon.

It was exciting to see the water flowing freely through the long wooden chute and to throw in the first shovels of pay dirt. I shoveled and washed gravel for ten days before I shut water out of the sluice box and made my first cleanup, and in those ten days I washed $180 worth of gold!

Early in June, Caesar and Little Jimmy, Chief Smith and Oaltal, Meegan and old Dentiah, returned with their families from their spring beaver hunt. A few days later two of the men took off with

The wild rose of the North
A willow grouse

Barren-ground caribou
A grizzly bear
Bearberries in flower

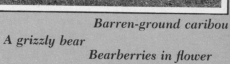

pack dogs and headed for Lower Post with the winter's catch of furs. While they were gone Caesar and his wife came to the cabin one evening. I shared my tobacco with them and as we smoked we reached an agreement for him and Little Jimmy to work for me at the mine.

Neither of the Indians had ever used a pick or shovel, but they soon got the hang of it and were able to keep the tailings clear at the lower end of the sluice box as fast as I shoveled gravel in at the head. Then suddenly high water interrupted us. With the melting snow the Finlayson began to roar down its canyon, and rocks half as big as bushel baskets came grinding along with the current. We loaded boulders on top of the flume intake to hold it in place, and went on with our work as soon as we could. Gold mining, I was learning, meant twelve to sixteen hours a day of hard labor.

The long days of summer came and crested. Wild fruit was ripening everywhere now and I feasted on currants and raspberries and then, in August, on blueberries. Grouse were plentiful and fat, and as often as I needed it I shot a moose. I'd planted a small garden with seeds I had brought in back in the fall. Now it began to pay off. Radishes, lettuce, and carrots grew in profusion, and turnips and other vegetables did reasonably well. I was living a king's life, working hard but enjoying it, fit and muscular as a man could get. The Indians fully accepted me now, and at least two, sometimes three, were working with me at the mine every day. Every ten days I cleaned up the box and added the take of gold to my pokes. I was averaging eight to ten ounces of gold a week, and I felt like a millionaire.

Fortunately the Indians showed no interest in nuggets or dust, but they took great delight in the twenty-dollar gold pieces with which I paid them. They understood and accepted gold coins but had absolutely no confidence in paper money—maybe because few of them could read and so could not tell one denomination from another.

The days began to shorten, and at the first hint of autumn I was suddenly lonely to see white faces again, to listen to dance music and eat fancy food. I realized I did not want to spend another

324

solitary winter at Frances Lake, at least not now. I needed a holiday.

I laid my plans carefully. I'd keep on working at the Half-Moon until mid-September, as Amos and I had done the year before. Then I would go to Vancouver. I wanted to see a city again and I could sell my gold at Vancouver's government assay office. That way I could keep my discovery concealed.

Fall came quickly that year, with heavy frosts at night. Ice began to rim the sluice boxes and the edges of the flume. It was mid-September, time to shut down. With the help of my crew I pulled the flume apart and stacked it and the boxes at the foot of a steep slope, safely out of reach of the river. The Indians and I had a last feast on the beach, then I shut the cabin door, put the dogs in the boat, and was off. At dark the next evening I was at the foot of Frances Lake. I pulled the boat up and turned it over, and at first light the following morning we took the trail that would end at Telegraph Creek.

It was a trip without incident—even the four hundred miles of trail seemed shorter than they had the previous November. When we arrived at Telegraph Creek, I spent an evening with my friend Harry Dodd, the gold commissioner. He was the only person to whom I had confided the story of Half-Moon. Then I made the trip downriver to Wrangell on the *Hazel B.*

I found it hard to believe the changes in me in almost three and a half years. I had wanted to hear English speech and dance music. But the voices sounded too loud and the jazz music in the cafés grated on my wilderness-attuned ears. There seemed to be nowhere I could go to get away from the noise. I also discovered that my sense of smell had become highly refined; I could scent a horse a block away, or chickens that were out of sight in a backyard. And now, after a diet of moose and caribou, I found beef flat and tasteless.

But there were some things about civilization that I still delighted in: fresh butter and oranges, tomatoes and cake, and the luxury of a hot bath in a tub. To inquisitive strangers who spotted me as a prospector and inquired what luck I had had, I showed only some

325

samples of the high-grade galena ore that lay waiting on the east arm of Frances Lake.

I loafed for two days in Wrangell, then left my dogs with a trapper friend and boarded the *Princess Louise* for a leisurely three-day cruise south through the Inside Passage to Vancouver.

5. Joyce

My first errand in Vancouver was at the government assay office, where in return for my gold I was given a check for $2280, in those days a small fortune for a man of twenty-six. That sum of money then had eight to ten times the purchasing power it would have today.

The next thing I did was to buy some new clothes. Then I moved into a quiet hotel, where I had a fine room overlooking the ocean and mountains. I had had friends in Vancouver before going north and I got in touch with them now. Invitations came thick and fast, to parties and dances and beach picnics. My holiday was turning out exactly as I had wanted it to.

Among my friends was Sergeant Jim Cunningham of the British Columbia provincial police. One Friday I invited him and another officer to dinner at my hotel. But I paid little attention to them that evening, for seated at a corner table was a guest I had not seen before.

She was a girl, apparently in her late teens, with a young and slender body and dark auburn hair that fell in waves to her waist. I thought her the prettiest girl I had ever laid eyes on. I remarked about her to my two companions, but drew only the kidding retort that I had been in the woods so long I was vulnerable. That did nothing to change my mind.

After dinner I saw her again in the hotel lobby. She was sitting beside a dignified old lady whom I had met earlier. When I walked up, the lady had no choice but to introduce me. I found myself looking into a pair of clear hazel eyes that looked levelly back at me, and suddenly I was aware that my heart was pounding.

326

Her name was Joyce Curtis, and she was seventeen. Her father was a doctor back in Rochester, New York, and she was in Vancouver by herself, ready to begin training as a nurse.

I think we both knew in the first instant our eyes met that we were meant for each other. She was fascinated by my stories of the North country I loved, of my months of solitude at Frances Lake, and of my Indian neighbors. We sat and talked late into the night. We met again for breakfast the next morning and spent most of that Saturday walking in Stanley Park, a beautiful place of huge fir trees and moss-covered trails, with glimpses of the ocean on three sides. I had always been one to make quick decisions, and the moment we found ourselves in a place of privacy under a towering fir, I held out my arms to Joyce.

She came to me, and our lips met in a long and ardent kiss. When we broke apart I said, "When will you marry me, Joyce?"

"Will Monday be soon enough?" she answered half teasingly.

Our engagement lasted through the rest of Saturday and Sunday. I knew a minister in Vancouver, and I went to him on Monday morning and told him what I wanted. At first he said it would be impossible. But I refused to take no for an answer, and in the end he yielded. He got his church heated up, I collected half a dozen friends, and Joyce's sister and brother-in-law hurried north from Seattle. At eight o'clock that Monday evening the lovely seventeen-year-old I had met three days earlier was my wife. I told myself I was the luckiest man alive.

We rented a house in West Vancouver that winter of 1926–1927 and started to make plans to go back to the Half-Moon. I had warned Joyce of the cold and the hardships, the primitive way of life. But she had fallen in love with the North without even seeing it, and she was as eager to be away as I was.

I went to wholesale houses in Vancouver and arranged to send two tons of supplies and household goods north in charge of my friend Van Gorder at the Pelly Banks post. From there we would take the lighter items to Frances Lake over the Finlayson River trail by pack dog, and when the first snow came in the fall we'd move the heavy stuff by toboggan.

We headed north in early March. The cruise up the Inside Passage was pure delight, but before we reached Wrangell something more than a minor hitch developed. Joyce announced that she thought she was pregnant.

We were warmly welcomed in Wrangell. But to our dismay we learned that the only doctor in town had moved south. The nearest physician now was in Juneau, another half day north by steamer.

The doctor there quickly confirmed Joyce's suspicions, and we gave up all thought of going to Frances Lake that spring. We'd stay on here, where Joyce could have the best of care. I took a job at an ore-milling operation in Juneau, and apart from our natural concerns as parents-to-be, the summer slipped by pleasantly enough.

Our son Sydney was born in the early fall of 1927, not quite a year after our marriage. He was a healthy, happy baby, and Joyce accepted her new role as a mother as easily as she had accepted wifehood.

Although we were proud and elated at becoming parents, we didn't really enjoy that winter in Juneau, for the weather was miserable much of the time. I wrote to the trapper in Wrangell to tell him I would need my dogs in Juneau by the first of March. We were eager to get away.

The dogs arrived on time, by steamer. We had a farewell party with our Juneau friends and headed north to Whitehorse. There we spent a week outfitting our new toboggan and driving the dogs out on test runs a few miles from town, checking the warmth and comfort of our down-filled arctic sleeping bags and the cold-weather clothing we had bought in Vancouver in anticipation of our journey into the northern wilderness.

Joyce and I each had long one-piece underwear of pure wool. In the temperatures we faced, wool next to the skin was essential. It would absorb perspiration and as we cooled off it would dry quickly. Any non-absorbent material would be dangerous, meaning a severe chill or actual freezing. Over our underwear we wore wool shirts and heavy wool sweaters. Woolen breeches were tucked snugly into the tops of three layers of heavy wool socks. For added warmth we

328

folded an oblong piece of thick wool around each foot and slid an Indian-made moccasin on over it. Our feet were well insulated from the cold, yet we could wiggle our toes freely. That was important. It is safer to run barefoot on dry snow at thirty below than to wear a tight shoe.

We had been fortunate in finding two excellent parkas at a surplus store. Made of light but windproof drill, they hung loosely to below the knees. They had big slash pockets, and the cuffs and hoods were trimmed with wolverine fur, the one material that stays free of ice in the bitterest cold. The moisture of human breath freezes quickly on any other fur, but the coat of the big weasel stays dry and protects the face from freezing.

Under the parka hoods we wore wool toques, and on our hands mooseskin mittens with undermittens of blanket-weight wool. The mittens were hung around our necks by a bright-coloured cord. At forty below it would not do to be bare-handed while we fumbled for a dropped mitten.

The baby had a thin wool shirt and socks, and a knitted bunny suit which covered him completely, except for his face. He wore tiny Indian moccasins, and was wrapped in a wool blanket.

Joyce and I studied maps and reports of the route we would be taking, and talked with local trappers and prospectors. Klondike Airways did not yet have actual air service, but it did run a tractor train from Whitehorse to Dawson City, about four hundred and fifty miles. That meant a wide, well-broken trail following the Nordenskiold River to where that stream joins the Yukon at Carmacks. From there we would go down the Yukon to Fort Selkirk, where the Pelly comes in, follow that river to Pelly Banks and then on to the Finlayson and so to Frances Lake. In all we had some seven hundred miles of dogsled travel ahead of us, the latter half of it through almost unpeopled country.

We would not need to carry a heavy load of food. I had checked with Taylor & Drury and found that our whole shipment—supplies for a year—was waiting for us now at Pelly Banks, seventy-five miles from the home cabin. We'd take only the minimum requirements for the trip itself—flour, rolled oats, rice, beans, dry milk, tea, sugar, butter and syrup, baking powder, salt and pepper, and of course dry formula for the baby. To that list of essentials we added a slab of bacon, dry soup mix, dried apples and peaches, raisins, and dehydrated vegetables—a new experiment then. For dog feed I bought a sack of smoked and dried salmon.

At last we were ready for the long trail.

WE DROVE out of Whitehorse on the tractor road that led north toward Dawson City at daybreak on a sparkling clear March morning when the temperature stood at twenty-five below.

The going was easy, and I was able to jog along behind the dogs without snowshoes on the hard-packed trail, hanging on to the handles of the sled. I had folded one of our sleeping bags to make a pad on top of the load, and Joyce rode there, with her legs protected in the second bag and Syd held on her lap. One thing we learned quickly. Extreme cold affects the kidneys of a baby more than it does those of a grown-up. Our little son wet himself about twice as frequently as normal.

Syd's meals on the trail posed no problems. In the tent at night Joyce simply added water to cans of dry baby formula and filled thermos bottles with the mixture. Changing him was another matter. We had to keep him as dry as possible for safety's sake as well as for his comfort, since at twenty-five to forty-five below zero the cold can be like a branding iron on the wet skin of an infant. Each change meant stopping and building up a big open fire. This slowed our travel, but enabled Joyce to take care of Syd's needs in complete safety.

Late on the afternoon of the fourth day we came to a tree that had fallen across the trail. I shouted to the dogs to gee into the timber around it. The leader, Rogue, and Rascal and Runt, the two dogs behind him, made the detour without mishap. But as the team pulled back onto the trail the fourth dog, Scotch, caught his harness on a snag. When he lunged ahead to free himself the ring that held his trace snapped in half. It was a key piece of the harness and had to be securely replaced.

I opened my emergency box of harness parts, found a spare ring

330

and a length of rawhide, and started to make the repair. It was getting on toward dusk, and in my anxiety to get farther along the trail and find a good camping spot, I did something I knew better than to do. I had to take off my mittens to tie the rawhide. That metal ring had thirty-five below zero on it, and without thinking I grabbed it with my warm fingers and thumb. The skin and flesh stuck as if welded to the metal.

I called to Joyce and she got the matches out of our grub box. Then she struck one match after another, holding the tiny flames against the ring on the side away from my fingers. Slowly the metal warmed enough to release my hand. But my first and second fingers were covered with the white blisters of frostbite, and the whole face of my thumb peeled off on the ring.

The pain of thawing hard-frozen flesh has to be experienced to be believed, and I cussed myself roundly. I had been guilty of carelessness, and as always in the North I had paid the penalty.

I was still in great pain two days later, when we came to the pretty little settlement of Carmacks, in a triangle of land where the Nordenskiold empties into the Yukon. We could see a roadhouse at the north end of town, but we headed instead for the Taylor & Drury trading post. Dan Snure, the trader there, insisted we stay in his bungalow, which gave us a welcome opportunity to wash our clothes and clean up.

While we were there, Dan told us of a shortcut to the Pelly River. Instead of going on to Fort Selkirk, as we had planned, we could go up the Yukon from Carmacks to the Little Salmon, follow that stream across some high country, and come down to the upper Pelly at Rose Creek. It would cut off two sides of a big triangle and save many miles of travel.

The next day we loaded up and mushed out onto the ice of the Yukon, turning upriver. The tractor trail was behind us now, but a good dog trail had been broken on the river and we had no trouble following it.

The winter silence was complete here, broken only by the crunch and creak of my snowshoes and of the hickory boards of the toboggan sliding over the dry snow. This was winter travel at its best, through country of great beauty, and Joyce and I found ourselves singing to the dogs as we went.

Having a family along meant a great deal more work for me on the trail. Traveling by myself, I had rarely bothered to pitch a tent unless the weather was bad, sleeping instead in my bag on top of the toboggan, or at most under a fly in front of my campfire. Now I had to put up the little silk tent each night, floor it with spruce boughs, install the small camp stove, and cut firewood. Joyce would keep herself and the boy snug by the open fire until the tent was ready and she could start cooking supper. To make seven or eight hours of travel a day meant getting up at four or five o'clock in the morning and breaking camp in the dark. We would mush out by daylight, and at the end of each day I was about as exhausted as a man can be. But having my wife and son with me made it more than worthwhile.

Our first stopover after Carmacks was the trading post at Little Salmon. From there we went on to Magundy Lake in the higher country at the headwaters of the Little Salmon. We found the lake crisscrossed with fresh caribou tracks, so we decided to make camp for a day or two while I hunted some meat.

As soon as the tent was up and warm I took off, following the caribou. In a mile I came upon them browsing on sparse brush between the hummocks of this windswept plateau. Picking out a young bull, I dropped him with one shot, and we feasted that night on fresh liver and kidneys.

When we left Magundy Lake we followed a small west-flowing creek to its head. Beyond that the plateau was typical high-divide country, low hummocks and frozen swamps, so that our trail twisted and turned as it snaked its way through the stunted, scrawny spruce trees. We lost track of any worn trail and just kept our direction easterly, hoping to strike Rose Creek, which would take us off this barren plateau and down to the Pelly River.

The trail got rougher as a strong wind started blowing and driving a heavy snow in our faces. Joyce slid deeper into the sleeping bag. I looked desperately about for a place to make camp, but saw no shelter from the increasing storm and no trees fit for tent poles or firewood.

332

We were in danger! We had to get into the shelter of heavy timber or we could freeze to death. I shouted at the dogs, urging them for more speed, but they were tired and their eyes were rimmed with ice. Taking the jerk line, I snowshoed alongside them, pulling desperately.

In ordinary travel the jerk line is allowed to trail behind, and when the musher is not steering with the handles of the sled he holds it in his mittens so he can jerk it to right or left and avoid trees or other obstacles in the trail. Now I was using it to help pull the load and to encourage the dogs to stay with it. I was proving the truth of an old saying among veteran mushers that when driving dogs with a heavy load the man is the hardest working member of the team.

The wind groaned in our ears as it drifted the snow into every crack and crevice on the toboggan. Darkness fell suddenly, shutting off the sight of the horizontally driven snow, but we could feel the sting of the icy flakes as they drove against us. Somewhere ahead there must be timber, shelter, safety.

I had spent three winters alone in the wilderness, but I'd never been out on a night worse than this. Snow seethed along the sides and over the top of the toboggan, menacing my loved ones. Even the dogs pulled their heads down sideways to avoid the worst of the stinging snow. The icy wind sucked the breath out of my lungs as I gasped from the exertion of lugging on the jerk line.

Suddenly out of the dark I became aware of tall shadows—and of the wind whistling and howling high overhead in the tops of trees. In this sheltered spot there was no wind, no snow. The moment I shouted "Whoa" to the dogs, they just dropped on their bellies, exhausted.

I got a huge blaze going as quickly as I could, then pitched the tent. Joyce fed Syd while I tied the dogs and gave them a generous feeding. Then, too worn out to want supper for ourselves, we slid into our bedrolls and were instantly asleep.

For two days we rested in that camp. On the third morning we took the trail once more and soon struck the steep valley of Rose Creek, where we had shelter again in heavy timber.

Near the mouth of the creek we met a trapper mushing a fine string of six dogs. He was the first human we had seen since leaving the post at Little Salmon, and we pulled off the trail to make tea and chat. To our astonishment, he told us that he had expected to meet us. At Ross River post on the Pelly, many miles ahead, he had heard that we were on the trail. Somehow the word had traveled ahead of us, probably from an Indian trapper who had heard about us at Carmacks. The efficiency with which messages traveled via that moccasin telegraph never ceased to amaze me.

Two days later we pulled into the tiny settlement at Ross River post, where a dozen cabins occupied a high terrace on the bank of the Pelly at its junction with the Ross. Roy Tuttle, the Taylor & Drury trader at Ross River, greeted us with the usual warm welcome. Other men found places to keep the dogs, and a cabin was made available to us.

We stayed there for two days while Joyce did laundry and all three of us rested up. The morning we left, the weather turned mild, making the trail heavy and the going hard. We knew there was one more bad spot ahead, the dreaded Hoole Canyon, and we camped early at the mouth of a creek below it. The Pelly was so narrow here and the current so fast that it formed whirlpools a hundred feet across in the middle of the river.

In summer no boat could possibly get through, and even in the winter those tumbling caldrons never froze. However, there was a shelf of ice close to the canyon walls on each side, and we decided to travel there.

The shelf was rough, and in places it sloped dangerously down toward the water. To slide into one of those whirlpools would mean certain death. But I took no chances, and the hazardous canyon was soon behind us.

The third afternoon after leaving Ross River post we arrived at Pelly Banks, where Van Gorder was expecting us. We moved into the cabin where I had stayed on my visit two years earlier, and arranged to hire four Indians with good dog teams to help us freight our outfit to Frances Lake. The first two pulled out on Easter morning. We followed with the others the following day. We found the first two waiting for us at Finlayson Lake, with a freshly killed moose.

Two items in our loads slowed us down. The first was a new kitchen stove that kept getting caught on trees because it was wider than the toboggan. The other was six ready-made window frames, complete with glass panes, protected between sheets of veneer. I had plans for a far better cabin than the one I had built originally.

On the third day, in a blizzard so thick we could not see Frances Lake, our five teams pulled up to the snug little cabin I had left a year and a half before. It was dry and in order, my stack of firewood waiting where I had left it. Even the dogs seemed happy to be tied again in their old kennels. After six hundred and fifty miles of hard winter travel Joyce and the baby and I were home.

I arranged with the four Indians to make a second trip from the post at Pelly Banks and bring the rest of our outfit to us. They took off, and when Joyce and I awoke the next morning the storm had ended. The sun climbed above the sawtooth mountains to the southeast, and the view across the lake, white and still under its blanket of snow, was one to take the breath away.

Joyce threw her arms around my neck and drew me close. "I love this place," she whispered.

THE LOCAL INDIANS, as I had expected, were away on their winter trapping grounds. We would have Frances Lake to ourselves until they came back, shortly before the spring breakup.

My first job was to get the fishnet working. Then, as soon as the Indian dog teams arrived with the rest of our outfit, I felt free to leave Joyce and the baby and go hunting.

I left early one morning, with the dogs, and headed for the sheep lick twelve miles above the lake. The sheep were still there and I killed three fat rams in a few minutes. I skinned them carefully, knowing the skins would be needed for mattresses, and dressed them out. Then I loaded the meat on the toboggan and started home.

The late-winter dusk was deepening when I drove up to the cabin, and I experienced the deep satisfaction of returning from a hunt to find an eager and excited wife waiting for me. Everything was double fun now.

It would be another month before I could begin work at the mine, so I put in my time improving the cabin. I made a crib for Syd and lined it with one of the sheepskins I had stretched and dried. The other two I stretched over a bed frame made of poles, lashing them in place with rawhide. The skins dried tight and flat, and made a fine, soft, full-sized mattress for Joyce and me. Then I fashioned some attractive odds and ends of furniture from peeled alder and willow trunks. I also built a snug outhouse, which I finished with a small window that could be removed and replaced with mosquito netting in the summer.

When the sap started to run I went back to the spruce stand on the Finlayson delta and began felling and peeling trees. The logs would season and dry through the summer, be light enough to handle by fall, and I would then begin work on a bigger and better cabin.

I taught Joyce to fire the guns, first the .22, then the .30-06. It was essential that she know how to feed herself and Syd in case some mishap befell me. And I knew that could happen, despite the care I took in everything I did. She was an apt pupil and learned readily.

One afternoon four Indian families drove their dog teams up to our cabin on the way to their campground. My friends from two summers before—Caesar, Little Jimmy, Oaltal, and Meegan— had seen smoke rising from our cabin and knew I was back. They had halted their teams, fastened plumes on the dog harnesses, and put on their brightest bandannas. They made a fine sight as they drove up.

Joyce came running out to watch, with Syd in her arms, and mother and son created an instant sensation. None of the Indian women and children, and few of the men, had ever seen a white woman or a white child before. Syd, who by now had a shock of curly blond hair, and Joyce were almost too much for them to believe. They crowded around, laughing and jabbering with excitement.

The Indian families camped below the cabin for three days, visiting us much of the time. I traded for some of their furs: mink, marten, lynx, even a few wolf, fisher, and otter pelts. The men agreed to work for me again at the gold digging when they came back from their spring beaver hunt. Then, with no announcement and no fanfare, the Indians were gone, fading swiftly up the rivers that flowed into Frances Lake, each family with its camp gear and the children loaded into a carryall on the toboggan.

My last chore before spring breakup was to build a smokehouse. It was eight feet by ten, with four corner posts eight feet high, but the walls extended only halfway up the posts; the upper half and the roof I covered with netting. Inside I built a series of racks. That smokehouse would take care of the problem of winter dog food and also store an emergency supply of smoked fish and meat for us.

Breakup came first in the Finlayson itself. Huge chunks of ice came thundering down through the canyon, piling up on the beach around the mouth of the river and smashing their way out into the still-frozen lake for half a mile, grinding and groaning and rumbling. Now I could go back to gold washing.

Until the Indians returned I'd have to work alone, but I was used to that. Right after breakfast each morning I walked the three miles from the cabin to the gold diggings, taking one or two of the dogs with me. The others I left at the cabin as company for Joyce and protection against bears. I shoveled gravel into the sluice boxes for about eight hours, and left Half-Moon in late afternoon, in time to be back at the cabin before dark.

Every evening after supper I tended the fishnet and showed Joyce how to cut and dry the fish. Some evenings we fished for trout from the bank at the mouth of the river with fly rods. We caught so many whitefish with our net that I finally pulled it out of the water. We were taking too many for our current use, and it was too early in the year to store dog food for next winter. Also, the fish were thin now, after a winter spent half dormant. The fat, full-fed ones of fall would be much better for storage.

Spring came fast as June approached, the days becoming longer and longer, the nights little more than brief twilights. The snow had melted on the lake and open water extended for half a mile from the beach now. Despite its chill, several times Joyce and I stripped our clothes off and went swimming, reveling in the freedom from convention in our far-off wilderness. When the ground thawed sufficiently we planted a vegetable garden in front of the cabin. Then the Indians came back and settled into their camps for the summer.

A strong wind smashed the last ice off the lake on June 10. The Finlayson was at flood stage, and I had moved my sluice boxes and flume back out of reach of the high water. But I had not moved them far enough. A torrent pouring over huge boulders at the head of Half-Moon carried three lengths of flume downstream overnight and broke them up.

I had no lumber to replace them, and I could not afford to delay my gold washing while I whipsawed more boards. It was a minor disaster, but I soon hit on a remedy. I'd tear up the boards I needed from the floor of the cabin. They could be replaced later, in a few evenings of whipsawing. Joyce once more proved herself completely the frontier wife. She never so much as hinted at any objection when I ripped up half the cabin floor.

The floorboards were twelve feet long, and although they were dry they still weighed about twenty pounds apiece. The three-mile trail to the mine ran mostly uphill, between trees part of the way. Each of us (Caesar and Little Jimmy and Oaltal were helping me now) carried three boards—a sixty-pound load—first on one shoulder, then on the other, and finally on top of our heads. We got the job done, but not without some very fluent cussing in both English and the local Tahltan dialect.

In the hot sun of the subarctic summer our garden sprouted almost overnight. In three weeks we had lettuce full-headed from seed. Radishes, chard, cabbage, and carrots began to find their way onto the table. And then the wild fruit started to ripen. There were gooseberries, raspberries, currants, and, toward the end of summer, blueberries, which Joyce converted into mouthwatering fruit pies.

The summer fled swiftly. I spent the long sunlit days working at

338

A stretch of the Yukon river

A group of caribou with their young

*The blue jay is
a common North
American bird*

the mine. Joyce tended the cabin and helped Syd take his first uncertain steps. Mosquitoes were a problem, but bacon fat for Joyce and olive oil for Syd served well as repellents. I had gained a high degree of immunity, simply by letting the mosquitoes bite me at will in the early spring, probably the same procedure that rendered the Indians almost entirely oblivious to the bites.

One evening I rigged a packstack so I could carry Syd, and sometimes I took him and Joyce up to the mine with me to spend the day. Our weeks were an unending honeymoon, blessed by perfect health and extraordinary happiness. Our marriage, we realized, was as good as a human relationship can possibly be.

But one thing bothered our Indian friends. They could not understand my keeping a wife who did not know how to tan mooseskins and convert them into clothing, who was not even able to make moccasins, and who did not carry a forty-pound pack and go along with me when I went hunting. The Indian men had urged me repeatedly to take another wife, an Indian girl who could do these things for me. Part of the time they kidded me about it, for we had come to be on close and friendly terms. I laughed the suggestion aside, but they were entirely serious about it, and as summer ended, the matter finally came to a head.

Two of the women, Caesar's wife Maddie and Little Jimmy's wife, came to the cabin one evening with Caesar's fifteen-year-old daughter, Adzina. Joyce made them a pot of tea and they sat for a long time, squatting on the floor, sipping their tea, and saying nothing. But plainly they had something of importance to communicate. Both the women spoke a little broken English, and I had learned some words of Tahltan and passed them along to Joyce. So the language barrier between Joyce and the women was not insurmountable. At last Maddie broke the silence.

"Adzina stay," she said. "Adzina make good wife for fine white man. Adzina will live here." The word stay, with the inflection Maddie had given it, meant that the girl would come to us because she wanted to and not because of an order.

We had no wish to offend our Indian neighbors, and after all, what they proposed was entirely in accordance with their moral

340

code. Eventually we decided on a way out. Through the men we thanked the band and explained that our customs did not permit a man to have two wives, adding that with so many fine friends here at the lake, I could trade for skin clothing and moccasins and snowshoes, and so did not need a second wife. It was all done politely and gravely, and in the end everybody appeared satisfied. But I kidded Joyce all through the winter about my having passed up the only opportunity I would ever have to be a bigamist.

IT WAS IN THE SPRING of 1928, a short time after Joyce and I had arrived at Frances Lake, that we first saw the three grizzlies. They made an attractive trio as they climbed a grassy slope directly across from our cabin. There was a big silvertip whose thick, lustrous fur rippled like molten silver when she walked. Following her up the slope came another large bear and then a cub.

There were anthills on the slope, and the winter snows had flattened some of them to four or five feet across. While we watched, the big silvertip lay down with her head in the middle of what was surely a crawling mass of ants. Through binoculars we saw her long red tongue work in and out, presumably licking up ant eggs. But she must have gotten a lot of live ants along with the eggs, for suddenly she stood up, shook her head, and charged off down the slope into the icy water of the lake. Again and again she plunged her head under the water, raised it up, and shook it, like a dog shaking itself to get dry. It was a thoroughly amusing performance.

We named all the animals we saw close to the cabin; inevitably the big bear was called Silver. Joyce named the smaller one Emma, because she reminded us of a rotund Indian woman we knew.

We saw the three bears a few more times during the next weeks, and then in June another group showed up. It consisted of a huge boar, much bigger than Silver, a large enough sow, a youngster probably three years old, and a small cub, not yet six months old. To the huge male we gave the name Glahzer, the local Indian word for grizzly, and Joyce tacked the whimsical name of Petunia onto the female.

We first saw this foursome walking along the beach toward the cabin, silhouetted against the sunlit water of the lake. They were a beautiful sight, but we did not want them for visitors. I went into the cabin to get my .30-06 just as the dogs spotted them and set up a terrific commotion, barking and lunging on their chains. The bears stopped a moment, then took off into the timber.

I had had my first meeting with a grizzly back in the fall of 1923, while I was duck hunting with Cap Conover, an old-time trapper. As we were on our way home, our packsacks bulging with our kill, a queer feeling of uneasiness suddenly came over me. Some subtle sense of danger made a cold shiver creep up my spine. It was like the shock a man feels when he's out alone and hears the drawn-out howl of a timber wolf. My shotgun was empty; the last two shells I had borrowed from Cap were gone.

I glanced at Cap and saw his jaw muscles twitch a little as he held his 12-gauge loosely in front of him. I looked past him to the edge of the timber and there, facing us, was a massive grizzly sow, with two cubs beside her.

Cap and I made tracks for the timber farthest from her, but before we had taken ten steps she ripped the evening stillness apart with a bawling roar. With a gasp I turned and saw the huge sow start toward us on the run, her mane bristling over the huge hump above her shoulders, her enormous head hung low and swinging from side to side. She looked as big as a mountain.

We were backed almost to the edge of a precipice. There was nowhere to run, no tree to climb, and it was impossible to climb down the sheer wall behind us. I looked at Cap. My chance of life lay in his hands.

His face was set. His firm jaw stuck out a little as he watched the oncoming half-ton of fury.

With a bellow the sow started the final charge. Cap did not move. He just stood there, his gun held lightly in front of him, both barrels loaded and cocked.

Those moments seemed like a thousand years. I could see the mean beady eyes, the huge slavering jaws. On she came—one hundred feet, fifty, thirty. Would Cap never fire? Slowly he raised his gun. Deliberately he took aim and waited. The bear was almost on top of us when, with a deafening roar, the shot from both barrels smacked into that enormous shaggy head.

Cap and I both jumped aside. The impetus the huge beast had gained in her mad charge carried her past us, and in a flash she was over the precipice. I heard a bellow, followed by the slide of rocks as she struck the broken basalt two hundred feet below.

A hoot owl sounded off in the distance as we threaded our way homeward. Praise beyond words for Cap's nerve choked in my throat.

REMEMBERING that experience, I couldn't shake off a certain uneasiness at the idea of having several grizzlies around the cabin, but I thought we could get along with them if we observed their rules. It is rare for a grizzly or any other animal to make an unprovoked attack on a human being. The attack may *appear* unprovoked, but in the mind of the bear there is a reason for it. The person may be too close to her cubs, as Cap and I had been.

But there was a time, at the end of summer, when Petunia and Glahzer gave us a few bad moments. One morning just before daylight we were awakened by the barking of the dogs. I suspected that a moose might be traveling toward timberline for mating, and I stumbled out into the predawn darkness with the .30-06. As my eyes got used to the dim light I saw the two grizzlies a hundred yards up the lake. They were out in water about two feet deep, clawing our fishnet ashore and feasting on the catch.

Joyce came to the door and I told her to stand by with the shotgun. This was a dangerous situation. There is nothing a grizzly is more reluctant to do than give up food, and if this pair decided to make trouble, they could be at the cabin in two streaks. But I couldn't stand by and let them destroy the net. With spare shells in my hand, ready for instant reloading, I fired two shots close over their heads. They dropped the net and stood erect on their hind legs to stare in our direction. They made a magnificent sight, standing there side by side like two prehistoric monsters. Joyce did the right thing; she lit our camp lantern, ran to the door, and hung it on a peg behind me. It threw enough light on the bears that I could have killed both of them, but that was the last thing I wanted to do.

I sent a third shot whistling over their heads, and that and the light proved too much for them; they dropped down on all fours and ran into the timber of the delta.

Not all our encounters with grizzlies were scary. Joyce and I were hunting grouse one day, following a trail that ran down the lake close to the beach. A couple of miles from the cabin we stopped to look through our binoculars at a bay. A movement caught my eye, and after watching it a moment I handed the glasses to Joyce. Petunia was lying flat on her back, and the little cub was nursing greedily, sprawling its fat little body all over its mother's belly. The older youngster, too big for such privileges, kept jumping on his mother and biting at her. She pushed him away with one foreleg and cradled the cub with the other. This charming maternal performance made it hard to believe that such an animal could suddenly become ferocious and deadly.

6. Winter of Solitude

Frosts came about mid-August, and by the middle of September ice was forming and we had to close down the mine. I paid the Indians off with gold pieces and trade goods, and my crew finished the year well satisfied.

The time had come to fill the larder in preparation for the long winter. Our garden had produced a fabulous crop, and we were ready now to store the potatoes, carrots, turnips, and onions. I dug a cellar under the floor of the cabin and fashioned a trapdoor over it of floorboards. Then we cleaned the vegetables, put them in sacks that had held some of our freight from Pelly Banks, and filled the cellar. Our cabbages we left in the ground to freeze. We would cook them by plopping them into boiling water unthawed, for cabbage that has been frozen and then thawed turns mushy on cooking.

By that time we had chosen the location for our new cabin. The logs were waiting, peeled and dry. As soon as the first snow fell we'd start hauling them from the delta to the cabin site. We were looking

344

forward to that new home as eagerly as any city couple planning to move to more comfortable quarters.

Now that fall was approaching, we had the net back in the lake, and some evenings we caught as many as fifty fish at one haul— mostly whitefish, with a scattering of lake trout. We pulled the net onto the beach, killed the fish, cleaned and split them, then hung them over the racks in the smokehouse to smoke and dry for three days. Then we put them in gunnysacks and stored them on the high cache. By the middle of September our catch totaled about two thousand. We pulled the net and began to lay plans for a fall hunt.

Syd's first and my twenty-eighth birthday were only two days apart, and a hunt seemed the ideal way to honor the occasions. We loaded the boat with a camping outfit and plenty of fresh food, and the morning Syd was a year old we hoisted the sail and started down the lake with a fair wind pushing us along. The weather was beautiful and the scenery breathtaking. The high mountains hemming the lake were capped with their first snow now, and lower down, along the shore, poplar and cottonwood and willow were decked in glorious fall colors.

In midafternoon we landed and made camp where the east arm enters the west arm. We had turned the dogs loose when we left our home place, taking only Rogue with us in the boat and leaving the others to run along the beach, keeping abreast of us. That night we cooked our supper over an open fire, and then sat up late watching the stars come out, listening to the soft lapping of waves on the beach. There could be no happier way to celebrate birthdays.

Two days later we made camp at the mouth of the creek where the silver-lead claims were. The dogs, who were still running along the beaches during the day, keeping up with us, came panting in almost at once. This part of the creek was an excellent campsite, sheltered by spruce timber, and we decided to stay there while I hunted in the mountains. With the dogs tied in camp, Joyce would be safe enough in my absence. She would have the shotgun and the .22, and it was agreed that if I heard a shot fired I would hurry back. In turn, if something happened to me I'd fire three signal shots. Joyce would then let two dogs loose and start for me with Rogue on a chain. The remaining three dogs would stay tied to protect Syd.

It was a fine morning for a hunt. The air was clean and pine-scented. Late-fall flowers were still abundant and berry bushes hung heavy with fruit, but a tang in the wind spoke of snow to come. Above timber, at four thousand feet, I sat down and with my binoculars scanned the swampy flats and patches of spruce I had climbed through.

Presently a movement caught my eye. A mile away, his head and antlers showing above the willows at the edge of a stand of timber, stood a bull moose.

I got up on him by making a big circle all the way back to the shore of the lake. Then I shed my packsack and edged ahead toward the open glade where I had seen him. I must have been within a hundred yards of him when I stopped dead in my tracks. Standing beside a tree not fifty yards ahead was another moose, a huge cow. She was facing in the direction of the bull and had neither heard nor winded me, although I could smell her strongly.

I debated what to do. If I tried to get around her, she would be almost sure to spook and scare the bull off, and I'd lose both. In the end I killed her with a shot through the heart. As I expected, the bull ran crashing away through the brush. I gutted, skinned, and quartered the cow, covered the meat with the hide to keep flies off, and returned to camp.

We started for the moose right after breakfast the next morning. Rogue was with us and the other dogs followed, chained together so they would tangle quickly around a tree if they stampeded at the scent of game. Joyce carried the shotgun, and I had Syd in the packsack. I also carried the .30-06, in case a grizzly had taken possession of my kill. But we found the carcass just as I had left it, and the dogs packed the meat down the mountain to our camp. The nights were cold enough now that we did not need to worry about its spoiling. It would freeze hard in three weeks, and would keep until May if stored in shade.

I cut off all the fat for rendering. It would supply us with cooking fat and "butter" for the winter, and once the meat had frozen I would give it a light coating of the fat to keep it from drying out

346

when the temperature fell to thirty and forty below. Meat kept that way is as tasty as when freshly killed.

Light snow covered the brush and the tent that night. I still hoped to take a young mountain goat, and we needed more ducks and geese if we could get them, as well as at least one more moose to assure us an adequate supply of meat for the winter.

I hiked away from camp the next morning. The moose were near the peak of their mating season now, and their tracks were everywhere. I followed some that looked like those of a young bull, to where he had bedded at the edge of a meadow. Then I took the fresh tracks that led away from the bed.

I was approaching a willow swamp when I heard a sudden loud crashing in the brush ahead. I stopped dead still to listen, and the crashing noise came again, louder and more prolonged. Creeping closer, I reached a half-open place and suddenly, thirty yards off through the trees, I saw the young bull I had been tracking. Facing him was an older one, heavier and with a splendid spread of antlers. Both were pawing the ground and grunting. The older bull was bleeding from a wound in the right shoulder. A hundred yards behind them, a cow watched unconcernedly.

The young bull took a few steps, lowered his head, and made a rush for his rival. The older animal reared, came down, and charged. They met with a loud crash of horns and for a minute wrestled head to head. Then they pulled apart, and with vicious swings of his antlers each tried to rip the other in the side or shoulder. The younger one reared to strike with his front hoofs, but before he could land the blow, a tine of the big bull's rack drove deep into his neck and a stream of blood gushed out. The fight was over.

They stood for a moment only a pace apart. Then the youngster turned and staggered slowly downhill in my direction. In spite of a limp, the conqueror strode arrogantly toward the waiting cow with antlers held high. As he joined her a second cow stepped out of the brush and sidled up to him, and the three of them went out of sight into the timber.

The young bull was in bad shape, blood spurting from his neck,

347

and I spared him further suffering with a shot through the heart.

Two days later we awoke to find six inches of snow on the ground, and since we had just about enough meat, I decided to give up my goat hunt. We stayed in camp another day and I netted five fat mallards and five geese.

It took us two days to get home, but they were clear bright days with the October sun glinting on the water and on the snow-blanketed mountains, and we gloried in the peacefulness and beauty.

It was indeed a happy homecoming. Winter was close now, but our larder was full and we were ready for it. The Indians had scattered to their traplines, and Joyce and Syd and I could expect to be by ourselves for the next five months—three contented people in the wilderness with everything they needed or wanted.

THE FIRST BLIZZARD came upon us in early November. It heaped huge drifts around the cabin and along the beach, but we stayed snug and warm in our home. Then abruptly the storm ended, and we awoke one morning to a world of unbelievable stillness.

The snow was deep enough now for hauling the logs from the delta for our new cabin. There were about fifty to be brought in, and with Joyce and Syd as passengers in the toboggan, I broke and packed down a quarter mile of trail until it was hard and slick. Then Joyce and I started skidding the logs home one at a time, lashing one end to the toboggan and letting the other end drag in the snow. The logs were dry now and weighed no more than half their weight when green.

We managed to notch and lay one round of logs a day and the cabin walls took shape quickly. With the axe I planed boards smooth for the door and window frames. Six weeks after we laid the first round of logs we had a beautiful new cabin completed except for the interior. It measured twenty-two by twenty-four feet and to us it seemed roomy and luxurious.

Syd, more than a year old now, was a strong and healthy little boy. He was beginning to talk, and he was big enough to haul himself up on benches and get into everything. He enjoyed being

348

outdoors, even when the temperature was well below zero, and we found him a sheer delight. I had taught Joyce to set snares for rabbits. I made a small sled for the boy, and she took him along when she made her rounds of the snares.

A week before Christmas, to our surprise, Caesar and his family arrived at their campground a mile below the cabin. A kind, mild-mannered man of about forty, Caesar took in any child who had been orphaned or, as sometimes happened, deserted. He had fourteen children with him that winter, and Maddie, his happy, wide-grinning wife, made them all welcome.

One of his boys had cut his foot with an axe some time before. The wound had not been kept clean and now the foot was infected and swollen painfully. Joyce and I treated it as best we could, opening the cut, soaking the foot in water as hot as the boy could tolerate, and putting on a poultice.

Soon the foot was much improved, the swelling almost gone. To Caesar this was wonderful "medicine," by which we knew he really meant witchcraft. It would go far to cement our growing friendship and respect for each other.

The family's arrival was greatly to my liking. I had wanted to make the trip to Pelly Banks, where we had several hundred pounds of new supplies waiting for us, but I did not want to take Joyce and Syd along and neither was I willing to leave them alone. I talked it over with Caesar, and he agreed to stay close by and let Joyce continue to take care of his boy's foot, while I made a quick trip to the Pelly Banks post.

I started before daylight the next morning and made the seventy-five mile trip over a rough trail in a day and a half. I made a deal with Van Gorder to send Indian drivers with most of my freight as soon as they came in from their traplines. The following morning I loaded six hundred pounds on my own toboggan, got an early start, and was back at our cabin at dusk on the second day. I was pleased to get home. Christmas was only two days off.

Christmas Day broke clear and cold and we made it as festive as possible. We had presents hidden for each other and Syd. My big surprise for my wife was a Belgian .410-gauge double-barreled shotgun, a lightweight, beautifully-made firearm. She was completely delighted.

Our Christmas dinner consisted of a roast goose, wild cranberries dug from under the snow, a plum pudding Joyce had made from dried fruit, and pumpkin pie. The pumpkin was the only item that came from a can. We had brought in small candles for birthday cakes, and now we used them as decorations for the Christmas tree, a small spruce I had cut, along with strings of cranberries and cotton wool from our first-aid supplies. Our little cabin glowed with warmth and happiness.

Soon after Christmas four Indians arrived from Pelly Banks with the rest of our supplies. What we could not store on the high cache we put in the old cabin. The interior of our new cabin was complete now except for a few floorboards, so we moved our furniture in, and that night we slept in it for the first time.

By now the other Indians had come in. I traded some jewelry and dress goods for their mink, marten, and lynx pelts, and just before New Year the whole band departed, making a colorful spectacle as one dog team after another crossed the lake, pompoms waving from the top of each dog's collar and bright ribbons streaming from the harnesses.

Daily the cold grew more intense. When I went out the snow crunched under my snowshoes as if I were walking on soda crackers. Our spirit thermometer, hanging free of the cabin wall in front of a window, was calibrated to register down to eighty degrees below zero. On New Year's Day, 1929, the red liquid dropped into the bulb, about four degrees below the lowest reading. That meant a temperature of eighty-four degrees below zero! It was by far the coldest day I had ever experienced.

The temperature stayed that low for three days. I went outdoors only long enough to split a little wood, and even that posed the danger of frosted lungs. As soon as I began to feel the chill of that terrible cold in my chest I took refuge in the cabin.

We felt some concern about how the dogs would fare in such cold. But our worries were groundless, and Joyce and I laughed as often as we looked out at them. Each dog would curl contentedly in the snow *on top* of his kennel, his nose tucked down in the shelter of his tail, frost covering the rest of his head. They appeared not to care one iota about the low temperatures.

The cold broke at last and clear sunny days followed one another through January. We built more furniture and shelves, and we divided our new cabin into three rooms by hanging lengths of cloth from the ceiling.

Our water came from a hole I kept chopped open in the ice of the lake. By midwinter the ice was five feet thick, and I had to cut steps in it to get down to the water safely. I covered the hole with a lid made of boards, partly to keep it from freezing over quickly, partly to make sure that Syd did not toddle out on the lake and fall in.

He delighted now in following my snowshoe trails, and he had given us one bad fright when he wandered by himself to the outdoor toilet and fell in deep snow just off the trail. We missed him, searched frantically, and found him there, too smothered in snow to get back on his feet but none the worse for the experience. We pulled him out and his mother carried him, laughing and proud of himself, back to the cabin.

February passed as quickly as January, and the storms of March were not too severe. The sun climbed higher in the south, and I spent my days getting ready for summer, cutting enough wood to last until fall, repairing the net; and, while the ice was still good on the river, hauling extra lumber up to the mine.

By mid-April slush and water covered the lake, and not long afterward the river broke. As soon as the water started to run I set the flumes and sluice boxes in place and began washing gold from the gravel in the canyon.

The Indians came back for the summer, and Caesar worked steadily at the mine; Little Jimmy and Oaltal and Meegan took turns helping. It was becoming harder to find rich pay dirt, but we were still recovering enough gold to make the work worthwhile. By the time we closed the mine down in mid-September of 1929 we had a really good stake. Caesar's wife Maddie had made pokes of tanned mooseskin for us. There were seventeen of them stacked in the cabin now, from our two summers of work, and as nearly as we

351

could calculate, each one contained almost a thousand dollars' worth of gold! Joyce and I were planning a trip outside, but we would not leave until the following March, when sled travel would be at its best. We'd go well-heeled indeed. When the Indians left we told them we would be gone before breakup but that we planned to return in a year.

The winter passed smoothly and swiftly. Syd had learned to ride on Rogue's back, hanging on to the dog's collar with both hands. Rogue was trustworthy, and obviously loved the boy. I no longer had to pack Syd on my back when we went on hikes.

As spring of 1930 approached we stored our leftover supplies on the high cache and braced the cabin roof with extra stanchions against the weight of heavy snows. By the middle of March, when the sun was swinging north once more and a heavy crust had formed on the snow, we were ready to leave.

We were eating supper our last night in the cabin when my wife, forever full of surprises, said casually, "You're going to be a father again, darling."

On that happy note we took our departure at daybreak.

7. Outside!

All through the preceding summer Joyce and I had known exactly what we wanted to do. We were eager to see our families again and show off our son. So first we'd book passage for England, where we'd visit my relatives. Then we'd come back and stop in Rochester, New York, Joyce's hometown. We expected to return to the Half-Moon late the following winter.

We had a fine morning for the start of our long trip out. The bright March sun struck the mountains across the lake, backlighting the snowy peaks in golden flame and causing the lake to sparkle like an enormous field of gems.

I had loaded the toboggan the day before. Now Joyce climbed into the carryall and settled Syd on her lap under the robes while I hitched up the dogs. Then I loosed the jerk line of the sled from the hitching stump and shouted, "Mush, Rogue!" We were away. Ahead of us lay six hundred and fifty miles of sled travel, out to Whitehorse.

There would be no packed trails to follow for the first part of this trip. We would go up the Finlayson to the Pelly Banks post, down the Pelly to where it flowed into the Yukon at Fort Selkirk, then up the Yukon and the Nordenskiold to our destination. With luck I figured we'd be at Whitehorse in about three weeks.

We reached Pelly Banks by sunset the second day, and said good-by to Van Gorder. Two days later we arrived at Hoole Canyon. It was a place we dreaded, rock-strewn, with water too swift to freeze. But we made it through safely, picking our way along the shelf of rough but safe ice on the south wall. Long before dark on our fifth day we drove the dogs up the steep bank of the Pelly to the Ross River post.

We laid over at Ross River, luxuriating in hot baths and clean laundry, and when we pulled out at dawn two days after our arrival, we found to our surprise a freshly broken snowshoe trail leading downriver for about three miles. There were eight white men at the post, all trappers and prospectors except Roy Tuttle, the trader, and Sergeant Tidd, a Royal Canadian Mounted Police officer.

One of the men had broken that trail to give us a good send-off. We never found out who the Good Samaritan was, but that little act of kindness was typical of the North and of the hardy breed of men that peopled it. They were rough and strong, yet slow to anger, and there was not one of them who would not give a stranger in need the shirt off his back.

Although the sun was melting the surface of the snow at noon now, temperatures fell to fifteen to twenty below each night. The crust stayed firm, and in the mornings I was able to jog behind the toboggan without snowshoes, or even ride for a few miles. But we knew we had no time to lose. Soon snow melt would be running down the creeks into the river, and slush would replace the hard snow.

Not far above the roadhouse at Pelly Crossing, forty miles from Fort Selkirk, we came to the camp of Van Bibber, a famous hunting guide. His family welcomed us to a full dinner table, and for the first time in two years we heard news of the outside world. Fur prices were high, the guide said, which delighted us. Then he added something we could not comprehend, about people in the cities going broke because of a stock-market crash in the autumn of 1929. Until then we'd had no inkling of the Great Depression that now held Canada and the United States in its grip. But gold, Van Bibber told us, was still selling at twenty dollars an ounce; the eternal treasure had not suffered from the slump.

We reached the Pelly Crossing roadhouse two weeks after leaving Frances Lake, and found good lodgings. We also learned that the winter "stage" to Whitehorse, the way we were headed, was due that evening.

The stage consisted of a tractor pulling two or three sleds behind it. One of these would be loaded with mail, and for a fare of a hundred and fifty dollars you could sit on the mail sacks and ride along. Each night the little convoy stopped at a roadhouse, running the tractor and loads into a barn, while the travelers found accommodation inside.

Joyce and I reached a decision quickly. She and Syd would go on to Whitehorse on the stage, which would be fast and would allow them the comforts of a roadhouse every night. From Whitehorse they would take the train to Skagway and then go on to Vancouver by steamship. I'd catch up with them there. First I'd finish the sled trip to Whitehorse, where I'd trade our furs and sell our gold.

It would have been shorter and faster for me to leave the rivers here and follow the stage road, but I knew that at this time of year there would be too many miles bare of snow. I'd have to keep to the river ice, forty more miles down to Fort Selkirk, then up the Yukon, past Carmacks to Whitehorse.

The stage came roaring in as darkness fell. I saw my family off the next morning and then mushed the dogs to Fort Selkirk. There I found a telegraph station and sent a cable to my parents in England to let them know we were on our way. There, too, I slept in a bed for the first time in two years.

I hit the trail at the first streaks of dawn the next morning, under

354

crystal-clear skies with the temperature holding around forty below. I was on the homestretch now, with three hundred miles to go to Whitehorse, and there'd be frequent roadhouses at Carmacks, Big Salmon, Yukon Crossing, and Little River.

The days went by quickly, but a thaw set in, the temperature suddenly warming to forty above during the day. Afternoon sled travel became impossible, for the melting crust would no longer hold the dogs.

We camped each day at noon and mushed out at night as soon as falling temperatures hardened the surface. Even on cloudy nights the snow reflected enough light for travel, and I knew I could trust Rogue not to lead the team onto unsafe ice. He seemed to have a sixth sense that warned him of danger.

Two hours after breaking camp in the darkness, on what I figured was our last day, we struck the foot of Lake Laberge. The lake is about twenty-eight miles long, and much of the snow had melted off now, leaving glare ice, slick and smooth, on which the dogs could find no footing. The ice was about five feet thick, but the water was rising fast under it and the thundering booms that signify cracking ice rumbled across the lake like muffled drums. The toboggan slid this way and that, and I strained to hold it on course.

Around midnight clouds cleared away, and I pulled ashore to make tea and rest for an hour. When I pulled onto the lake again I drove the dogs out half a mile from the bank to avoid any danger of thin ice, knowing that lakes thaw first along the beach. The groaning and booming under our feet was an eerie sound and it stirred a vague sense of danger in me. But the dogs kept their steady pace, tails held high.

The night was one of rare beauty, with a pale moon casting its ghostly light over the shore, where the trees stood freighted with snow. The toboggan made a soothing, rustling sound as it swished over the snow and patches of ice.

I was very tired, and the stillness of the night and the song of the sled were lulling me into drowsiness. Then Rogue stopped dead in his tracks, so suddenly that the rest of the team piled up on top of one another.

My drowsiness was gone in an instant. I knew my lead dog had a good reason for what he had done.

I went ahead to untangle the snarling team, and as they quieted I thought I heard the sound of water, like small waves breaking on a beach. I hushed the dogs to complete silence and listened intently.

The sound was unmistakable. It *was* water, and it was lapping against the ice just ahead. I knew what had happened and I broke into a cold sweat. The ice in the river above the head of the lake had cracked, and running water was now lapping against the rotting ice of the lake itself.

In all my years in the Yukon I had had no closer call than that. I had been too near to sleep to sense the danger and halt the dogs in time. Had Rogue led the team into that danger zone and gone through, he almost certainly would have taken the sled with him and I would have followed. The current under the ice would have swept everything with it—instantly, too.

I wasn't drowsy now. I turned the dogs back on their own trail, returned to the shore, and fought through tangles of timber onto higher ground. Daylight was only an hour or two away, and, with thirty very tough miles ahead to Whitehorse, I decided to make camp and rest awhile.

When I started the next day the river ice was gone. I was several miles from the winter tractor road, which, even if I reached it, would have long stretches of bare ground. There was nothing for it but to fight my way through timber and underbush, breaking trail in the deep and slushy snow, clawing around trees and thickets and along steep hillsides. It was arduous work, and I was bone-tired at dusk when I made camp.

I awoke to find the sky clear and the sun high. I was sure we were only a few miles from Whitehorse now and I began breaking trail again, helping the dogs through the wet snow. Suddenly, just before dark, we came out on a well-used trail where the travel was easy. The team perked up, and in another few miles the trail ran into the winter tractor road. The hardships were behind us.

The lights of Whitehorse shone in the darkness ahead. When we passed the first outlying cabins I halted my team and tied sleigh bells to the top of each harness. We'd end this winter odyssey in style. There must have been two hundred sled dogs in the town that night, and the musical jingle-jangle of those bells set them howling in unison. What a grand and suitable announcement of our arrival!

We drove up in front of the Whitehorse Inn, with its wide double doors, and lights burning in the lobby. It stood as the symbol of everything I had dreamed about for months. George King, the handsome and very pleasant Japanese who owned the place, stood on the porch at the top of a flight of wide snow-covered steps, waving a welcome.

I ignored the hitching posts at the foot of those steps and shouted happily to the dogs, "Mush, you fellows! Up there, Rogue! Mush!"

King threw the double doors wide open and the team piled up the stairs. They were across the lobby when I halted them with a sharp "Whoa!" The toboggan came to rest in front of the roaring fire in the lobby fireplace.

King helped me unharness the dogs and took them out through the back door to kennels. I threw off my parka and sprawled spread-eagled in a big leather armchair. George shoved a glass of hot buttered rum into my hand and reported that Joyce and Syd had taken a train to the coast three days before. He also told me that some of the men in town, learning of my progress via the single-wire Yukon telegraph line, had laid plans to go out and look for me if I did not show up by noon the next day.

For the next three days I slept and partied. Friends came into the lobby and unpacked some of my furs and shook them out, testing the fineness of the silky marten and mink skins. They untied a poke of the gold, weighing the nuggets in the palms of their hands, estimating their worth. Thieving was practically unknown in the Yukon before World War II, and I am confident that I did not lose a single nugget during that time.

Three days later I took the gold across the street to Jim Wheeler at the Canadian Bank of Commerce. He emptied each poke into the pan on one side of the huge gold scales on the counter, added brass weights on the other pan until the scales balanced, and when he had finished, credited my account with close to $17,000! A fortune. In

357

purchasing power it would be equal to about eight times that amount today—more than $135,000.

I took my furs to the Taylor & Drury store and cashed them in, then went over to the railroad depot and bought deluxe passage via Canadian Pacific train and steamer for the family to England.

George King had promised to look after my dogs until we came back to our gold diggings at the Half-Moon, which we planned to do late the following spring.

This was going to be the grandest vacation any family ever had. But we had plenty to come back to. The satisfaction of mining gold on our own claim. The hard work. The glory and peacefulness of the wilderness. The fishing, the hunting, the great inner feeling of independence and freedom and accomplishment. We knew that the wild and beautiful and lonely North would be there to welcome us home.

This was the North—the good life—we loved.

Anton Money

As it turned out, the Moneys did not return to Frances Lake until 1936, when they spent a year developing the Half-Moon, eventually selling it to a mining company. In the meantime their second son, Tony, had been born. A steady job looked attractive, and for a while Mr. Money worked as a field scout for two companies with mining interests in the Yukon and British Columbia.

When World War II forced the closing of the mines, the Canadian government sent Anton Money to supervise a large explosives plant near Toronto. He managed to get out of that job to go to the North again, running twelve dog-team crews surveying a route over the McKenzie Mountains for the Canol Pipeline.

Anton Money now lives in retirement in Santa Barbara, California, but he will never forget his pioneering days. As he puts it, "That North still lives—bright as a nugget inside me."

Anton Money, 1925

Joyce Money, 1928

SHARPE'S GOLD
Bernard Cornwell

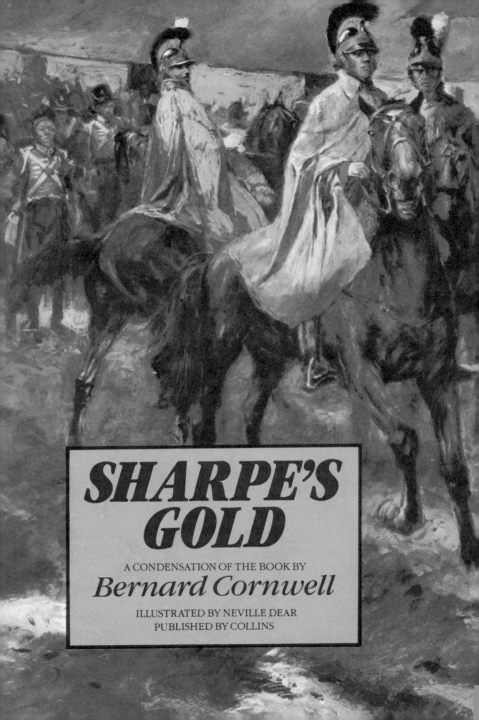

SHARPE'S GOLD

A CONDENSATION OF THE BOOK BY

Bernard Cornwell

ILLUSTRATED BY NEVILLE DEAR
PUBLISHED BY COLLINS

Never in the course of the Peninsular War have things looked so bleak for the British as in this summer of 1810 Napoleon's troops are pushing them farther and farther into Portugal, funds are desperately low and Wellington cannot even afford to pay his demoralized army. An ignominious defeat seems inevitable.

Then news reaches the general of a secret cache of Spanish gold, abandoned behind enemy lines. He knows of only one man with the courage and bravado to recover the gold: Captain Richard Sharpe of the South Essex Light Company. Danger threatens the expedition not only from the French invaders but from the Spanish partisans—in particular the ruthless guerrilla leader El Católico, who claims the gold for himself. And the rivalry between the two men deepens when Sharpe meets the lovely Teresa, one of the fiercest fighters in El Católico's band.

Richard Sharpe will be familiar to readers of *Sharpe's Eagle* (a recent Condensed Books selection) as a cool fighter, and a gallant leader of his devoted company. Here in hostile country, surrounded by enemies, he faces the most desperate challenge of his military career.

1

The war was lost; not finished, but lost. Everyone knew it, from generals of division to the whores of Lisbon; that the British were trapped, trussed, ready for cooking, and all Europe waited for the master chef himself, Bonaparte, to cross the mountains and put his finishing touch to the roast. Then, to add insult to imminent defeat, it seemed that the small British army was not worthy of the great Bonaparte's attention.

The drumbeats rattled through France and a hundred thousand fresh troops followed their Eagles across the Pyrenees to join the quarter of a million Frenchmen who waited for the orders that would march them westward. West towards Lisbon, and all that stood in their way were thirty thousand British troops with their allies, the Portuguese.

Spain had fallen. The last Spanish armies had gone, butchered into the history books, and all that was left was the fortress harbour of Cádiz and the Spanish peasants who fought the "guerrilla", the "little war", with ambush and terror, till the French troops loathed them. But the little war was not the war, and that, everyone said, was lost. Not yet finished, but lost.

All London knew it, all Britain, and the letters came from officers in Portugal that told of the huge odds, of the mustering French, and asked their families to air the mattresses, unpack the wardrobes, and with any luck Masséna would kick them home before the start of the hunting season.

Captain Richard Sharpe, once in the ranks of His Majesty's 95th Rifles, now Captain of the Light Company of the South Essex Regiment, was in a foul mood, morose and irritable. Rain had fallen since dawn, turning the road's dusty surface into mud and making his rifleman's uniform clammy and uncomfortable. He marched in solitary silence, listening to his men chatter, and Lieutenant Knowles and Sergeant Harper, who both would normally have sought his company, left him alone.

Knowles had commented on Sharpe's mood, but the huge Irish sergeant had shaken his head. "There's no chance of cheering him up, sir. He likes being miserable, so he does, and the bastard will get over it."

Knowles shrugged. He rather disapproved of a sergeant calling a captain a "bastard", but there was no point in protesting. Patrick Harper had fought beside Sharpe for years; both were big men, the Irishman immensely strong, and both confident in their abilities. Knowles could never imagine either out of uniform. It was as if they had been born to the job and it was on the battlefield, where most men thought nervously of their own survival, that Sharpe and Harper came together in an uncanny understanding.

Knowles stared up at the sky, at the low clouds touching the hilltops either side of the road. "Bloody weather."

"Back home, sir, we'd call this a fine day!" Rain dripping off his shako, Harper turned to look at the company who followed the fast-marching figure of Sharpe. They were staggering a little, slipping on the road, and he raised his voice. "Come on, you Protestant scum! The war's not waiting for you!" He grinned at them as he shouted, proud that they had outmarched the rest of the regiment, and happy that, at last, the South Essex was marching north to where the summer's battles would be fought. The South Essex was pitifully understrength. Replacements had sailed from Portsmouth in March, but the convoy had been hit by a storm and, weeks later, word came of hundreds of bodies washed ashore on the southern

366

Biscay beaches and now the regiment must fight with less than half its proper number. Harper did not mind. Like everyone, he had heard the rumours of the French armies and their new commander, Masséna, but he did not intend to lose any sleep over the future. Tonight, in the town of Celorico where the army was gathering, there would be women in the streets and wine in the shops. Life could be a lot worse for a lad from Donegal and he began whistling.

Sharpe heard the whistling and checked his impulse to snap at the sergeant. Sharpe did not believe the rumours of coming defeat — to a soldier defeat was something that happened to the other side — yet the remorseless logic of numbers was haunting him. Defeat was in the air, and as the thought came to him again he marched even faster as if the aching pace could obliterate his pessimism. A year before, in 1809, the British had beaten the French at Talavera. Since then, however, the South Essex had patrolled the bleak, southern border between Spain and Portugal, and it had been a long, boring winter. The sun had risen and set, they had watched the empty hills, and there had been too much leisure, too much softness. And weddings. Twenty alone in the last three months so that, miles behind, the other nine companies of the South Essex were leading a motley procession of women and children.

But now, at least, they were doing something. In an unseasonably wet summer, they were marching north, to where the French attack would come, and where all doubts and fears would be banished in action.

The road reached a crest, revealing a shallow valley with a small village at its centre. There were cavalry in the village, presumably summoned north like the South Essex, and wearing the blue of the King's German Legion. Sharpe respected the Germans who fought France in Britain's army. They were professional soldiers and Sharpe, above everything else, was a professional. He had to be. There was no money to buy promotion and his future lay only in his skill. He had been a soldier for seventeen of his thirty-three years, first as a private, then a sergeant, then the dizzy jump to officer, and all the promotions had been earned on battlefields.

He halted the company in the village street under the curious gaze of the cavalrymen. One of them, an officer, hitched his curved sabre off the ground and walked over to Sharpe. "Captain?" The cavalryman made it a question because Sharpe's only signs of rank were the faded scarlet sash and the sword.

Sharpe nodded. "Captain Sharpe. South Essex."

The German officer's eyebrows went up. "Captain Sharpe! Talavera!" He pumped Sharpe's hand. They had all heard of him; the man whose company had captured the French Eagle at Talavera. The German beamed. "It was well done!" He clicked his heels to Sharpe. "Lossow. Captain Lossow at your service. You going to Celorico?" His English was accented, but good. His men, Sharpe knew, would probably speak no English. Sharpe nodded again.

"And you?"

Lossow shook his head. "The River Coa. Patrolling. The enemy are getting close so there will be fighting." He sounded pleased and Sharpe envied the cavalry. What fighting there was to be had was all taking place along the steep banks of the Coa.

Lossow was a square-faced man, with a ready smile, and eyes that looked shrewdly from the web of lines traced on his face by staring too long at enemy-held horizons. "Oh, one more thing, Captain. The bloody provosts are in the village." The phrase came awkwardly from his lips as if he did not usually use English swearwords, except to describe the provosts when any language's curse would be inadequate.

Sharpe thanked him and turned to the company. "You heard Captain Lossow! There are provosts here. So keep your thieving hands to yourselves. Understand?" They understood. No one wanted to be hanged on the spot for looting. "We stop for ten minutes. Dismiss them, Sergeant."

The Germans left, cloaked against the rain, and Sharpe walked up the only street towards the church. It was a miserable village, poor and deserted, and the cottage doors swung emptily because the inhabitants had gone south and west as the Portuguese government had ordered. When the French advanced they would find no crops, no animals, wells poisoned with dead sheep. Patrick Harper fell into step beside his captain. "Nothing here to loot, sir."

Sharpe glanced at the men stooping into the cottages. "They'll find something."

The provosts were beside the church, three of them, Horse Guards mounted on black horses and standing like highwaymen waiting for a plump coach. Their equipment was new, their faces burned red, and Sharpe guessed they were fresh out from England. He nodded civilly to them. "Good morning."

One of the three, an officer's sword jutting from beneath his cloak, nodded back. He seemed, like all of his kind, to be suspicious of any friendly gesture. He looked at their green riflemen's jackets. "There aren't supposed to be any riflemen in this area," he said. "You have orders?"

"The general wants to see us, sir." Harper spoke cheerfully.

A tiny smile came and went on the provost's face. "You mean Lord Wellington wants to see you?"

"As a matter of fact, yes." Sharpe's voice had a warning in it, but the provost seemed oblivious. He was looking Sharpe up and down, letting his suspicions show. Like the other eighteen riflemen in the company, Sharpe had kept his old uniform out of pride, preferring the dark green to the red of the line battalions. Sharpe's green jacket, faded and torn, was worn over French cavalry overalls, while on his feet were tall, leather boots that had originally been bought in Paris by a colonel of Napoleon's Imperial Guard, and on his back, like most of his men, he carried a French pack, made of oxhide. His officer's epaulettes had gone, leaving broken stitches, and even his sword was irregular. As an officer of a light company he should have carried the curved sabre of the British light cavalry, but Richard Sharpe preferred the straight-bladed sword of the heavy cavalry. Cavalrymen hated it; they claimed its weight made it impossible to parry swiftly, but Sharpe was six feet tall and strong enough to wield the thirty-five inches of ponderous steel with ease.

The provost officer was unsettled. "What's your regiment?"

"We're the Light of the South Essex."

The provost responded by spurring his horse forward so he could see down the street and watch Sharpe's men. There was no immediately apparent reason to hang anyone so he looked back at the

369

two men, and his eyes widened with surprise when he saw Harper's shoulder. The Irishman, four inches taller than Sharpe, was a daunting sight at the best of times, but his weapons were even more irregular than Sharpe's big sword. Besides his rifle he carried a brute of a gun: a seven-barrelled, squat menace. The provost pointed. "What's that?"

"Seven-barrelled gun, sir." Harper's voice was full of pride in his new weapon. Sharpe grinned. The gun had been one of Henry Nock's less successful inventions, and it was obvious that the provost had never seen one before. Only a few hundred had ever been made, for the navy. Seven barrels, each twenty inches long, were all fired by the same flintlock and it was thought that sailors, perched precariously in the fighting tops, could wreak havoc by firing down onto the enemy's crowded decks. One thing had been overlooked. Seven half-inch barrels, fired together, made a fearful discharge that broke the shoulder of any man who pulled the trigger. Only Harper, in Sharpe's acquaintance, had the brute strength to resist the gun's crashing recoil.

The provost sniffed. "Where did you get it?"

"I gave it to him," Sharpe said.

"And you are?"

"Captain Richard Sharpe. South Essex. You?"

The provost stiffened. "Lieutenant Ayres . . . sir." The last word was spoken reluctantly.

"And where are you going, Lieutenant Ayres?" Sharpe was annoyed by the man's pointless display of his power, and he edged his question with a touch of venom. "Where, Lieutenant?"

"Celorico, sir."

"Then have a good journey, Lieutenant."

Ayres nodded. "I'll look round first, sir. If you don't mind."

Sharpe nodded and they rode off, rain beading the wide, black rumps of their horses. They were determined, he knew, to find something. "I hope you're right, Sergeant."

"Right, sir?"

"That there's nothing to loot."

Almost immediately there was a shout from behind the cottages.

370

Sharpe's men tumbled from doorways as Private Batten was dragged out by a triumphant provost.

"A looter, sir. Caught in the act." Ayres was smiling.

Batten, who grumbled incessantly, who moaned if it rained and when it stopped made a fuss because the sun was in his eyes. Private Batten, who thought the whole world was conspiring to aggravate him, and who now stood flinching beneath the grasp of one of Ayres's men. If there was any one member of the company whom Sharpe would gladly have hanged it would be Batten, but he was damned if any provost was going to do it for him. Sharpe looked up at Ayres. "What was he looting, Lieutenant?"

"This." Ayres held up a scrawny chicken. Its neck had been well-wrung, but the legs still jerked and scrabbled at the air. Sharpe felt anger come inside him, not at the provosts but at Batten. "I'll deal with him, Lieutenant." Batten cringed away.

Ayres shook his head. "You misunderstand, sir." He spoke with silky condescension. "Looters are hanged, sir. On the spot, sir. As an example."

There was a muttering from the company, broken by Harper's order for silence. Batten's eyes flicked left and right as if looking for an escape from this latest example of the world's injustice. Sharpe snapped at him. "Batten! Where did you find the chicken?"

"It was in the field, sir. It was a wild chicken."

Ayres snorted. "He's lying. I found him in a cottage."

Sharpe believed him, but he was not going to give up. "Who lives in the cottage, Lieutenant?"

Ayres raised an eyebrow. "Really, sir, I have not exchanged cards with every slum in Portugal." He turned. "String him up."

"Lieutenant Ayres." The tone of Sharpe's voice stopped any movement in the street. "The village is deserted. You can't steal a chicken from nobody."

Ayres thought about his reply. The village inhabitants had gone away from the French attack, but absence was not a relinquishing of ownership. He shook his head. "The chicken is Portuguese property, sir." He turned again. "Hang him!"

"Halt!" Again movement stopped. "You have no proof. The man

was in the cottage. I suggest that he went there after catching the chicken in the field. You're not going to hang him, so go your way."

Ayres swivelled back to Sharpe. "He was caught red-handed and will hang. Your men need an example, and they will get one — "

A click interrupted him. He looked down and his anger was replaced by astonishment. Sharpe held his Baker rifle, cocked, the barrel pointing at Ayres. "Let him go, Lieutenant."

Ayres sagged back in his saddle. Sergeant Harper, instinctively, came and stood beside Sharpe. Ayres stared at the two men. Both tall, both with hard, fighters' faces, and a memory tickled at him. He looked at Sharpe's face, the scar that ran down his right cheek, and he suddenly remembered. The South Essex Light Company. Were these the two men who had captured the Eagle, who had hacked their way into a French regiment and come out with the standard? He could believe it. Sharpe watched the lieutenant's eyes waver and knew that he had won, but it was a victory that would cost him dearly. The army did not look kindly on men who held rifles at provosts, even empty rifles. Ayres pushed Batten forward. "Have your thief, Captain. We shall meet again."

Sharpe lowered the rifle. Ayres waited until Batten was clear of the horses, then wrenched the reins and led his men away towards Celorico. "You'll hear from me!" His words were flung back. Sharpe could sense the trouble like a boiling, black cloud on the horizon.

He turned to Batten. "Did you steal that hen?"

"Yes, sir." Batten flapped a hand after the provost. "He took it, sir." He made it sound unfair.

"I wish he'd bloody taken you. I wish he'd spread your guts across the bloody landscape." Batten backed away from his anger. "What are the rules, Batten? You know them — tell me."

The army issued regulations that were inches thick, but Sharpe gave his men three rules. They were simple, they worked, and if broken the men knew they could expect punishment.

Batten cleared his throat. "To fight well, sir. Not to get drunk without permission, sir. And . . ."

"Go on."

"Not to steal, sir, except from the enemy or when starving, sir."

372

"Were you starving?"

"No, sir."

Sharpe hit him, all his frustrations pouring into one fist that slammed Batten's chest, winded him, and knocked him down into the mud. "You're a bloody fool, Batten, a wingeing, slimy fool." He turned away. "Company! Into ranks! Packs on! March!"

Batten picked himself up, brushed ineffectively at the water that had flowed into the lock of his gun, and then ran shamblingly after his silent companions. "He's not supposed to hit me," he muttered.

"Shut your mouth, Batten!" Harper's voice was as harsh as his captain's. "You know the rules. Would you rather be kicking your useless heels at the end of a rope?" The sergeant shouted at the company to pick up their feet, bellowed the steps at them, and all the time he wondered what faced Sharpe now. A complaint from the provost would mean an inquiry and probably a court martial. And all for the miserable Batten.

Lieutenant Knowles shared Harper's thoughts as he fell in step beside the Irishman. The war was lost, it was still raining, and tomorrow Captain Richard Sharpe would be in provost trouble, real trouble, right up to his sabre-scarred neck.

2

If anyone needed a symbol in impending defeat then the church of São Paolo in Celorico, the temporary headquarters of the South Essex, offered it in full. Sharpe stood in the choir watching the priest whitewash a gorgeous roodscreen. The screen was made of solid silver, ancient and intricate, a gift from some long-forgotten parishioner whose family's faces were depicted on the grieving women and disciples who stared up at the crucifix. The priest, standing on a trestle, dripped thick lime paint down his cassock, looked from Sharpe to the screen and shrugged. "It took three months to clean off last time."

"Last time?"

"When the French left." The priest sounded bitter. He dabbed angrily at the delicate traceries. "If they knew it was silver they would carve it into pieces and take it away." He splashed the nailed, hanging figure with a slap of paint and then, as if in apology, moved the brush to his left hand so that his right could sketch a perfunctory sign of the cross on his spattered gown.

They know, thought Sharpe, they all know that the French are coming and the British falling back. The priest made him feel guilty, as if he were personally betraying the town and its inhabitants, and he moved down the church into the darkness by the main door where the battalion's commissariat officer was supervising the piling of fresh baked bread for the evening rations. The door banged open, letting in the late afternoon sunlight, and Lieutenant Colonel the Honourable William Lawford, dressed in his glittering best uniform, beckoned at Sharpe. "Ready?"

"Yes, sir."

Major Forrest was waiting outside and he smiled nervously at Sharpe. "Don't worry, Richard."

"Worry?" Lawford was angry. "He should damned well worry." He looked Sharpe up and down. "Good Lord, Richard, you look like a tramp. Is that the best you can do?"

Sharpe fingered the tear in his sleeve. "It's all I've got, sir. Uniform's in Lisbon, sir. In store. Light companies should travel light."

Lawford snorted. "Just because you captured an Eagle doesn't mean you can do what you like." He crammed the tricorne hat onto his head. "Come on, we don't want to be late."

Sharpe followed Lawford with Major Forrest through the crowded streets towards Wellington's headquarters. It was strange,

374

he thought, seeing the colonel's exquisite uniform and expensive accoutrements, how Lawford summed up all the things he disliked about privilege and wealth, yet he liked Lawford and was content to serve under him in the South Essex. They were the same age, thirty-three. Lawford was ambitious, as was Sharpe, but the colonel had the birth and the money for great things. He'll be a general, Sharpe thought, and he grinned because he knew that Lawford would still need him or someone like him. Sharpe was Lawford's eyes and ears, his professional soldier, the man who could read the faces of the failed criminals, drunks and desperate men who had somehow become the best infantry in the world. And more than that, Sharpe could read the ground, could read the enemy, and Lawford, for whom the army was a means to a glorious and exalted end, relied on him.

Lawford led them through the press of officers and townspeople. Major Forrest kept glancing at Sharpe with an avuncular smile that made him look, more than ever, like a kindly country vicar who was dressed as a soldier for the village pageant. He tried to reassure Sharpe. "It won't come to a court martial, Richard. You'll have to apologize or something, and it will all blow over."

Sharpe shook his head. "I won't apologize, sir."

Lawford stopped and turned round, his finger pushed into Sharpe's chest. "If you are ordered to apologize, Richard Sharpe, you will damned well apologize. You will grovel, squirm, cringe and toady to order. This is a general court-martial offence. Do you understand?"

Sharpe clicked the heels of his tall French boots together. "Sir!"

Lawford was not placated by Sharpe's crestfallen expression. "And do not think, Captain Sharpe, that just because the general has ordered us here he will look kindly on your action. He's saved your miserable skin often enough in the past and he may not be of a mind to do it again. Understand?"

He strode on, and Sharpe followed. Lawford could be right. The general had summoned the South Essex, no one knew why, and Sharpe had hoped that it was for some special task, something to wipe out the memory of the winter's boredom. But the scene with

Lieutenant Ayres could have changed all that for him, condemning him to a court martial instead, to a future far more dreary even than patrol work on an empty border.

Four ox-carts stood outside Wellington's headquarters, another reminder that the army would move soon, but otherwise everything was peaceful. The only unusual object was a tall mast that jutted from the roof of the house, topped by a crosspiece from which hung four tarred sheep bladders. Sharpe looked at them curiously. This was the first time he had seen the new telegraph and he wished that it was working so that he could watch the inflated bladders running up and down on their ropes and sending messages, via other similar stations, to the far-off fortress of Almeida and to the troops guarding the River Coa. He had heard that a message could travel twenty miles in less than ten minutes. The system had been copied from the Royal Navy and sailors had been sent with huge naval telescopes to man the telegraph. Each letter of the alphabet had its own arrangement of the four bladders and common words were abbreviated to a single display.

As they came close to the two bored sentries guarding the general's headquarters he forgot the telegraph and felt a twinge of fear at the coming interview. In a curious fashion his career had been linked to Wellington. They had shared battlefields in Flanders, India, and now in the Peninsula. In India, Wellington, then Sir Arthur Wellesley, had made him into an officer at the battle of Assaye, and now the same man who had rewarded him then must decide on his fate again.

"His Lordship will see you now." A suave young major smiled at them in the cool hallway of the house as though they had been invited for tea. It had been a year since Sharpe had seen Wellington, but nothing had changed; still the table covered with papers, the same blue eyes that gave nothing away above the beak of a nose, and the handsome mouth that was grudging with smiles. Sharpe was glad there were no provosts in the room so at least he would not have to grovel in front of them, but even so he felt apprehensive. He watched, cautiously, as the quill pen was laid quietly down.

376

"Did you threaten Lieutenant Ayres with a rifle, Captain Sharpe?"

"Yes, sir." This was no man to play games against.

Wellington nodded. He looked tired. He stood up and moved to the window. There was silence in the room, broken only by the jingle of chains and rumbling of wheels as a battery of artillery drove by in the street. The general turned back to him. "Do you know, Captain Sharpe, the damage it does our cause if our soldiers thieve or rape?"

"Yes, sir."

"I hope you do, Captain Sharpe, I hope you do." He sat down again. "Our enemies are encouraged to steal because that is the only way they can be fed. The result is that they are hated wherever they march. I spend money, my God, how much money, on providing rations and transport and buying food from the populace so that our soldiers have no need to steal. We do this so they will be welcomed by the local people and helped by them. Do you understand?"

Sharpe wished the lecture would end. "Yes, sir." There was suddenly a strange noise overhead, a shuffling and rattling, and Wellington's gaze shot to the ceiling as if he could read what the noise might mean. It occurred to Sharpe that the telegraph was working, the inflated bladders running up and down the ropes, bringing a coded message from the troops facing the French. The general listened for a few seconds then dropped his face to Sharpe again. "Your gazette has not yet been ratified."

There were few things the general could have said more likely to worry Sharpe. Officially he was still only a lieutenant, his captaincy given him by a gazette awarded by Wellington a year ago. If Whitehall did not approve, and he knew they usually rejected such irregular promotions, then he was soon to be a lieutenant again. He said nothing as Wellington watched him. If this was a warning shot then he would take it in silence. The general sighed, picked up a piece of paper, put it down again. "The soldier has been punished?"

"Yes, sir."

"Then do not, pray, let it happen again. Not even, Captain Sharpe, to wild chickens."

My God, thought Sharpe, he knows everything that happens in this army. There was silence. Was that the end of it? No court martial? No apology?

Wellington stood again. "I would quite happily, Captain Sharpe, string up you and that damned sergeant of yours. But I suspect we need you." He used one of his few, thin smiles, "What do you think of our chances this summer?"

Again there was silence. The change of tack had taken them all by surprise. Lawford cleared his throat. "There's clearly some concern, my lord, about the intentions of the enemy and our response."

Another wintry smile. "The enemy intends to push us into the sea, and soon. How do we respond?" Wellington, it occurred to Sharpe, was using up time. He was waiting for something or someone.

Lawford was clearly uncomfortable. The question was one he would rather hear answered by the general. "Bring them to battle, sir?"

"Thirty thousand troops, plus twenty-five thousand untried Portuguese, against three hundred and fifty thousand?" Wellington let the figures hang in the air like the dust that shifted silently in the slanting sunlight over his desk. Overhead, the feet of the men operating the telegraph still shuffled. The figures, Sharpe knew, were unfair. The French commander, Marshal Masséna, needed thousands of men simply to contain the *guerrilleros*, the partisans. Even so, the disparity in numbers was appalling.

There was a knock on the door. Wellington sniffed. "Come in."

"Sir." The major who had shown them into the room handed a slip of paper to the general, who read it, closed his eyes momentarily, and sighed. "The rest of the message is still coming?"

"Yes, sir. But the gist is there."

The major left and Wellington leaned back in his chair. The news had been bad, but not, perhaps, unexpected. Sharpe watched the fingers drum on the edge of the table. The eyes came up again, flicked to Lawford. "Colonel?"

"Sir?"

"I am borrowing Captain Sharpe from you, and his company. I doubt whether I need them for more than one month."

"Yes, my lord." Lawford looked at Sharpe and shrugged.

Wellington seemed to be relieved, as if a decision were made. "Though I know my confidence is not universally shared, gentlemen, I believe that the war is *not* lost. We may bring the French to battle, and if we do, we will win." He opened a map, stared at it, then let it snap shut again into a roll. "But if we win we will only delay their advance. No, gentlemen, our survival depends on something else. Something that you, Captain Sharpe, must bring me. Must, do you hear? *Must.*"

Sharpe had never heard the general so insistent. "Yes, sir."

Lawford coughed. "And if he fails, my lord?"

The wintry smile again. "He had better not." He looked at Sharpe. "You are not the only card in my hand, Mr. Sharpe, but you are . . . important. There are things happening, gentlemen, that this army does not know about. You are now under my orders, Captain Sharpe. Your men must be ready to march this night. They must not be encumbered with wives or unnecessary baggage, and they must have full ammunition."

"Yes, sir."

"You will receive your orders, Mr. Sharpe, not from me but from an old companion of yours. Major Hogan."

Sharpe's face betrayed his pleasure. Hogan, the engineer, the quiet Irishman, was an old friend.

"But before that, Mr. Sharpe, you will apologize to Lieutenant Ayres." Wellington watched for Sharpe's reaction.

"But of course, sir. I had always planned to." Sharpe looked shocked at the possibility that he might ever have contemplated another course of action and, through his innocently wide eyes, he wondered if he saw a flicker of amusement behind the general's cold gaze. Wellington turned to Lawford, and with his usual disarming speed suddenly became affable. "You're well, Colonel?"

"Thank you, sir. Yes." Lawford beamed with pleasure. He had served on Wellington's staff, and knew the general well.

"Join me for dinner tonight. The usual time." The general looked at Forrest. "And you, Major?"

"My pleasure, sir."

"Good." The eyes flicked at Sharpe. "Captain Sharpe will be too busy, I fear." He nodded a dismissal. "Good day, gentlemen."

Outside the headquarters the bugles sounded the evening and the sun sank in magnificent crimson. Inside the quiet room the general paused a moment before plunging back into the paperwork that must be done before dinner. Hogan, he thought, was right. If a miracle was needed to save the campaign, and it was, then the rogue he had just seen was the best man for the job. More than a rogue; a fighter. But, thought Wellington, a damned rogue all the same.

3

After leaving Wellington, Sharpe was shown into a large room to find a reception committee, formal and strained, flanking a wretchedly embarrassed Lieutenant Ayres.

An unctuous major smiled at Sharpe as though he were a valued and expected guest. "Ah, Captain Sharpe. You know the provost marshal, you've met Lieutenant Ayres, and this is Colonel Williams. Gentlemen?" The major made a delicate gesture as if inviting them all to sit down and take a glass of sherry.

It seemed that Colonel Williams, plump and red-veined, was deputed to do the talking. "Disgraceful, Sharpe, Disgraceful!"

Sharpe stared a fraction of an inch over Williams's head and stopped himself from blinking. It was a useful way of discomfiting people and, sure enough, Williams wavered from the apparent gaze. "You imperilled Lieutenant Ayres's authority, overstepped your own. A disgrace!"

"Yes, sir. I apologize."

"What?" Williams seemed surprised at Sharpe's sudden apology. Lieutenant Ayres was squirming while the provost marshal seemed impatient to get the charade done. Williams cleared his throat. "You apologize?"

"Yes, sir. Unreservedly, sir. Terrible disgrace, sir. I utterly apologize, sir, regret my part very much, sir, as I'm sure Lieutenant Ayres does his."

Ayres, startled by a sudden smile from Sharpe, nodded hastily and agreed. "I do, sir. I do."

Williams whirled on his unfortunate lieutenant. "What do you have to regret, Ayres? You mean there's more to this than I thought?"

The provost marshal sighed and scraped a boot on the floor. "I think the purpose of this meeting is over, gentlemen, and I have work to do." He looked at Sharpe. "Thank you, Captain, for your apology. We'll leave you."

As they left, Sharpe could hear Colonel Williams interrogating Ayres. Almost immediately the door opened once more and Michael Hogan came into the room. The small, neat Irishman shut the door carefully and smiled. "As graceful an apology as I might have expected from you, Richard. How are you?"

They shook hands, pleasure on both their faces. The war, it turned out, was treating Hogan well. An engineer, he had been transferred to Wellington's staff, and promoted to major. He spoke Portuguese and Spanish, and added to those skills a common sense that was rare. Sharpe raised his eyebrows at Hogan's new, elegant uniform. "So what do you do here?"

"A bit of this and the other." Hogan beamed at him, paused, then sneezed violently and held out his snuff box. "Can't get Scotch Rappee here, only Irish Blackguard. I warn you, it's like sniffing grapeshot straight up the nostrils."

"Give it up".

Hogan laughed. "I've tried, but I can't." His eyes watered as another sneeze gathered force.

"So what do you do?" Sharpe persisted.

Hogan wiped a tear from his cheek. "Not so very much, Richard. I sort of find things out, about the enemy, you understand. And draw maps. Things like that. We call it Intelligence, but it's a fancy word for knowing a bit about the other fellow. . . . I get by. And I have some duties in Lisbon occasionally."

Lisbon, where Josefina was. The girl whom Sharpe had loved so briefly, for whom he had killed, and who had then left him for a cavalry officer. He still thought of her, but this was no time or place for that kind of memory. He pushed the thought of her away, the jealousy he felt for Captain Claud Hardy, and changed the subject. "So what is this thing that I 'must' bring back for the general?"

Hogan leaned back. "Nervos belli, pecuniam infinitam."

"You know I don't speak Spanish."

Hogan gave a gentle smile. "Latin, Richard, Latin. Your education was sadly overlooked. Cicero said it. 'The sinews of war are unlimited money'."

"Money?"

"Gold, to be precise. Bucketsful of gold. A king's ransom, my dear Richard, and we want it. No, more than we want it, we need it. Without it —" He did not finish the sentence, but instead just shrugged.

"You're joking, surely."

The light beyond the windows was fading now and Hogan lit a candle. He spoke quietly. "I wish I was. We've run out of money. You wouldn't believe it, but there it is. Eighty-five million pounds is the war budget this year, can you imagine it? And we've run out."

"Run out?"

Hogan gave another shrug. "We're paying all Portugal's expenses, arming half the Spanish nation. . . . It's what, I think, you would call a local embarrassment. We need some money fast, in a matter of days. We could force it out of London in a couple of months, but that will be too long. We need it now."

"And if not?"

"If not, Richard, the French will be in Lisbon and not all the money in the world will make any difference. So you go and get the money."

"I go and get the money." Sharpe grinned. "How? Steal it?"

"Shall we say borrow?" Hogan's voice was serious. "There is a problem, Richard, which is that the gold belongs to the Spanish government. In a manner of speaking. . . ."

"What manner of speaking?"

"Who knows where the government is? Is it in French-occupied Madrid? Or is it in Cádiz?"

"And where's the gold? Paris?"

Hogan gave a tired smile. "Not quite that far. Two days' march." His voice became formal, reciting instructions. "You leave tonight, march to Almeida. The crossing of the Coa is guarded by the 60th, they're expecting you. In Almeida you meet a Major Kearsey. From then on you are under his orders. We expect you to take no longer than one week and should you need help, which pray God you will not, here is all you're going to get."

He pushed a piece of paper over the table. Sharpe unfolded it to read: "Captain Sharpe is directed by my orders and all officers of the allied armies are requested and instructed to offer Captain Sharpe any assistance he may require." The signature was a simple, "Wellington".

"There's no mention of gold?" Sharpe had expected elucidation at this meeting. He seemed to find only more mysteries.

"We didn't think it wise to tell too many people about a great pile of gold that's looking for an owner. It sort of encourages greed, if you follow me."

A moth flew crazy circles round the candle flame. Sharpe heard dogs barking in the town, the tramplings of horses in the stables behind the headquarters. "So how much gold?"

"Kearsey will tell you. It can be carried."

"God Almighty! Can't you tell me anything?"

Hogan smiled. "Not much. I'll tell you this though." He leaned back, locked his fingers behind his head. "The war's going bad, Richard. It's not our fault. We need men, guns, horses, powder, everything. The enemy gets stronger. There's only one thing can save us now, and that's this money."

"Why?"

"I can't tell you." Hogan sighed, pained by hiding something from a trusted friend. "We have something that is secret, Richard." He waved down an interruption. "It's the biggest damned secret I've ever seen and we don't want anyone to know, anyone. You'll know in the end, I promise you; everyone will. But for the moment we've just got to get the gold, which will pay for the secret."

THEY HAD MARCHED at midnight. As they crossed the narrow, high bridge that spanned the River Coa, the shadowy sentries had stamped their feet and waved at the dark hills. "No patrols yesterday. You should be all right."

Now, with dawn bleaching the sky, the Light Company was climbing the river gorge towards Almeida. Jagged rocks loomed over the path, and the creeping dawn showed a savage landscape half hidden by mist from the water. Almeida, a mile or so ahead, was a Portuguese fortress town, manned by the Portuguese army under British leaders, but the countryside around was in French hands. Soon the French would have to take Almeida, and batter their way through its famous walls so they could march on safely towards Lisbon.

The Light Company were not worried by the French. If Richard Sharpe wanted to lead them to Paris they would go, blindly confident that he would see them through. They were to march behind the enemy patrols and for once Sharpe was worried. Now he was remembering Hogan's final words. He had been pushing and probing, trying for information that Hogan was not giving. "Why us? It sounds like a job for cavalry."

Hogan nodded. "The cavalry tried, and failed. Kearsey says the country's not good for horses."

"But the French cavalry use it?"

Another tired nod. "Kearsey says you'll be all right."

There was silence in the room. "You don't think we'll succeed, do you." Sharpe made it a statement, not a question.

Hogan looked up. "No."

"So the war's lost?" Hogan nodded. "So why the hell don't you send three regiments in? Four? Send the bloody army! Make sure you get the gold."

"It's too far, Richard, there are no roads beyond Almeida. If we attract attention then the French will be there before us. The regiments would be outnumbered. No. We're sending you."

And now he was climbing the tight bends of the border road, watching the dull horizon for the telltale gleam of a drawn enemy sabre, and marching in the knowledge that he was expected to fail. He hoped this Major Kearsey, waiting for the company in Almeida, had more faith, but Hogan had been guarded about the major. Sharpe had probed again. "Is he unreliable?"

Hogan shook his head. "He's one of the best, Richard, one of the very best. But he's not exactly the man we'd have chosen for this job." He refused to elaborate. Kearsey, he told Sharpe, was an exploring officer, one of the men who rode fast horses behind enemy lines, in full uniform, and sent back a stream of information, dispatches captured from the French by the partisans, and maps of the countryside. It was Kearsey who had discovered the gold, informed Wellington, and only Kearsey knew its exact location. Kearsey, suitable or not, was the key to success.

The road flattened on the high crest of the Coa's east bank and ahead, silhouetted in the dawn light, was Portugal's northern fortress, Almeida. It dominated the countryside for miles around, a town built on a hill that rose to the huge bulk of a cathedral and a castle side by side. Below those massive and challenging buildings, the thick-tiled houses fell away from the steep streets until they met Almeida's real defences, low, grey granite ramparts, a scientifically designed maze of ditches and hidden walls, built only seven years before. Sharpe did not envy the French. They would have to attack across open ground, and all the time they would be enfiladed by dozens of masked batteries that could pour canister and grape into the killing ground between the long, sleek arms of the starlike fortifications.

The old days of sheer, high walls were past and the best modern fortresses were surrounded by smooth, gently sloping hummocks like the ones the Light Company now approached. These deflected the besiegers' cannon shots, sent the balls and shells ricocheting into the air, over the defences. And when the infantry attacked, up the gentle, innocent grass slopes, they would find hidden at the top a vast ditch, at the far side of which was a granite-faced wall, topped by belching guns, and even if that were taken there was another behind, and another.

The Portuguese defenders were as impressive as their walls. The company marched through the first gate, a tunnel that took two right turns beneath the first massive wall, and Sharpe was pleased at the look of the Portuguese. They were confident, with the arrogance of soldiers secure in their own strength. The town's steep streets were virtually empty of civilians, most of the houses were barred shut, and from the guns on the inner walls to the bales of food stacked in courtyards, the fortress was supplied and ready. It was Portugal's front door and Masséna would need all his foxlike cunning to open it.

Brigadier Cox, the English commander of the garrison, had his headquarters at the top of the hill, but Sharpe found him in the main plaza, watching his men roll barrels of gunpowder into the door of the cathedral. Cox, tall and distinguished, returned Sharpe's salute.

Sharpe glanced at the barrels going into the dark interior of the cathedral. "You seem well prepared, sir."

Cox nodded happily. "We are, Sharpe, we are. Filled to the gunwales and ready to go." He nodded at the cathedral. "That's our magazine."

Sharpe showed his surprise and Cox laughed. "The best defences in Portugal and nowhere to store the ammunition. Can you imagine that? Luckily they built that cathedral to last. Walls like Windsor Castle and crypts like dungeons. Hey presto, a magazine. No, I can't complain, Sharpe. Plenty of guns, plenty of ammunition. We should hold the Froggies up for a couple of months." He looked speculatively at Sharpe's faded green jacket. "I could do with some prime riflemen, though."

Sharpe could see his company being ordered onto the main ramparts and he swiftly changed the subject. "I understand I'm to report to Major Kearsey, sir."

"Ah! Our exploring officer! You'll find him at the top of the castle. Can't miss it, right by the telegraph. Your lads can get breakfast in the castle."

"Thank you, sir."

Sharpe climbed the winding stairs of the mast-topped turret and came out into the early sunlight. Beyond the wooden telegraph with its four motionless bladders, identical to the arrangement at Celorico, he saw a small man on his knees, wearing the uniform of the Prince of Wales Dragoons, an open Bible lying next to a telescope at his side. Sharpe coughed and the man opened one fierce eye. "Yes?"

"Sharpe, sir. South Essex."

Kearsey nodded, shut the eye, and went back to his prayers. When he had finished he took a deep breath, smiled at the sky as if his duty were done, and turned abruptly on Sharpe. "Kearsey." He stood up, his spurs clicking on the stones. He was a foot shorter than Sharpe, but he seemed to compensate for his lack of height with a look of Cromwellian fervour. "Pleased to meet you, Sharpe." His voice was gruff and he did not sound in the least pleased. "Do you pray?"

"No, sir."

Kearsey snorted. "I'll talk to you about that later. Glad you're here, Sharpe. Now we can get going. You know what we're doing?" He did not wait for an answer. "One day's march over the River Agueda to Casatejada, pick up the gold, escort it back to British lines, and send it on its way. Clear?"

"No, sir."

Kearsey had already started walking towards the staircase and, hearing Sharpe's words, he stopped abruptly, swivelled, and looked up at the rifleman. "What don't you understand?"

"Where the gold is, who it belongs to, how we get it out, where it's going, do the enemy know, why us and not cavalry, and most of all, sir, what it's going to be used for?"

"Used for?" Kearsey looked puzzled. "Used for? None of your business, Sharpe."

"So I understand, sir."

Kearsey was walking back to the battlement. "Used for! It's Spanish gold. They can do what they like with it."

"I thought the gold was for us, sir. The British."

Kearsey started barking and Sharpe realized, after a moment's panic, that the major was laughing. "Forgive me, Sharpe. For us? What a strange idea. It's Spanish gold, belongs to them. Not for us at all! Oh no! We're just delivering it safely to Lisbon and the Royal Navy will ship it down to the Spanish government in Cádiz." Kearsey started his strange barking again, repeating to himself, "For us! For us!"

Sharpe decided it was not the time, or place, to enlighten the major. It did not matter much what Kearsey thought, as long as the gold was taken safely back over the River Coa. "Where is it now, sir?"

"I told you. Casatejada." Kearsey sat on the edge of the telegraph platform and riffled the pages of his Bible as he talked. "It's Spanish gold. Sent by the government to Salamanca to pay the army. The army gets defeated, remember? So the Spaniards have a problem. Lots of money in the middle of nowhere, no army, and the countryside crawling with the French. Luckily a good man got hold of the gold, and told me."

"Who's the 'good man', sir?"

"Ah. Cesar Moreno. A fine man, Sharpe. He leads a guerrilla band. He brought the gold from Salamanca."

"How much, sir?"

"Sixteen thousand coins."

The amount meant nothing. It depended how much each coin weighed. "Why doesn't Moreno bring it over the border, sir?"

Kearsey stroked his grey moustache, seeming unsettled by the question. "Problems, Sharpe, problems. Moreno's band is small and he's joined up with another group, a bigger group, and the new man doesn't want us to help! This man's marrying Moreno's daughter, has a lot of influence, and he's our problem. He thinks we just want to steal the gold! Can you imagine that?" Sharpe could, very well. Kearsey slapped at a fly. "Wasn't helped by our failure two weeks ago."

"Failure?"

Kearsey looked unhappy. "Cavalry, Sharpe. My own regiment, too. We sent fifty men and they got caught." He chopped his hand up and down as if it were a sabre. "Fifty. So we lost face to the Spanish, they don't trust us, and they think we're losing the war and planning to take their gold. El Católico wants to move the gold to Cádiz by land, but I've persuaded them to give us one more chance!"

"El Católico, sir?"

"I told you! The new man. Marrying Moreno's daughter."

"But why is he called the Catholic?"

The major sounded gloomy. "He prays over his victims before he kills them. The Latin prayer for the dead. Just as a joke, of course." His fingers riffled the pages as if he were drawing strength from the psalms and stories. "He's a dangerous man, Sharpe. Ex-officer, knows how to fight, and he doesn't want us."

Sharpe took a deep breath, walked to the battlement, and stared at the rocky, northern landscape. "So, sir. The gold is a day's march from here, guarded by Moreno and El Católico, and our job is to persuade them to let us take it, and escort it safely over the border."

"Quite right."

"What's to stop Moreno already taking it, sir? I mean, while you're here."

Kearsey gave a single snorting bark. "Thought of that, Sharpe. Left a man there, one of the regiment, good man. He's keeping an eye on things, keeping the partisans sweet." Kearsey stood up and pushed the Bible into his slung sabretache. "Moreno trusts us, it's only El Católico we have to worry about and he likes Hardy. I think it will be all right."

"Hardy?" Sharpe had somehow sensed the feeling of an incomplete story.

"That's right." Kearsey glanced sharply at the rifleman. "Captain Claud Hardy. You know him?"

"No, sir."

It was true. He had never met his usurper, just watched Josefina walk away to Hardy's side. He had thought that the rich young cavalry officer was in Lisbon, dancing away the nights, and instead he was waiting a day's march away. Sharpe stared westward at the deep, shadowed gorge of the Coa that slashed across the landscape.

Kearsey stamped his feet. "Anything else, Sharpe?"

"No, sir."

"Good. We march tonight. Nine o'clock."

Sharpe turned back. "Yes, sir."

"One rule, Sharpe. I know the country, you don't, so no questions, just instant obedience."

"Yes, sir."

"Company prayers at sunset, unless the Froggies interfere."

"Yes, sir." Good Lord!

Kearsey returned Sharpe's salute. "Nine o'clock, then. At the north gate!" He turned and clattered down the winding stairs and Sharpe went back to the battlement, leaned on the granite, and stared thoughtfully at the huge sprawl of the defences beneath him.

As he looked at the rough countryside to the north he tried to force his mind to think of the gold, of El Católico and Cesar Moreno. But to do the job with Josefina's lover? "God damn it!" he said aloud.

"I beg your pardon, sir?" A midshipman, fifteen years old and far from the sea, had come onto the turret to man the telegraph and he looked uncertainly at the tall, dark-haired rifleman with the scarred face.

Sharpe turned. "Nothing, son, nothing." He grinned at the bemused boy. "Gold for greed, women for jealousy, and death for the French. Right?"

"Yes, sir. Of course, sir." The boy watched him go downstairs.

390

4

On foot Kearsey was, to Sharpe's eyes, ludicrous. On horseback, though, he was at home, as if he had been restored to his true height. Sharpe was impressed by the night's march. The moon was thin and cloud-ridden, the country difficult, yet the dragoon major led the company unerringly down to the River Agueda where they waited for the first sign of dawn.

Kearsey certainly knew the countryside, the villages, the paths, the rivers and where they could be crossed; and within the countryside he knew the guerrilla bands and where they could be found. Sitting in the mist that ghosted up from the Agueda he talked about the partisans. Sharpe and Knowles listened, the unseen river a sound in the background, as he talked of ambushes, murders, the secret places where arms were stored, and the signal codes that flashed from hilltop to hilltop. "Nothing can move here, Sharpe, nothing, without the partisans knowing. The French have to escort every messenger with four hundred men. Imagine that? Four hundred sabres to protect one dispatch and sometimes even that's not enough."

Sharpe could imagine it, and even pity the French for it. Wellington paid hard cash for every captured dispatch, and the war in the hills between French soldiers and Spanish partisans was a terrible tale of pain.

"By day the men are shepherds, farmers, millers, but by night they're killers. For every Frenchman we kill, they kill two."

Knowles stretched his legs. "Do the women fight, sir?"

"They fight, Lieutenant, like the men. Moreno's daughter, Teresa, is as good as any man. She knows how to ambush, to pursue. I've seen her kill."

Sharpe looked up and saw the mist silvering overhead as the dawn leaked across the hills. "Is she the one who's to marry El Católico?"

Kearsey laughed. "Yes." He was silent for a second. "They're not all good, of course. Some are just brigands, looting their own people." He was silent again.

"Do you mean El Católico, sir?" Knowles asked.

"No." Kearsey seemed uncertain. "But he's a hard man. You must understand, Lieutenant, how much they hate. Teresa's mother was killed by the French and she did not die well." He peered up at the lightening mist. "We must move. Casatejada's a two-hour march." He stood up. "You'll find it best to tie your boots round your neck as we cross the river."

"Yes, sir." Sharpe said it patiently. He had probably crossed a thousand rivers in his years as a soldier, but Kearsey insisted on treating them all as pure amateurs.

Once over the Agueda, Kearsey rode ahead searching the landscape for signs of the enemy. The hills were the French hunting ground, the scene of countless small and bloody encounters between cavalrymen and partisans, and Kearsey led the Light Company on paths high up the slopes so that, should an enemy patrol appear, they could scramble quickly into the high rocks where horsemen could not follow. The company seemed excited, glad to be near the enemy. Sharpe had twenty riflemen now, including himself and Harper, the best of them all. They were good men, the Green Jackets, and he was proud of them. Daniel Hagman, in his forties, was the oldest man in the company, but the best marksman. A Cheshire man, raised as a poacher, Hagman could shoot the buttons off a French general at three hundred yards. Parry Jenkins, five feet four inches of Welsh loquaciousness, could tease fish out of the most reluctant water, while Isaiah Tongue, educated in books and alcohol, believed that Napoleon was an enlightened genius but nevertheless fought with the cool deliberation of a good rifleman.

The other thirty-three were all redcoats, armed with the smooth-bore Brown Bess musket. Most were criminals, avoiding justice by enlisting, and nearly all were drunks, but they had proved themselves at Talavera and in the tedious winter patrols. Sharpe nodded at James Kelly, an Irish corporal who had stunned the battalion by marrying Pru Baxter, a widow who was a foot taller and two stones heavier than the skinny Kelly, but the corporal had hardly stopped smiling in the three months since the marriage. Lieutenant Knowles, although still awed by Sharpe, was a good officer, decisive and fair.

Sergeant Harper moved alongside Sharpe. Over his shoulder he had slung two packs belonging to men who were failing with tiredness after the night's march. He nodded ahead. "What's next, sir?"

"We pick up the gold and come back. Simple."

Harper grinned. "You believe that, sir?"

Sharpe had no time to reply. Kearsey had stopped two hundred yards ahead, and dismounted. His arm pointed left, up the slope, and Sharpe repeated the gesture. The company moved quickly off the path and crouched while Sharpe, puzzled, ran towards the major. "Sir?"

Kearsey nodded at a hilltop, half a mile away. "See the stones?"

Sharpe could see a heap of boulders on the peak of the hill. "Yes, sir."

"There's a white stone showing, yes?" Sharpe nodded. "That means the enemy are abroad."

The major led his horse into the tangle of rocks and Sharpe followed patiently, wondering how many other secret signs they had passed in the night. The company were curious but silent, as Kearsey led them over the crest into a rock-strewn village.

"They won't be up here, Sharpe."

"Where then?"

"Casatejada." Kearsey nodded ahead, worried, past the head of the valley to the village where the gold should be waiting.

To the north, over the hilltops, a bank of cloud was ominous and

393

still on the horizon, but otherwise the sky was arching an untouched blue over the pale grass and rocks. Everything seemed innocent, a high valley in morning sunshine.

A mile up the valley, as the sides began to flatten out into a bleak hilltop, Kearsey tethered his horse to a rock, and turned back to Sharpe. "Come on. Keep low."

The skyline proved to be a false crest. Beyond was a gully, shaped like a bowl, and as Sharpe ran over the lip he realized that Kearsey had brought them to a vantage point that was overlooked only by the peak with its white, warning stone. It was a steep scramble over the edge, and the company tumbled into the bowl and sat, grateful for the rest. Kearsey beckoned Sharpe to the far side. "Keep low!" The two officers used hands and feet to climb the bowl's inner face and then they were peering over the edge. "Casatejada." He spoke almost grudgingly as if not wanting to share this high and secret village with another Englishman.

Casatejada was beautiful, built in a valley where two streams met and irrigated enough land to keep forty or so families supplied with food. Sharpe began to memorize the layout of the village, two miles away, from the old ruined fortress-tower at one end of the main street, a reminder that this was border country, past the church, to the one large house at the far end of the street, built round a lavish courtyard. He asked Kearsey about the house.

"Moreno's house, Sharpe."

"He's rich?"

Kearsey shrugged. "Used to be. The family own the whole valley and a lot of other land. But who's rich with the French here?"

There were no animals in sight, no humans on the single village street, just the wind stirring the barley that should have been harvested. Sharpe let his eyes travel beyond the church, across a flat pasture to an orchard and there, half hidden by trees, was another church and a bell tower. "What's the far church, sir?"

"Hermitage," Kearsey grunted. "Some holy man lived there, long ago. It's not used now, except that the graveyard's there." Sharpe could see the walled cemetery through the trees. Kearsey nodded at the hermitage. "That's where the gold is."

394

"Where's it hidden?"

"In the Moreno vault, inside the hermitage." Kearsey was chewing his grey moustache, glancing up at the white stones on the hilltop, back to the village. "They must be there."

"The French?" Sharpe was beginning to realize how little he knew of this kind of warfare.

"An ambush." Kearsey spoke quietly. "The weather vane on the church. It's moving. When the partisans are in the village they jam it so you know they're there. There are no animals. The French have butchered them for food. They're waiting, Sharpe, in the village and they want the partisans to think they've gone."

"Will they?"

Kearsey gave his bark. "No. They're too clever. The French can wait all day."

"And us, sir?"

Kearsey flashed one of his fierce glances. "We wait, too."

The sun's heat increased, baking the rocks. Most of the company used their weapons to support spread greatcoats to give themselves shade and slept, heads pillowed on haversacks, while single sentries watched the empty landscape. Sharpe was frustrated. He could climb the gully's rim, see where the gold was stored, hidden in a seemingly uninhabited valley, yet he could do nothing. As midday approached he slept himself.

"Sir!" Harper was shaking him. "We've got action."

He had slept no more than fifteen minutes. "Action?"

"In the valley, sir."

The company was stirring, looking eagerly up at Sharpe, but he waved them down. They would have to stifle their curiosity and watch, instead, as Sharpe and Harper climbed up beside Kearsey and Knowles on the rock rim. Kearsey was grinning at them. "Watch this."

From the north, from a track that led down from high pastures, five horsemen trotted slowly towards the village. Kearsey had his telescope extended and Sharpe reached for his own. "Partisans, sir?"

Kearsey nodded. "Three of them."

Sharpe pulled out his glass and found the small group of horse-men. The Spaniards rode straight backed and easy, looking relaxed and comfortable, but their two companions were quite different. Naked, the men were tied to the saddles, and through the glass Sharpe could see their heads jerking with fear.

"Prisoners." Kearsey said the word fiercely.

"What's going to happen?" Knowles was fidgeting.

"Wait."

Nothing stirred in the village. If the French were there then they were well hidden.

The horsemen had stopped. One Spaniard held the reins of the prisoners' horses while the others dismounted. The naked men were pulled from their saddles and the ropes that had tied their legs beneath the horses' bellies were used to lash their ankles tightly together. Then more rope was produced, and the two Frenchmen were tied behind the horses.

Knowles had borrowed Sharpe's telescope. "They won't gallop far," he said, half in hope.

Kearsey shook his head. "They will."

Sharpe took the glass back. The partisans were undoing their saddle bags, going back to the horses with their roped men who would be dragged over the ground.

"What are they doing, sir?"

"Thistles."

Sharpe understood. Along the paths and in the high rocks huge purple thistles grew, often as high as a man, and the Spanish were thrusting the heads of the spiny plants beneath the empty saddles. The first horse began rearing up, but was held firm, until with a final crack over its rump the beast was released and sprang off, infuriated by the pain. The prisoner was jerked by the legs and scraped in a cloud of dust behind the angry horse.

The second horse followed, pulling left and right, zig-zagging behind the first towards the village. The three Spaniards mounted and stood their horses quietly. One had a long cigar and, through the telescope, Sharpe saw the smoke drift over the fields.

"Good God!" Knowles stared unbelieving.

"No need for blasphemy." Kearsey's reprimand was gruff.

The two tied men were invisible in the dust, but, as the horses swerved at a rock, Sharpe caught just a glimpse, a flash through the cloud, of a body streaked red, and then the horses were running again.

By now the Frenchmen would be unconscious, the pain gone. But the partisans had guessed right and the gates of Cesar Moreno's big house were thrown open. Cavalry hussars, hidden all morning, rode onto the street. Sharpe saw sky-blue trousers, brown jackets, and the tall fur helmets.

The hussars cantered down the street to rescue the two bloody and battered Frenchmen at the northern end of the village. But then the two horses became aware of the cavalry and stopped. Suddenly they whirled and galloped away from the hussars, splitting apart in a mad, thistle-driven panic. Kearsey nodded. "They won't go near French cavalry, not unless they're ridden. They're too used to running from it."

There was chaos in the valley. The horses circled crazily in the fields while the hussars, all order gone, tried to ride them down. Sharpe guessed there were a hundred Frenchmen, in undisciplined groups, crossing and recrossing the fields. He wondered how he would feel if those two bodies were his men, and he knew that he would do what the French had done; try to rescue them.

One of the horses had been caught and quieted, and dismounted French cavalrymen were unbuckling the girth and untying the prisoner. And at that exact moment El Católico launched his own horsemen from the northern hills. Kearsey barked out a description, "Grey cloak, grey boots, long rapier, black horse," but even without it Sharpe would have recognized the tall man as the leader.

They came down onto the scattered and outnumbered French in a long line, blacks and browns and greys, swords held over their heads, the dust spurting behind them, while from the rocks of the hillside Sharpe saw muskets firing over their heads at the surprised French.

Kearsey slammed his fist against the rock. "Perfect!"

The ambushers had been ambushed.

5

Kearsey was thumping his fist on the rock, willing the partisans on, closer and closer to the wheeling French. Sharpe scanned the guerrilla line, looking for the blue and silver of a Prince of Wales Dragoon, but he could see no sign of Hardy. He remembered Kearsey saying that El Católico's betrothed, Teresa, fought like a man, but he could see no woman in the charging line, just men screaming defiance as the first horses met and the swords chopped down on the outnumbered French.

In the village trumpets split the quiet; men scrambled onto mounts, sabres hissed from scabbards. But El Católico was no fool — he was not going to fight a regiment. Sharpe saw him waving at his men, turning them back, and the rifleman searched with the telescope in the obscuring dust for clues to what was happening. The French, outnumbered two to one, had been hard punished. They had fallen for the lure, and then had been savagely hurt in one quick charge. Sharpe admired the action. It was hardly two minutes since the Spanish had appeared and already, hidden by dust, they were returning to the hills. One man alone stayed in the valley.

El Católico stood his horse and watched the hussars. Close to him were the survivors of the charge and they now spurred their horses to the attack. El Católico seemed unconcerned. He urged his horse into a canter, circled away from the safety of the hills, looking over his shoulder as the French came close. A dozen men were chasing him, leaning over the manes of their horses, sabres stretched out, and it was certain that the tall partisan leader must be taken until, at the last moment, his horse sidestepped, the thin rapier flashed, one Frenchman was down and the big, black horse with its grey rider was in full gallop to the north and the hussars were milling in uncertainty where their leader lay dead. Sharpe whistled softly.

Kearsey smiled. "He's the finest swordsman on the border. Probably in Spain."

Sharpe stared into the valley. A hundred hussars had ridden out to rescue the two prisoners and now two dozen of them were dead or captured. The partisans had lost none, and their leader, staying till the end, had slapped French pride in the face. The black horse was cantering to the hills, its strength obvious, and the French would never catch El Católico.

"That's how it's done." Kearsey slid down from the rock.

Sharpe nodded. "Impressive. Except for one thing."

The dragoon's eyebrow shot up. "What?"

"What are the French doing in the village?"

"Clearing out a hornet's nest." Kearsey waved southwards. "Remember their main road is down there. All the supplies for the siege of Almeida go through this area and they don't want partisans in their rear. They're trying to clear them out."

The answer made sense to Sharpe, but he was still worried. "And the gold, sir?"

"It's hidden."

"And Hardy?"

Kearsey was annoyed by the questions. "He'll be somewhere, Sharpe; I don't know. At least El Católico's here, so we're not friendless!" He gave his bark of a laugh and then pulled at his moustache. "I think it would be sensible to let him know we've arrived." He slid down the inner side of the gully. "Keep your men here, Sharpe. I'll ride to El Católico, round the back of the village. I'll see you again tonight sometime, probably late. Don't light any fires!" He strode away.

Harper waited till he was out of earshot. "What did he think we were going to do? Borrow a light from the French?" He looked at Sharpe. "Bloody muddle, sir."

"Yes." But it was not too bad, Sharpe decided. The French could not stay for ever, the partisans would be back in the village, and then there was only the small problem of persuading El Católico to let the British "escort" the gold towards Lisbon. He turned back to the valley, watched as the hussars walked their horses disconsolately towards the village, then raised his eyes and looked at the hermitage. Although it was the far side of the valley, beyond the village, he was tempted to search the place that night, Kearsey or no Kearsey. The idea refused to go away and he lay there, the sun hot on his back, and thought of a dozen reasons why he should not make the attempt, and one huge, overriding reason why he should.

The valley settled in peace. The sun burned down on the grass, and still, on the northern horizon, the great cloud bank loomed. There would be rain in a couple of days. Sharpe let his imagination play with the idea of finding the gold in the middle of the night, just two hundred yards from a French regiment, and bringing it safely back to the gully. What if the hermitage was locked? A lock was no problem: a dozen men in the company had once earned a living by opening up locks. Kearsey had said the gold was in the Moreno vault, which should be easy enough to find. . . .

Sharpe lay in the westering sun, looking at the valley. It could be done. A pox on Kearsey. What if there was more gold than they could carry? Then they must carry what they could. He wondered about a diversion, a small group of riflemen in the southern end of the valley to distract the French, but he rejected the idea. Keep it simple. Night attacks could go disastrously wrong and the smallest complication could turn a well-thought plan into a horrid mess. His excitement grew. They could do it!

AT FIRST the trumpet was so faint that it hardly penetrated Sharpe's consciousness. Rather it was Harper's sudden alertness that stirred him, dragged his mind from the gold beneath the Moreno vault, and made him curse as he looked at the road disappearing to the northeast. "What was that?"

400

Harper stared at the empty valley. "Cavalry. Nearer to us than the partisans were, sir. Something's happening up there."

They waited, in silence, and watched the valley. Knowles climbed up beside them. "What's happening?"

"Don't know." Sharpe turned and called to the sentry on the far side of the gully. "See anything?"

"No, sir."

"There!" Harper was pointing to the road. Kearsey was in sight on his big roan covering the rough ground towards the slopes where the partisans had disappeared. And behind him were rank upon rank of enemy horsemen in blue and yellow, each one wearing a strange, square, yellow hat, and carrying lances instead of swords, long, steel-tipped weapons with red and white pennants. As Sharpe watched, the lancers kicked in their heels, dropped their points, and the race was on.

Knowles shook his head. "What are they?"

"Polish lancers." Sharpe's voice was grim. The Poles had a reputation in Europe; nasty fighters, effective fighters. These were the first he had encountered in his career. He wondered how many regiments of cavalry the French had thrown up into the hills to wipe out the guerrilla bands, and how long they would stay.

"They won't get him, sir." Knowles sounded very sure.

"Why not?"

"The major explained to me, sir. His horse is fed on corn, and most cavalry horses are grass-fed. A grass-fed horse can't catch a corn-fed horse."

Sharpe raised his eyebrows. "Has anyone told the horses?" He snapped his glass open, found Kearsey, and saw the major look over his shoulder and urge his horse on. The big roan responded, widening the gap from the nearest lancers, galloping easily. Kearsey had not even bothered to unsheath his sabre and Sharpe was just relaxing when suddenly a bird flew up, startled, right beneath the horse's nose. It reared, twisted sideways, and Kearsey fell.

Sharpe focused the glass again. Kearsey was on his feet, reaching up desperately to put his foot in the stirrup. The trumpet sounded again, the sound delayed by the distance, but Sharpe had already seen the lancers spurring their horses, and he gritted his teeth as Kearsey seemed to take an age in swinging himself into the saddle.

"Where's El Católico?" Knowles asked.

"Miles away." Harper sounded gloomy.

The horse went forward again, Kearsey's heels raking back, but the lancers were desperately close. The major turned downslope towards the village, but the roan's head tossed nervously, and at the moment when Sharpe knew the lancers must catch him the major realized it as well. He circled back, sword drawn.

Four lancers were closest to the major. He spurred towards them, and Sharpe saw the sabre being held, point downwards, high in Kearsey's hand. His horse had calmed, was responsive and, as the lancers thundered in, Kearsey touched the spurs, leaped forward, and had turned the righthand lance to one side, swivelled his wrist with the speed of a trained swordsman, and one Pole lay beheaded, on the ground.

Kearsey was through, crouching on his horse's neck, urging it on towards the hills, but the first squadron of lancers was close behind their fellows, at full gallop, and the effort was useless. The dustcloud engulfed the Englishman, the silver lance points disappeared in the storm, and Kearsey was trapped with only his sword to save him. The dust billowed like cannon smoke. Lances were forced upwards in the press and once Sharpe thought he saw the flashing light of the lifted sabre. It was magnificent, quite hopeless, one man against a regiment. Sharpe watched the commotion subside, and the lance points sink to rest. It was over.

"Poor bastard," Harper muttered.

"He's alive!" Knowles was pointing. "Look!"

It was true. Sharpe rested the glass on the rock rim of the gully and saw the major riding between two of his captors. There was blood on his thigh, but only a smear. It was a good capture for the Poles: an exploring officer whom they could keep for a few months before exchanging for a Frenchman of equal rank.

Half the lancers rode with their prisoner to the village, but the other half, in a curving column, trotted towards the graveyard and its hermitage. Sharpe cursed beneath his breath. There was no hope now of finding the gold that night, the only chance left was to wait until both the French and the Poles had gone. And when they went El Católico would come, and Sharpe had no doubt that the tall, grey-cloaked Spaniard would use every effort to stop the British taking the gold. Only one man stood a chance of persuading the partisan leader, and that man was a wounded prisoner. He eased back from the skyline, turned and stared at the company.

Harper slid down beside him. "What do we do, sir?"

"Do? We fight. We've been spectators long enough. We get the major out, tonight."

Knowles heard him, scrambled down the slope. "Get him out, sir? There's two regiments there!"

"So? That's only eight hundred men. There are fifty-three of us."

"And a dozen Irish." Harper grinned.

Knowles looked at them with a disbelieving stare. "With respect, sir. You're mad." He began to laugh. "Are you serious?"

Sharpe nodded. There was no other choice. Fifty-three men must take on eight hundred, or else Wellington's hopes were dashed, and the war was lost. He grinned at Knowles. "Stop worrying! It'll be simple!" And how the hell, he thought, do we do it?

6

Sharpe mocked himself. So simple. Just release the major from two of the finest regiments in the French army. The wise course, he thought, was to go home. The French probably had the gold by now, the war was lost, and a sensible man would shoulder his rifle and think about making a living at home. Instead, like a gambler who had lost all but a handful of coins, he was staking everything on one last throw.

As the sun westered he lay on the gully's rim and watched the French preparations. They were thorough, but in their defence was their weakness: they expected an attack by partisans, by small groups of silent men and they had prepared themselves for that ordeal. They had no outlying sentries. To put a small group of men out in the fields was to write their death sentence and the French, accustomed to this kind of fighting, had drawn themselves into make-shift fortresses. Most of the cavalry were in Cesar Moreno's house with its ample stabling and high, encircling wall. The only other building with a wall high and strong enough was the hermitage with its cemetery. Both buildings would be crowded, but both safe from the silent knives, and to make them safer every tree, every door, every stick of furniture had been piled into heaps that could be lit so an attacking partisan would be denied the gift of darkness. In their wildest dreams the French would not imagine the sudden appearance of British infantry, the crossbelts vivid in the defensive firelight, the muskets flaming disciplined death. Or so Sharpe hoped.

He had one other advantage, slight but important. Kearsey had obviously given his parole, a gentleman's promise to his captors that he would not attempt to escape, and Sharpe had seen the small major limping round the village. Each time Kearsey had gone back to Moreno's house and finally, as the light faded, Sharpe had seen the major sitting on a balcony, on one of the few pieces of furniture left, so at least the rescuers knew where their goal lay. All that remained was to break into the house and for that speed was vital.

Now, as the company filed down a goat track in the darkness, Sharpe dared not hurry the men for fear of getting lost. They slipped and cursed on the stones, squinting in the tiny light that came from the sickle moon hazed by the northern clouds. To the east stars pricked at the outline of the hills and, as they neared the valley floor and midnight approached, the French lit fires that beckoned in the dark night.

Harper was beside Sharpe. "They'll blind themselves, sir."

"Yes." The French, in the security of their firelight, would see nothing beyond a musket shot from their walls. The circling night would be a place of fantasy and strange shapes.

They neared the village, feeling naked and obvious in the wide valley. Sharpe strained his senses for a telltale sign that a sentry, high on Moreno's house, had been alerted. The click of a carbine lock, the scrape of an officer's sword, or the sudden stab of flame as a picquet saw dark shapes in the field. The crunching of the dry soil beneath his feet seemed to be magnified into a terrible loudness, and —

A flash of light. "Down!" Sharpe hissed. Flames whipped crazily into the night, spewed sparks that spiralled away in the breeze, and then Sharpe realized that the cavalrymen had lit another fire, one of the timber piles out in the cleared space. He stayed on the ground, listening to the pounding of his heart, and searched the dark shapes of the deserted cottages to his front. He took a breath. "Sergeant?"

"Sir."

"You and me. Lieutenant?"

"Sir?"

"Wait here."

Sharpe and Harper went forward, dark uniforms blending with the night. Sharpe could hear every rustle of his jacket and creak of his belt, and the looming walls seemed to hold danger in every shadow. He felt himself tense with anticipation as his hand reached out and touched a drystone wall, leading into an alleyway that stank of manure. Harper, a vast shadow, crossed the alley and crouched by the main street. A fire flickered at its end, sending crazy shadows, but the cottages were deserted and Sharpe relaxed. They went back to the outer wall and Harper whistled softly, and the shadows in the barley humped and moved forward.

Sharpe found Knowles. "We stay on this side of the house. Rifles first. Wait for the signals."

Knowles nodded and his teeth flashed white. Sharpe could feel the excitement of the company, their confidence, and he marvelled at it. They were enjoying it, taking on sixteen times their number, and he did not understand why. Harper knew, Knowles knew, that the tall rifle captain who was not given to rousing speeches could nevertheless make men feel that victory was just a commonplace where he led. "Come on!"

They went in fits and starts beside the outer walls, the riflemen scouting the dark shadows, the company catching up, and the only breath-stopping moment was as they passed beneath the tall, dark tower of the church. A sound came from the belfry, a musical whisper, and the men froze, their eyes suddenly scared, and then came a white flash, beating wings, receding in the blackness, and the company sighed together as the owl, which had brushed a wing against the hanging bell, disappeared on its own hunt.

"Halt!" Sharpe's voice was scarcely above a whisper. He pointed. "In there."

The company crowded into an alley, the firelight uncomfortably close, and Sharpe peered cautiously into the street. For the first time he could properly see the front of Moreno's house. The great double gate through which the farm animals could be driven was still wide open. Inside he could see white faces, staring at the fires that were the main defence and behind the faces the dim shadows of mounted men.

The front wall of the courtyard had no firestep, no platform on which men could stand and keep watch, so the French had no choice other than to keep the gate open and light the area in front beyond the range of a musket shot. The only danger from the front would be an attack by trained troops and that, the French knew, was an impossibility. Sharpe grinned.

The fire in front of the gate crackled and roared and its noise covered the scuffling in the alley as the redcoats of the South Essex struggled from their greatcoats, rolling them up and strapping the bundles to their packs. The riflemen crouched near him, some fidgeting with excitement, all wanting to start the action, to dispel the nervous thoughts of anticipation. Knowles passed through the men. "Ready, sir."

Sharpe turned to the riflemen. "Remember. Go for officers."

The Baker rifle, although slow to load, was a deadly weapon, more accurate than any gun on the battlefield. The muskets, under Lieutenant Knowles, could spread death in a wide arc, but the rifles were instruments of precision. Sharpe turned again towards the house. Forty yards. He could hear the mutter of voices, the trampling of hooves in the yard, a man coughing, and then he touched Harper's shoulder and the riflemen slithered into the street, crawling on their bellies, hiding in the shadows. They would go first, to draw the enemy fire, to start the chaos, and the rest was up to Knowles. Sharpe waited. He inched the sword out of its scabbard, laid it in front of him, and waited as his men put the long bayonets on their rifles. It had been so long since he had faced the enemy.

"Come on!" He had ordered them to scream, to shout, to sound like the fiends of hell, and they scrambled over the rubble, the long rifles silent, and the guards at the gate whirled, jerked up carbines and fired too soon. Harper ran forward to the fire and grabbed, with both hands, the unburned end of a baulk of timber. He hurled the flaming wood at the waiting horsemen. It struck the ground, exploded in sparks, and the horses reared up and Sharpe's sword was reaching for the first guard who had dropped an empty carbine and was trying to snatch up his sabre. The sword took the hussar in the throat, the man grabbed at the blade, seemed to shake his head and slumped. Sharpe turned to the riflemen. "Forward!"

They knelt and aimed at the firelit space. Voices shouted in strange languages, bullets chipped at the cobbled entrance, and Sharpe heard the first distinctive cracks of the Baker rifles. He turned and saw the redcoats running round the fire, being formed up, their muskets deliberately untipped by bayonets, so as not to slow the loading of fresh rounds, and then Harper's voice bellowed at him. "Sir!"

He turned. A lancer was riding for him. The horse tossed its head, eyes reflecting firelight; the rider was crouched on its neck, the steel blade reaching for Sharpe, and he slammed himself to one side, hitting the gatepost, saw the spear go past, and the horse stank in his nostrils, was past, a rifle spat, and the beast screamed.

The Pole's arms went up and man and horse fell sideways, and Sharpe was running forward, into the courtyard.

Everything was too slow! Horses were tethered and he hacked at the ropes. "Hup! Hup! Hup!" A man swung a sabre at him, missed, and Sharpe rammed his sword into his chest. Riflemen ran past, screaming incoherently, long bayonets driving scattered Frenchmen into dark doorways. Harper stamped forward, bayonet

outstretched, driving back an officer who screamed for help. The man tripped, fell backwards, the screams becoming panic as he fell into a fire and Harper turned, forgot him, and Sharpe yelled to him to get out of the way. "Rifles!"

He blew his whistle, shouted at them, brought them over to the building where he stood. Stray horses skittered in the yard, reared as the company, white belts gleaming, filled the entrance, and

Lieutenant Knowles began the terrible commands that would chill any Frenchmen who knew the firepower of British infantry. "Present! Front rank only! Fire!"

It was the last thing the hussars and lancers could have expected. Instead of brigands and silent knives they were fighting a clockwork machine that could spit out four volleys a minute. The muskets flamed, smoke gouted into the courtyard, the three-quarter inch musket balls hammered between the walls. "Rear rank! Look to the roof!" The front rank were already taking the next cartridge from their ammunition pouch. The left hand held the top of the barrel, the right poured the powder, the left gripped the paper and tore it off while the right kept the priming between finger and thumb. The bullet was pushed loosely into the muzzle, the other three fingers of the right hand had the ramrod, up in the air, and down with the steel rod, and out again, the gun swung up, and all the time they had to ignore the shouts of the enemy, the carbine bullets, the screaming horses, the fires, and put the pinch of powder into the pan after the flint was dragged back, and the rear rank had fired, flash and explosion in their ears, as Lieutenant Knowles, his voice calm, was ordering the slaughter. "Present! Fire!" The clockwork killing – no infantry in the world did it better. Fire, reload, present, fire, until their faces were blackened with powder, their eyes smarting with the grains of powder thrown up by the priming just inches from their cheeks, their shoulders bruised by the kick of the gun, and the courtyard ahead was littered with the bodies of their enemy, and all the time Knowles had taken them forward, two steps at a time, and the maddened horses had escaped behind them and Hagman's group of four riflemen had shut the gates. Hardly a minute had passed.

"Inside!" Sharpe kicked at a door, Harper hit it, and the riflemen were inside the house. Someone fired at them, a pistol, but the bullet went wide and Sharpe was hacking with the sword. "Bayonets!" The riflemen formed line, snarled forward, and Sharpe saw they were in a hall which was officer country, the table littered with used bottles, stairs leading to bedrooms.

Now there was trouble. Officers at the top of the stairs had seen

410

what was happening, found mattresses and the furniture they had kept for their own use and were throwing up a barricade. Sharpe needed to clear the stair's top.

It would be suicide on the stairs, and Sharpe stopped Harper as he took a pace towards the steps. "Give me the gun!" he demanded.

Harper looked at the seven-barrelled gun, grinned, and shook his head. Before Sharpe could stop him the sergeant had leaped to the bottom step, pointed the fearful weapon upwards, and pulled the trigger. It was as if a small cannon had gone off in the room. It belched smoke and flame, stunned the eardrums, and to Sharpe's horror the sergeant fell backwards.

Sharpe ran to him, fearing the worst, but the Irishman was grinning as he scrambled to his feet. "Bloody recoil!"

"Up!" Sharpe took the stairs two at a time, the sword ahead, seeing an officer aiming a pistol. There was nothing Sharpe could do. He saw the trigger pulled, the cock fall forward, and nothing happened. In his panic the Frenchman had forgotten to prime the pan. It was his death sentence. The sword slammed down, cutting skull and brain, and Sharpe seized the mattresses and threw them aside, slashing at the slim sabres of the two men who had survived the seven-barrelled gun.

"Rifles!" Harper pounded up the stairs followed by green-jacketed men. Behind him, Sharpe lunged, wounded a man, stepped aside as another swung wildly and then Harper was beside him, sword bayonet stabbing. Soon the landing was clear.

"Kearsey!" Sharpe yelled, forgetting niceties of rank. Where was he? "Kearsey!"

"Sharpe?" The major was in a doorway, buckling his trousers.

"Get out of here, Major!"

"My parole!"

"You're rescued!"

Kearsey suddenly seemed to wake up. "That way!" He pointed at two closed doors. "You drop outside the house."

Sharpe nodded. The landing seemed safe. The riflemen were reloading, waiting for orders, and Sharpe went to the stairhead. Downstairs was chaos. The room was filled with musket smoke that

411

was lanced, second by second, with the stabbing flames as the redcoats fired at windows, doors and passageways. Knowles had long stopped controlling the volleys. Now each man fired as fast as he could and the burning paper wads, spat after the musket balls, were setting fire to rush mats and hanging curtains. Sharpe cupped his hands. "Lieutenant! There's a way out up here!"

Knowles nodded and turned back to his men. Sharpe found Kearsey at his side, hopping on one leg as he pulled on a boot. "The rifles will cover them as they come up, Major! Take over!"

Kearsey nodded, showed no surprise at Sharpe's peremptory commands, and the tall rifleman turned to the closed doors. The first was not locked. The room was empty, the window invitingly open, and Harper went through to knock out the remaining glass and frame. Sharpe tried the other door, it resisted, and he hit it with his shoulder, the wood round the lock splintering easily, and he stopped.

On the bed, hands and feet tied to the four stubby posts, was a girl. Dark hair on a pillow, a white dress, and eyes that glared at him over a gag. She was struggling to free herself, and Sharpe was struck by her fierce beauty. The shots still sounded downstairs, a sudden cry, the smell of flames catching wood.

Harper came in and saw the girl. "God save old Ireland."

"Cut her free!"

Sharpe could hear Knowles downstairs, counting the men off, sending the wounded up first. He ran to the window, smashed panes with the sword, and saw the empty darkness outside. They could make it! The first redcoats were at the head of the stairs, and Sharpe whipped round to see that the slim, dark-haired girl was free, rubbing her wrists.

"Patrick! Get the men in here. Through the window! And next door!" The girl looked at Sharpe, then ran out of the door, ignoring the fight, and turned right. Sharpe was thrown off balance by her beauty, hardly hearing the commands from the landing, the banging muskets. He followed her, caution gone, just the instinct left that some things, just one thing perhaps, could turn a man's life inside out.

412

7

Knowles had done well. The hall was on fire, but empty of the enemy, and the redcoats backed up the stairs, still loading and firing their muskets, ignoring the fresh blood that made the steps slippery, and then the riflemen took over, the Bakers spitting into the hallway below and Major Kearsey, sabre in hand, was pushing the men into a bedroom, towards a window and shouting "Jump!"

The girl had run through a door and Sharpe followed, noticing, irrelevantly, a small statue of the Virgin Mary with a host of candles flickering at its base. He was grateful for the light because the stairs beyond the door were pitch-dark, and he grabbed a candle and followed the fading footsteps. He hurried, cursing his impetuosity. His place was with his men, not chasing some girl because she had long black hair, a slim body, and a beauty that reminded him of his old love. But this was not a night for sensible action, it was a mad darkness, and he rationalized that if she had been kept a prisoner then she was important to the enemy, and so important to ˙him.

The stairway plunged below ground level, into the cellars, and he was still hurtling down, half out of control with the candle flame blown out, when a white arm shot out and her voice hushed him. They were by a door; light leaked through its gaping planks. Sharpe pushed it open, ignoring her caution. In the cellar a lantern hung from a hook, and beneath it, fear across his face, was a lancer holding a musket and bayonet. He lunged at Sharpe, thinking to kill with a blade rather than pulling a trigger, but Sharpe had cut his teeth on just such fighting. He let the bayonet come, stepped aside, and used the enemy's own momentum to run the sword blade into his stomach. Sharpe stepped over the body, and then he nearly gagged.

Wine racks stood by the walls, looted empty, but the floor was black with blood, strewn with mutilated bodies obscene as nightmare. Young, old, men and women, Spaniards all killed horribly. It struck Sharpe that these people must have died the day before, as he watched from the hilltop, killed as the French pretended the village was empty. He had lain in the gully, the sun warm on his back, and in the cellar the Spanish had died, slowly. Sharpe felt an impotent rage as the girl stepped past him, and from far away, as if across a whole town, Sharpe heard a volley of shots. They must get out! He grabbed the girl's arm. "Come on!"

"No!"

She was searching, pulling at the bodies. Sharpe pushed past her, took the lantern. He had heard a moaning from the far, dark end of the wine cellar. The girl heard, too. "Ramon!"

Sharpe stepped on dead flesh, flinched from a spider's web, and then, dimly at first, he saw a man by the far wall. He took the lantern closer and saw that the man was nailed to the wall, alive.

"Ramon!" The girl was past Sharpe, pulling ineffectively at the nails, and Sharpe put the lantern down, and hammered at the nail heads with his sword's brass hilt. He knocked them left and right, and then one nail was loose, blood trickling afresh, and he pulled it out and started on the second hand, hammering desperately until the prisoner was free. He gave the girl his sword and heaved Ramon, if that was his name, onto his shoulder. "Go on!"

The girl took the lantern and led him past the doorway they had come through, past the blood and bodies, to the far corner of the cellar. A trapdoor was revealed in the lantern light and she gestured at it. Sharpe dropped his moaning burden, reached up, heaved, and a sudden breeze of welcome night air dispelled the foul stench of blood and death. He pulled himself up. The trapdoor emerged outside the house walls. He looked round and there was the company, forming up in the field. "Sergeant!"

Harper turned, relief visible on his face in the light from the burning house. Sharpe dropped back into the cellar, heaved the wounded man up, leaped after him and reached down for the girl. She ignored him, pulling herself up. There were cheers from the men. Harper was there, thumping his back, saying something unintelligible about thinking Sharpe was lost, and then the sergeant had the wounded man and they were running towards the company and Sharpe, for the first time, saw horsemen in the darkness.

"Are they loaded?" Sharpe gestured at the muskets, screamed at Knowles over the sound of the burning house.

"Most, sir."

"Keep going!" Sharpe pushed Knowles on, driving the company towards the barley field and the darkness, and turned to face the cavalry. Harper was there, running backwards, the seven-barrelled gun threatening any horseman. It was no more than seven or eight minutes since they had burst through the gate: enough time for Sharpe's men to have fired seven or eight hundred shots into the astonished French, set fire to the house, and rescue Kearsey, the girl and the prisoner.

"Watch right!" Harper called. A dozen lancers were coming up in line, the wicked points held low so that they glittered by the ground. They were coming at a trot, to take the company in the flank, but there was still time. "Right wheel!"

The company turned, three ranks swivelling. "Halt!" A ragged line, but it would do. "Rear rank about turn. Hold your fire!" That looked after the rear. "Present! Aim at their stomachs, give them a bellyache! Fire!"

It was inevitable. The lancers became a turmoil of falling men and horses. "Right turn! Forward!" He had the small company in a column now. "Double!" There were more hoof beats behind, but not enough loaded muskets to fight off another charge. Time only to run. "Run!"

The company ran, sprinting despite their burdens, and Sharpe heard a wounded man groan. Time later to count the wounded. He saw lancers coming in desperate chase, one aiming at Harper, but the Irishman dashed the lance aside with the squat gun and reached up a huge hand that plucked the Pole clean out of the saddle. He held the lancer effortlessly, his huge strength making the man seem to be weightless, and then threw him at the feet of another horse. A rifle cracked behind Sharpe, another horse went down, and Hagman's voice came through the din. "Got him!"

Suddenly the barley was under Sharpe's feet and he ran into the field, and for a moment the trumpets meant nothing to him. Then he heard Harper's triumphant voice. "The recall! Bastards have had enough!" Harper was laughing. "You did it, sir!"

Sharpe slowed down, let the breath heave in his chest. It was strangely quiet in the field, the hooves muted, the gunfire stopped, and he guessed that the French refused to believe that just fifty men had attacked the village. The sight of red jackets and crossbelts would have convinced them that a hidden British regiment must be out in the darkness. He listened to the' men panting, the wounded moaning as they were carried, and he wondered what the price had been. "Are you all right?" he turned to Harper.

"Yes, sir. Yourself?"

"Bruised. What's the bill?"

"Don't know for certain, sir. Jim Kelly's bad. Cresacre's bleeding, says he's all right. We lost a couple though. Saw them in the courtyard."

"Who?" He should have known.

"Don't know, sir."

They climbed, up into the hills, up where horses could not go, back to the gully which they reached as the far hills were lined with the faintest grey of dawn. Men were posted as picquets at the gully's rim, and for the rest it was a time for sleep. The girl sat with the man Ramon, binding up his hands, while Knowles looked after the other wounded. Sharpe stood over him. "How bad?"

"Kelly's going, sir." The little corporal had a chest wound and Knowles had picked away the shreds of jacket to show a bloody horror of mangled ribs. It was a wonder he had lived this long. Cresacre had been shot in the thigh, a clean wound, and he dressed it himself, swore he would be all right, and apologized to Sharpe for making a nuisance of himself. Two others had sabre cuts but

416

they would live, and there was hardly a man who did not have a scratch, a bruise, some memento of the night.

Sharpe counted heads. Forty-eight men, three sergeants and two officers had left the gully. Four men had not come back. Sharpe felt the tiredness wash through him, tinged with relief. It was a smaller bill than he dared hope for, and the lancers must have lost three times as many men. He went round the company, those that were awake, and praised them. The men seemed embarrassed by the thanks, shaking as sweat dried on their bodies in the cold air.

"Captain Sharpe!" Kearsey was standing in a clear patch of the gully. "Captain!"

Sharpe went to him. "Sir?"

"Are you mad, Sharpe? What were you doing?"

"Doing, sir? Rescuing you." Sharpe had expected thanks.

Kearsey waved at the wounded, anger in his face. "You fool! How do you get them back?"

"We carry them, sir."

" 'Carry them, sir.' " Kearsey mimicked him. "Over twenty miles of country? You were only here to help carry the gold, Sharpe! Not fight a battle in the back of beyond!"

Sharpe took a deep breath, bit back his anger. "Without you, sir, we would have had no chance of persuading El Católico to let us take the gold. That was my judgment."

Kearsey looked at him, shook his head. "I doubt if the gold is there. The French probably have it."

Sharpe blinked. "Did they say anything about it to you, sir?"

"No, they said nothing." Kearsey sounded suddenly tired.

"So there's hope, sir?"

The major shrugged. "At least you rescued them." He waved at the two Spaniards.

Sharpe looked at the girl. "Them, sir?"

"Moreno's children. Teresa and Ramon. The French were holding them as bait, hoping Moreno or El Católico would try a rescue. At least we've earned their thanks and that's probably more valuable than carrying the gold for them. After all, the gold was only a gesture to the Spanish."

"Yes, sir." It was no time for an argument.

Kearsey sighed. "You'd better sleep, Sharpe. The French will be after us today. In a couple of hours you'll have to defend this place."

"Yes, sir." He turned away and, as he did, he caught Teresa's eyes. She looked at him without interest, as if the rescue and the killings meant nothing. El Católico, he thought, is a lucky man. . . . He slept.

8

Casatejada was like a shattered ants' nest. All morning the French patrols searched the valley, then galloped in their dustclouds back to the houses and the thin spires of smoke that were the only signs left of the night's activity. Others rounded up stray horses, circling the valley floor. In the gully Sharpe's men moved slowly, quietly. The elation of the attack had given way to weariness and sadness. Kelly's breath bubbled through the morning, and the men avoided him as if death were contagious.

Sharpe woke, told Harper to sleep, replaced the picquets, and struggled to scrape the clotted blood from his sword with a handful of wiry grass. The heat bounced from the rocky sides of the gully, and the girl sat by her brother, talking quietly to him, and giving him sips of tepid water from a wooden canteen.

Kearsey climbed up to lie alongside Sharpe and took the telescope so that he could spy down on the French. "They're packing up to move out."

"Sir?"

"Mules, Sharpe. String of them."

Sharpe took his telescope back and found the village street. Kearsey was right: he could see a string of mules with men lashing ropes over their burdens, but it was impossible to tell whether there was gold or just forage in the packs. "Perhaps they won't look for us," he said hopefully.

The major shook his head. "Bound to. Look at the track we left." Running across the barley field, like a giant signpost, was the trampled spoor of the company's retreat. "They'll want to look over the ridge, just to make sure you've gone."

Sharpe looked at the bare rocks and turf of the hillside. "Should we move?"

Another shake of the head. "Best hiding place for miles, this gully. You can't see it from any side, even from above it's difficult. Keep our heads down and we'll be all right."

Sharpe turned and nodded at Teresa and Ramon. "Do they know anything about the gold? About Captain Hardy?"

"They say not." Kearsey shrugged. "Perhaps El Católico moved the gold and Hardy went too. I ordered him to stay with the gold."

"Then surely the girl would know?"

Kearsey turned and spoke in staccato Spanish to her. Sharpe listened to her deep, husky reply, and even if he could understand little of the language he was glad to look at her. She had long, dark hair, as black as Josefina's, but there the resemblance ended. The Portuguese girl had been a lover of comfort and luxury, while this girl reminded Sharpe of a wild beast, with eyes that were deep, wary, and hawk-like. She was young — twenty-three, Kearsey had said — but either side of her mouth there were curved lines. Sharpe remembered that her mother had died at the hands of the French, and God knew what she herself had suffered. . . .

Teresa was looking at Sharpe as if she would have liked to claw out his eyes. "Stop staring at me!"

"You speak English?"

She shrugged, and Kearsey looked at Sharpe. "Her father's fluent, that's what makes him so useful to us, and she and her brother have picked up some of the language."

"But do they know anything about the gold?"

"She doesn't know a thing, Sharpe. They think the gold must still be in the hermitage, and they haven't seen Hardy."

"So the next thing we must do, sir, is search the hermitage."

Kearsey sighed. "If you insist, Sharpe. If you insist." He slid down from the edge of the gully. "But for now, Sharpe, watch for that patrol. It won't be long."

The major was right about that. Three hundred lancers rode from the village, and Sharpe watched them come. They carried carbines instead of lances and he knew they intended to search the hillsides on foot. He turned to the gully and ordered silence, explained that a patrol was coming, and then turned back to see the Poles dismounting at the foot of the steep rock-strewn slope.

They started to climb, their horses left with picquets below. They were stringing into a line, a crude skirmish order, and he could hear their distant voices. There was a chance that they would miss the gully, that by climbing obliquely up the slope they would emerge on the crest and never suspect that a whole company was in dead ground behind them. He breathed slowly, willed them to stay low on the slope.

He could hear Kelly's laboured breathing, someone else clearing a throat, and he flapped his hand for silence. A tall lancer, a suntanned sergeant with a black moustache, was climbing higher than the others. He was a big man, almost as big as Harper. Go down, Sharpe urged silently, go down, but the man kept coming on. Sharpe moved his head, found Harper, beckoned.

Now the Polish sergeant was just below Sharpe, who craned forward as far as he dared to see the yellow, square top of his headgear come closer and closer. He could hear the man grunting, the sound of his fingernails scraping on rock, the scrabble of his boots searching for a foothold and then, as if in a nightmare, a large brown hand with bitten nails appeared right by Sharpe's face and he summoned all his strength for a desperate act. He waited, it could only have been for a half second, but it seemed for ever, until the man's face appeared, the eyes widened in surprise and Sharpe put out his right hand and gripped the sergeant by the

420

windpipe, fingers closing like a trap on his throat. He thrust his left hand forward, found the lancer's belt, and half turning onto his back he pulled him up and over the rim, throwing him to the tender mercy of Sergeant Harper. The Irishman had his gun reversed and brought it down, sickeningly, on the man's head. Sharpe whirled back to face the slope. The line was still advancing! No one had seen, no one had noticed.

But the lancer was tough, was trying to stand up and face his opponent. The men in the gully were frozen, appalled by the enemy who had suddenly landed in their midst, and it was Teresa who reacted first. She picked up a musket, turned it, took four steps and swung its brass-tipped butt into the man's forehead. He slumped, tried to rise, but she swung again and felled the sergeant.

Harper shook his head. "God save old Ireland."

The girl gave Harper a pitying look and then scrambled up the slope to lie beside Sharpe and peer at the enemy. The search-line was climbing the hill in short, erratic bursts. They had not missed the sergeant, might not do so until they returned to the village. Their voices echoed and faded even further from the gully. Sharpe watched them disappear behind the summit and grinned at his sergeant who still stood over the unconscious lancer. "We're safe," he said.

Within two hours the lancers had been recalled, and Casatejada was thronged with Frenchmen as other cavalry units came in to join the Poles, stirring a dustcloud that would have befitted a whole army. Sharpe guessed that the village had been the centre of a huge operation to clear the partisans from Masséna's supply areas, and Kearsey agreed. And, in the midst of such a withdrawal, who would question too closely the absence of one particular Polish lancer?

As the cavalry left the village their ranks seemed endless, the glorious might of France that had ridden down the best cavalry in Europe, but could not defeat the *guerrilleros*. The only way to win was to kill them all, every one, young and old, and even that, as the French were finding, did not work. Sharpe thought of the bodies in the blood of the cellar.

They spent the night in the gully, cautious lest the French should still be watching, and some time in the small hours the breath stopped in Corporal Kelly's throat. Pru Kelly, though she did not know it, was a widow again. They buried him at dawn, in a grave scratched from the soil and heaped with rocks to keep away the vultures. Dust to dust, ashes to ashes, and in a few weeks, Sharpe thought, Pru Kelly would marry again because that was the way it was with women who marched with soldiers. Then the new day came, still hot, the rain still keeping away, and the Light Company marched down into the empty valley to find their gold.

9

It was a sweet smell, sticky-sweet. Sharpe had smelled it often enough, so had most of the company, and they knew it fifty yards from the village. It was not so much a smell, Sharpe thought, as a state of the air like an invisible mist.

Not even the dogs had been left alive.

Ramon told him in slow English that four dozen people had been left in the village, mostly the old or the very young, but they had all died. Sharpe stared at the wrecked houses, the blood splashed on low, white walls. "Why were they caught?"

Ramon shrugged, waved a bandaged hand. "French were good."

"Good? You mean clever?"

The young man nodded. He had his sister's nose, the same dark eyes, but there was a friendliness to him that Sharpe had not seen in Teresa. Ramon shook his head hopelessly, blinking back tears;

the dead had been of his village. "We went there." He pointed north. "They were before us. We were . . . " He described a circle with his two bandaged hands.

"Surrounded?"

"*Sí.*" He looked down at his right hand, at the fingers that poked from the grey bandage, and Sharpe saw the index finger moving as if it were pulling a trigger. Ramon would fight again.

The bodies were not just in the cellar. Some had been taken to the hermitage to meet their bitter end, and on the steps of the building Sharpe found Isaiah Tongue, the admirer of Napoleon, throwing up the dry bread that had been his breakfast. The company waited outside. The captured Polish lancer, tall and proud, stood by Sergeant McGovern, and Sharpe stopped by the Scotsman. "Look after him, Sergeant."

"Aye, sir. They'll not touch him." The sturdy face was twisted as if in pain. McGovern, like Tongue, had looked inside the hermitage. "Savages, sir, that's what they are, savages!"

Sharpe climbed the steps, his face a mask as the thick stench of the hermitage struck him.

"Out! Get them out!" He knew no other way to react to the small bodies of innocent children. "Bury them!"

Harper was crying, tears running down his cheeks. Kearsey stood there, with Teresa. The major flicked at his moustache. "Terrible. Awful."

"So is what they do to the French." Sharpe surprised himself by saying it, but it was true. He remembered the naked prisoners, wondered how the other captured hussars had died.

"Yes." Kearsey used the tone of a man trying to avoid an argument. The girl looked at Sharpe and he saw she was holding back tears, her face rigid with an anger that was frightening. Sharpe swatted at a fly. "Where's the gold?"

Kearsey led him in, spurs clicking on stone, and pointed at a stone slab that was flush with the hermitage floor. The building was not used for services. It was a place that was consecrated only to death. The major poked the stone slab with his toe. "Under there."

The gold. So close, so near to the war's survival, and instead of a feeling of triumph Sharpe felt stained, touched by a horror that brought an anger against his job. "Sergeant!"

"Sir!"

"Find a bloody pick! Smartly!" There was a comfort in orders, and Sharpe tried to ignore the sound of the bodies being dragged outside. He looked at the slab engraved with the name "Moreno" and beneath the letters an ornate and eroded coat of arms. The girl had her back to them and Sharpe realized that this was her family's vault. It made Sharpe wonder where his own body would finally rest. Beneath the ashes of some battlefield, or drowned like the poor reinforcements in their transport ships?

"Sergeant!"

"Sir?"

"Where's that pick?"

Harper had the pick, and he thrust it into the gap between the stones. He heaved, the veins on his face standing out, and with a shudder the slab moved, lifted, and there was a space large enough for Sharpe to slide a piece of broken stone beneath.

Teresa had gone to a second door, opening into the cemetery, and stood there as if not interested. Harper found another spot, levered again, and this time it was easier and there was enough space to take hold of the slab and pull it from the floor, swinging it like a trapdoor. Dark steps led down into blackness. Sharpe stood at the top, claiming the right to be first down. "Candle? Come on, someone! There's got to be a candle!"

Hagman had one in his pack, a greasy but serviceable stump, and there was a pause while it was lit. Sharpe stared into the blackness. Here was where Wellington's hopes were pinned? It was ludicrous.

He took the candle and began the slow descent into the tomb and to a different kind of smell. This was not a sweet smell, not rank, but dusty because the bodies had been here a long time; some long enough for the coffins to have collapsed and show the gleam of dry bones. Sharpe held the miserable light high, sweeping it round the small space and saw the flash of bright metal. But it was not gold, just a discarded piece of brass that had once bound

424

the corner of a casket. Sharpe turned to look at Kearsey. "There's no gold."

"No." The major looked round. "It's gone."

"Where was it stored?"

"There. Where you are."

"Then where's it gone, sir?"

Kearsey sniffed, drew himself up to his full height. "How would I know, Sharpe? All I know is that it is not here."

"And where's Captain Hardy?" Sharpe was angry. To have come this far, for nothing.

"I don't know."

Sharpe kicked the vault's wall and swore. The gold gone, Hardy missing, Kelly dead. He put the candle in a niche and bent down to look at the floor. The dust had been disturbed by long, streaking marks and he congratulated himself ironically for guessing that the smears had been made when the gold was removed. The knowledge was not much use now. The gold was gone. He straightened up. "Could El Católico have taken it?"

The voice came from above them, from the top of the steps, and it was a rich voice, deep and young. "No, he could not." The owner of the voice wore long, grey boots, and a long, grey cloak over a slim, silver scabbard. As he descended the steps into the dim light, he proved to be a tall man with dark, good looks. "Major. How good to see you back."

Kearsey preened himself, gestured at Sharpe. "Colonel Jovellanos, this is Captain Sharpe. Sharpe? This is . . . "

"El Católico." Sharpe's voice was neutral, showing no pleasure in the meeting.

The tall man, perhaps three years older than Sharpe, smiled. "I am Joaquím Jovellanos, once colonel in the Spanish Army, and now known as El Católico." He bowed slightly. He seemed amused by the meeting. "They use my name to frighten the French, but you can see that I am really harmless." Sharpe remembered the man's extraordinary speed with the sword, the bravery in facing the French charge alone. The man was far from harmless. Sharpe noticed the hands, long fingered, that moved with a kind of ritual grace when he gestured. One of them was offered to Sharpe. "I hear you rescued my Teresa."

"Yes." Sharpe, as tall as El Católico, felt lumpish beside the Spaniard's civilized languor.

The other hand came from behind the cloak, briefly touched Sharpe's shoulder. "Then I am in your debt." The words were given the lie by eyes that remained watchful. El Católico moved back and gestured at the tomb. "Empty."

"So it seems. A lot of money."

"Which it would have been your pleasure to carry for us. To Cádiz?" The voice was like dark silk. The Spaniard smiled, gestured again round the vault. "Alas, it is gone. The French have it. They captured it two days ago, along with your gallant Captain Hardy. We captured a straggler who told us so."

Kearsey coughed, looked to El Católico as if for permission to speak, and received it. "That's it, Sharpe. Hunt's over. Back to Portugal."

Sharpe ignored him, continued to stare at the watchful Spaniard. "You're sure?"

El Católico smiled, raised amused eyebrows, spread his hands. "Unless our straggler lied. And I doubt that."

Now it was Sharpe's turn to smile. "We have our own prisoner. I'm sure he can deny or confirm your straggler's story."

El Católico pointed a finger up the stairs. "The Polish sergeant? Is that your prisoner?"

Sharpe nodded. The lies would be nailed. "That's the one."

"How very sad." The hands came together with a graceful hint of prayerful regret. "I cut his throat as I arrived. In a moment of anger."

The eyes were not smiling, whatever the mouth did, and Sharpe knew this was not the moment to accept, or even acknowledge, the delicate challenge. He shrugged, as if the death of the sergeant meant nothing to him, and followed the tall Spaniard up the steps and into the hermitage that was noisy with newcomers who quietened as their leader appeared. Sharpe watched the grey-cloaked man move easily among his followers. Nothing had been admitted,

426

nothing openly said, but in the gloom of the vault, in the wreckage of British hopes, Sharpe had found the enemy and now, in the scent of death, he groped for the way to victory in this sudden, unwanted, and very private little war.

10

The rapier moved invisibly, one moment on Sharpe's left, the next, as if by magic, past his guard and quivering at his chest. There was enough pressure to bend the blade, for the point to draw a trace of blood, and then El Católico stepped backwards, flicked the slim blade into a salute, and took up his guard again. "You are slow, Captain."

Sharpe hefted his blade. "Try changing weapons."

El Católico shrugged, reversed his blade, and held it to Sharpe. Taking the heavy cavalry sword in return he held it level, turned his wrist, and lunged with it into empty air. "A butcher's tool. On guard!"

The rapier was as delicate as a fine needle yet, even with its balance and responsiveness, Sharpe could do nothing to pierce El Católico's casual defence. The partisan leader teased him, led him on, and with a final contemptuous flick he stopped his hand half an inch before he would have laid open Sharpe's throat. "You are no swordsman, Captain."

"I'm a soldier."

El Católico smiled, but the blade moved just enough to touch Sharpe's skin before the Spaniard dropped the sword on the ground and held out a hand for his own blade. "Go back to your army, soldier. The British are going, didn't you know? They're sailing home, Captain, leaving the war to us."

"Then look after it. We'll be back." Sharpe picked up his heavy sword, ignoring El Católico's laugh, and walked away towards the gate leading into the street. He was in the ruins of Moreno's courtyard, where Knowles had smashed the volleys into the lancers, and all that was left were bullet marks on the scorched walls. It had taken most of the day to clear up the village.

Cesar Moreno came through the gate and stopped. He seemed a decent enough man, Sharpe thought, but whatever prowess he had once had seemed to have drained away. Moreno was as grey as his future son-in-law's cloak; grey hair, grey moustache, his personality a shadow of what he had once been. He gestured towards the street. "Your men, Captain."

"Yes?"

"They're ready."

They walked towards the gate, to the fields where the dead of the British company would be buried. El Católico walked with them, and Sharpe sensed that Moreno was wary of his young colleague. The old man looked at the rifleman. "My children, Captain—"

Sharpe had been thanked a dozen times, more, but Moreno explained again. "Ramon was ill. Nothing serious, but he could not travel. That was why Teresa was here, to look after him."

"The French surprised you?"

El Católico interrupted. "They did. They were better than we thought. We knew they would search the hills, but in such strength? Marshal Masséna must be worried."

"Worried?"

The grey-cloaked man nodded. "His supplies, Captain, all travel on roads to the south. Can you imagine what we will do to them? We ride again tomorrow, to ambush his ammunition, to try to save Almeida." He turned his most charming smile on Sharpe. "Perhaps you will come? We could do with those rifles of yours."

Sharpe smiled back. "We must rejoin our army."

El Católico raised an eyebrow. "And empty-handed. How sad."

428

The guerrilla band watched them pass in silence. Sharpe had been impressed by them, by their weaponry, and by the discipline El Católico imposed. But was it likely, he wondered, that the French, having killed the old and young, and defiled the walls of the hermitage, would then carefully replace the stone lid of the family tomb? He stood in front of the waiting company and looked at Harper. The sergeant glanced at his captain and away. His face was unreadable, and Sharpe wondered what he had found. He had asked him to look round the village, explaining nothing, but knowing that the Irishman would understand.

After the burial service Kearsey marched across to stand beside Sharpe, his Bible still in his hand. He faced the company. "You've done well. Very well. Difficult countryside and a long way from home. Well done." They stared back at him with the blank look soldiers keep for encouraging talks from unpopular officers. "I'm sorry that you must go back empty-handed, but your efforts have not been in vain. We have shown, together, that we do care about the Spanish people, about their future, and your enthusiasm, your struggle, will not be forgotten."

El Católico clapped, beamed at the company, smiled at Kearsey. Sharpe's company stared at the two men as if wondering what new indignity would be heaped on them. Kearsey flicked at his moustache. "You will march tomorrow, back to Portugal, and El Católico, here, will provide an escort."

Sharpe kept his face straight, hiding his fury. Kearsey had told him none of this. The major went on. "I'm staying, to continue the fight, and I hope we will meet again." If he had expected a cheer he was disappointed.

Then it was the turn of the British to stand in the walled graveyard as the dead villagers were put into a common grave. The French had been here, too, as disturbed graves and burst-open sepulchres showed. The dead had been reburied, the damage patched up, but Sharpe wondered yet again at the savagery of such a war. He looked at Teresa, and she gave him one of her unconcerned stares. He told himself that there was already enough trouble looming on the horizon without planning to pursue El Católico's woman.

Ramon limped over to Sharpe. "You go tomorrow?"

"Yes."

"I am sad." He was genuine; the one friendly face in Casatejada. He pointed to Sharpe's rifle. "I like it."

Sharpe grinned, gave him the rifle to handle. "Come with us, you could become a rifleman."

There was a laugh and El Católico stood there. He cleared his throat. "A sad day, Captain."

"Yes, indeed."

El Católico was looking round the graveyard with an imperious eye. "Too many dead. Too many graves. Too many defiled graves."

Sharpe followed his eyes round the small graveyard with its smashed headstones. Had the French been looking for the gold, he wondered, or did they treat all cemeteries this way? Suddenly he saw a fresh grave, neatly piled with earth and waiting for its headstone. "They didn't open all the graves."

El Católico smiled at him. "Not all. Perhaps there was not time. I buried him six days ago. A servant, a good man."

There was a snap and they all looked at Ramon who was still fumbling with the Baker rifle. He had the small trap open in the butt, and seemed impressed by the cleaning tools hidden inside. He handed the rifle back to Sharpe. "One day I have one, yes?"

"One day I'll give you one. When we're back."

"You come back?"

Sharpe laughed. "We'll be back. We'll chase the French all the way to Paris."

He slung the rifle and walked across the cemetery and through a wrought-iron side gate that opened onto the wide fields. If he had hoped for fresher air, he was unlucky. Beside the gate, half hidden by dark green bushes, was a vast manure heap, stinking and warm. Sharpe turned to see El Católico had followed him.

"You think the war is not lost, Captain?"

Sharpe wondered if he detected a trace of worry in the Spaniard. He shrugged. "It's not lost."

"You're wrong." The Spaniard spoke loudly, almost sneeringly. "You have lost, Captain. Only a miracle can save the British now."

430

Sharpe copied the sneering tone. "We're all Christians, aren't we? We believe in miracles."

A peal of laughter checked them, swung them round, to see Teresa, standing at the hermitage door. The laugh stopped, the face became stern again, but for the first time, Sharpe thought, he had seen that she was not completely bound to the tall, grey-cloaked Spaniard. She even nodded to the rifleman, in agreement, before turning away.

11

The elation had worn them. Failure imposed its mocking price of depression and regret as Sharpe marched westward from Casatejada towards the two rivers that barred the Light Company from the British army. He felt sour, disappointed, and cheated. There had been little friendliness in the farewells. Only Ramon had embraced him, Spanish fashion, with a garlic kiss on both cheeks, and the young man had seemed genuinely sad at the parting. "Remember your promise, Captain. A rifle?"

Sharpe had made the promise, but he wondered, gloomily, how it was to be kept. Almeida must soon be under siege, the French would dominate the land between the rivers, and the British would be retreating westward towards the sea, to final defeat. And all that stood between survival and a silent, bitter embarkation was his suspicion that the gold was still hidden in Casatejada. He remembered Wellington's words. "Must, do you hear, must. . . ."

The rain clouds still built in the north, and Sharpe knew he must

431

stop soon and rest, but his men were uncomplaining, even the wounded, and they trudged on in the dusk towards the far blue line that was the hills around Almeida.

The escort of partisans rode on the spine of a low chain of hills to the south, Kearsey among them. El Católico had talked of ambushing the French convoys that would be lumbering with ammunition towards Almeida.

Patrick Harper caught up with Sharpe, glanced at his captain's face. "Permission to speak, sir?"

Sharpe looked at him sourly. "You don't usually ask. What is it?"

Harper gestured at the escorting horsemen. "What do they remind you of, sir?"

Sharpe looked at the long, black cloaks, wide hats, and long stirruped saddlery. He shrugged. "So tell me."

Harper grinned. "A bloody escort for prisoners, that's what this is. They're seeing us off their land, so they are."

"And what if they are?" The two men had quickened their pace so they were ahead of the company, out of earshot.

"The bastard is lying through his teeth. What did he say yesterday?" Harper meant El Católico, but the question did not demand an answer from Sharpe. The sergeant went on with enthusiasm. "We were standing by that grave, and he said that he had buried the man six days before. Would you remember that?"

Sharpe nodded. He had been thinking of that grave himself. "Yes. Go on."

"Yesterday was a Saturday. I asked the lieutenant, he can always remember the day and date. So that means the Spanish bastard buried his servant on the Sunday."

Sharpe looked at Harper, mystified. "What's wrong with that?"

"God save old Ireland, sir, they would not do that. Not on a Sunday. They're Catholics, sir, not your heathen Protestants. Or my name's not Patrick Augustine Harper. On a Sunday? Not at all!"

Sharpe walked on. Harper had reinforced his suspicions. The stone over the crypt, the speed with which El Católico had killed the Polish sergeant — surely that had been done so that the man did not blurt out the awkward fact that the French knew nothing

432

about the gold. It was not much of a reason for suspicion. In the short time that the lancer had been their prisoner Sharpe had not found a common language, but El Católico was not to know that.

The stone, the sudden death of the lancer, and now Harper's idea. Sharpe walked on, feeling the sweat trickling down his back, and tried to remember El Católico's exact words. His suspicion was drifting free and he had nothing to pin it on and justify the plan that was in his mind. He had no proof, just a certainty. He turned back to Harper. "You think the gold is in that grave?"

"There's something there, sir. Say you wanted to hide a few thousand gold coins, sir, and they were in the vault. If you had a grain of sense, you'd move them a short way, hidden by the walls of the burial yard, and bury them in a good fresh grave."

"But if I was a French officer," Sharpe was thinking out loud, "the first place I would look for anything hidden—guns, food, anything—would be a good fresh grave."

Harper nodded. "And if you found the corpse of a British officer, sir? What would you do then?"

Sharpe let the idea thread itself into his suspicions. Where the hell was Hardy? If the French found a British officer in a grave they would not disturb it, they would replace the earth, even say a prayer.

Harper interrupted his thoughts. "Did you talk, sir, with the girl's father?"

"Yes, but he knew nothing." Which was not true, Sharpe reflected. He had talked with Cesar Moreno, in the burned courtyard of the widower's house, and the grey hair had bowed when Sharpe had asked what had happened to Captain Hardy and the gold. "The gold! Always the gold!" the old man had shouted. "The French have it! There is no gold any more." There had been a note of desperation in his voice that had made Sharpe want to go on prying, but El Católico, Teresa with him, had appeared and the chance had gone. Yet now Harper was offering a new thought, that the grave in the walled cemetery held a body, and that the body was surrounded by gold.

Sharpe let the idea take wings, spin a fragile sequence of possibilities. The gold was in the graveyard, sitting there till the armies had moved on and El Católico could dig it up without fear of French patrols or zealous exploring officers. It was all a frail web of surmise, but he knew that if he did not take a decision then all would be irrevocably lost. He laughed out loud, at the absurdity of it all, at his worries that if the gold was there, then the company would have to carry it across twenty miles of hostile country, avoiding the French, but worse than that, fighting off the partisans who knew the territory and how to fight it. As if that mattered against the outcome of the summer's campaign.

Harper looked round, startled by the sudden laugh. "So we're going back?"

Sharpe nodded. "Not that anyone else needs to know. How did you guess?"

Harper looked shrewdly at Sharpe, as if gauging the wisdom of his answer, but he seemed to think it safe. "Because you want that woman."

Sharpe smiled. "And the gold, Patrick. Don't forget the gold."

They reached the Agueda in the dark. Sharpe was tempted to bivouac on the eastern bank, but knew that such an action would arouse the escorting partisans' suspicions, so the Light Company waded the river and went half a mile into the trees that fringed the western hills. The escort stood on the far bank watching them, and for a moment Sharpe wondered if the Spaniards suspected that the British soldiers would try to return to Casatejada in the night. Finally, however, they decided to leave and Sharpe, crouching in the shadows at the tree line, saw the horsemen wheel and spur their horses back to the east.

The company was alone. "Lieutenant!"

Knowles came to him. "Sir."

"We're going back. Tonight." He watched Knowles to see if there was any reaction, but the lieutenant nodded as if the news was not unexpected. Sharpe was obscurely disappointed. "We won't take the wounded. Sergeant Read can take them on to Almeida. Give him three men to help."

"Yes, sir."

"And we'll split up tonight. I'll go ahead with the riflemen, you follow. You'll find us in the graveyard at Casatejada."

Knowles scratched his head. "You reckon the gold is there, sir?"

Sharpe nodded. "Maybe. I want to look, anyway." He grinned at the lieutenant, infecting him with his enthusiasm.

There was a pause while Knowles shifted from foot to foot. "I thought Major Kearsey ordered you back to the army, sir. If he comes back and finds us poking round Casatejada he won't exactly be happy. And . . ." His voice trailed away. "He's a risk, sir."

"Well?" Sharpe knew his lieutenant was not lacking in courage.

"Well, sir." Knowles crouched down so he was closer to Sharpe, his voice even lower. "Everyone knows you were in trouble with the general after those provosts, sir. If Kearsey complains about you, sir, well . . ." He ran out of words again.

"I could be in even more trouble, yes?"

"Yes, sir. And it's not just that." His words suddenly tumbled out as if he had been storing the speech for weeks. "We all know the gazette hasn't come through, sir, and it's so unfair. Just because you were once a private they seem to be doing nothing."

"No, no, no." Sharpe stopped the flow. He was embarrassed, touched. "The army isn't unfair, just slow." He did not believe that himself, but if he let himself express his real thoughts then the bitterness would show.

Damn the army, damn the promotion system. He looked at Knowles. "How long have you been a lieutenant?"

"Two years and nine months, sir." The quick answer was not surprising. Most lieutenants counted the days until they had three years' seniority.

"So you'll be a captain by Christmas."

"Yes, sir." Knowles sounded embarrassed. "My father's paying, sir."

"You deserve it." Sharpe felt a pang of jealousy. He could never afford fifteen hundred pounds for a captaincy. He laughed, disguising his mood. "If my gazette fails, Robert, then by Christmas we'll have changed places!" He stood up, looked across the dark valley. "Time to go. God knows how we find the way. But good luck."

12

It was a nightmare journey. Only Hagman's instincts, honed by years of poaching, took the riflemen safely back over the dark pathways, and Sharpe wondered how Knowles was surviving. The moon was hidden behind looming clouds that slowly blotted out the stars, and a small, chill breeze that came from the north reminded Sharpe that the weather had to break. Let it not be tonight, he thought, for rain would slow them, and he needed to be in Casatejada while darkness still reigned. To his surprise, his pleasure, the news that they were not going on to Almeida seemed to have excited the men. They muttered that he was a bastard, but there was a restlessness about the company that spoke of a need to fulfil their job. And they made good time, cursing through the rocks, stumbling on the stream beds, going faster than the less well-trained men of the South Essex could travel.

Perversely the moon sailed clear of the ragged cloud edge as the green-jacketed men reached the final crest before the village. The men dropped to the ground, but nothing moved in the moonlight except the barley rippling in the breeze and the maize clattering on its long stalks.

Sharpe urged them on. The cemetery was on the far side of the village and the riflemen made a wide circuit, round the end of the valley, moving fast in the moonlight and hoping that if their shadowed bodies were dimly seen against the dark background of the hills the sentries in the village would think that it was one of

436

the wolfpacks that ran in the uplands. Sharpe kept looking towards the east, fearing the first silver of dawn.

"Down!" They dropped, panting, in a field of half cut barley that the French had trampled with their horses, and wriggled forward, the hermitage bell tower a quarter mile away, picking paths through the stalks where the crop had been flattened and where standing clumps gave them cover. Each man knew his job, and each knew, too, that the Spaniards could have watched them for the last five miles. Sharpe was haunted by the knife edge on which he had balanced the company.

Two hundred yards to go and he stopped, raised a hand, and turned to Hagman. "All right?"

The man grinned toothlessly. "Perfect, sir."

Sharpe looked at Harper. "Come on."

Now it was just the two of them, creeping forward into the growing stench of the manure, listening for the tiny sounds that could betray an alert sentry. The barley grew almost to the wall of the graveyard, but as they twisted their way closer to the high, white wall, Sharpe knew they could not hope to climb it unseen. He let Harper wriggle alongside and put his mouth close to the sergeant's ear. "You see the bell tower?"

Harper nodded.

"There has to be someone up there. We can't cross here. We'll be seen."

The sergeant put out a hand to the left. Sharpe nodded.

The bell tower, with its arches facing the four points of the compass, was the most obvious sentry post in the village. As they crawled, the stalks of the barley rustling deafeningly, Sharpe felt like a small animal creeping towards a trap. They reached the corner of the cemetery, stood against the wall and then, hidden from the tower, edged slowly down its lefthand side towards the gate, the bushes, and the rank heap of manure.

Nothing stirred. It was as if Casatejada was deserted. But Sharpe remembered Ramon, who could not yet ride, and his sister, Teresa, who had stayed to look after him, and he knew that the village was not empty. He peered through the wrought-iron gate. The graves were lit by the moon. It was quiet; the hairs on the back of his neck prickled. He twitched Harper's elbow, forcing the sergeant into the thick shadow of the bushes by the gate. "I don't like it," he whispered. "You stay here. I'll go in. If anyone interferes with me, use that damned gun."

Patrick Harper nodded. He watched Sharpe jump for the top of the wall, not trusting the hinges of the gate. Sharpe's scabbard scraped on the stones, there was a thump as he hit the ground, then he crouched inside the graveyard, his ears ringing with the noise he had made as he dropped over the wall. But nothing moved, nothing sounded except a curious deep background sighing where the wind passed through the bell tower and caressed the huge, metal instrument. And across the graveyard the fresh grave waited for him.

He could be seen, he knew, from the bell tower as he made his way across, but the die was cast and there was no going back. His belt buckle and buttons snagged on the dry earth as he crawled on his belly towards the heap of earth. He cursed this stupidity—why hadn't he marched straight in, bayonets fixed, and insisted on digging up the grave, instead of coming like a thief in the night? If he had been certain he could have done that, but nothing was certain. A suspicion, that was all, a flimsy suspicion that was buttressed by nothing more than Harper's insistence that a man would not be buried on a Sunday.

At last he came up beside the grave and began to dig, awkwardly, lying flat with a crooked arm and dragging back handfuls of earth from the grave. It was hard. Every handful of dry earth and flinty stone brought down a miniature landslide from the top of the ridge, and each time it seemed that the noise was deafening, but nothing moved. The bell moaned gently, but there were no other sounds. He looked up, saw the tinge of grey dawn that limited his time. The light was improving, disastrously, and what before had been mere humped shadows in the moonlight could now be seen as distinct, ornate gravestones.

There was no point in trying to hide any more. He knelt up and used both hands, pulling back the soil, delving down to whatever was in the grave. And there it was! Sackcloth. He scraped more

438

frantically, the soil caving in on the patch of sacking, and his mind whipped ahead to the thought of gold coins in thin sacks. He cleared the patch again, could see the sacking clearly, and he thrust at it with stiff fingers, splitting it, forcing his hand in to the coins. But there were no coins. Just a horrifying slime on his fingers, a gagging in his throat. This body, shrouded in plain, brown cloth, was not Captain Hardy, but in truth El Católico's servant who, for a reason that he would never know, had been undisturbed by the marauding Frenchmen. Failure, utter failure, and the end of a thousand hopes.

"Good morning." The voice was mocking, and Sharpe spun round to see El Católico standing in the door of the hermitage. "Good morning, Captain Sharpe. Do you often dig up corpses?"

Sharpe stood up, conscious of the filth on his uniform. He bent to pick up the rifle, but checked as he saw a musket barrel point at him from behind El Católico, and then suddenly a dozen men were in line either side of the Spaniard. He let the rifle stay on the ground.

"I asked if you often dug up corpses, Captain." The tall, grey-cloaked man chuckled, waved a hand in an elegant gesture. "You're not going to answer my question. I suppose you are searching for the gold? Am I right?" Sharpe said nothing and El Católico's voice became insistent. "Am I right?"

"Yes."

"You have a voice!" El Católico turned and spoke to one of his men, waited, and turned back holding something in his hand. A spade. "Then dig, Captain. Dig. We never had time to bury Carlos properly. We did it in a hurry last Saturday night, so you can do us a service." He threw the spade at Sharpe, the blade thumping into the soil next to his feet.

Sharpe did not move. Why the devil had Harper not appeared? Had they found him, too? He could not have been captured, not without a struggle that would have been audible a mile away, and Sharpe felt the faintest stirring of hope. Or had the bastards cut Harper's throat? Damn everything! Knowles would blunder into the same trap, and everything would fail.

El Católico took a step forward. "You won't dig?" He chopped
down with his left hand and Sharpe saw the musket barrel come
up, heard the bang, saw the stab of flame in the gout of smoke,
and the ball flattened itself on the wall behind him. "Dig, Captain,
dig! The gold! You must have the gold!"

"Joaquím?" Teresa's voice and suddenly she was there, in her
long white dress, and she stood beside her man, put her arm
through his, and asked what was happening. Sharpe heard her
laughter as El Católico explained.

He turned back. "Have you found your gold, Captain?"

Sharpe ignored the spade. "There is no gold."

"Ah!" El Católico's face showed mock horror. "Then go, Captain. Go, and take your men with you. You're not alone, are you?"

"No. And I didn't expect to find you here."

The Spaniard bowed. "An unexpected pleasure, then. Teresa's father is leading the ambush. I decided to come back."

"To protect your gold?"

El Católico put an arm round Teresa's shoulders. "To protect my treasure." The girl's face stayed as enigmatic as ever as El Católico waved at the gate.

"Go, Captain. I know your men are near. Go home, little grave-digger, and remember one thing."

"Yes?"

"Watch your back. Very carefully. It's a long road." He laughed, watched Sharpe bend down to retrieve his rifle. "Leave the rifle. It will save us picking it up from the road."

Sharpe picked it up, slung it defiantly on his shoulder, and swore uselessly at the Spaniard. El Católico laughed, shrugged, and gestured at the gate. "Go, Captain. The French have the gold, as I told you. The French."

The gate was not locked, it could have been opened easily, but Patrick Harper, with the blood of Irish heroes in his veins, chose to stand back and kick it with one enormous foot. It exploded inwards, the hinges tearing from the dry mortar, and there he stood, six feet four inches of grinning Irishman, filthy dirty, and in one hand his seven-barrelled gun pointed casually at El Católico. "Top of the morning! And how's our lordship this morning?" Sharpe was rarely given a glimpse of Harper's imitation of what the rest of the world thought of as Irish mannerisms, but this was obviously to be a rich performance. "And a fine morning it is, to be sure, your honour. I wouldn't move, your grace, not while I've got the gun on you. It could go off with a desperate bang, so it could, and take the whole of your darling head off." He glanced at Sharpe. "Morning, sir! Excuse my appearance." He was disgusting, covered with glistening manure. "Would you mind calling the lads, sir?"

Sharpe drew the whistle from its holster on his leather crossbelt and blew the signal that would bring the riflemen running to the village. Harper looked steadily at El Católico. "You were saying, your Holiness, that the French have the gold?"

El Católico nodded, said nothing. Teresa looked defiantly at Harper, then at Sharpe who now pointed his rifle at the small group of partisans. The Spaniards had guns, but none of them dared move while the vast muzzle of Harper's gun still stared at their leader.

"The French have the gold." Teresa's voice was firm, her tone almost contemptuous. "The French have the gold," she repeated.

"That's good, miss, so it is." Harper's voice was suddenly gentle.

"Because what you don't know about, as my old mother used to say, you won't miss. And look what I found in the dungheap." He grinned at them all, raised his free hand and from it, trickling in a glittering cascade, fell thick gold coins. The grin became wider. "The good Lord," said Patrick Augustine Harper, "has been kind to me this morning."

13

Sharpe put Hagman and three other crackshots in the bell tower with orders to shoot any horsemen spurring away from Casatejada. He needed all the time he could gain before El Católico's other band of partisans returned.

El Católico had said nothing. His men, disarmed, sat by the cemetery wall and watched five other riflemen, led by Harper, raking at the huge pile of manure with bayonets. They were pulling out leather bags filled with coins, and dumping them at Sharpe's feet; bag after bag, heavy with gold: more money than Sharpe had ever seen, a fortune beyond his imaginings.

El Católico crossed to Sharpe and gestured at the bags. "Spanish gold, Sharpe."

"So we take it to Cádiz for you. Do you want to come?"

"Cádiz!" For a moment the voice was a snarl of anger. "You won't take it to Cádiz! It will go back to England with your army, to buy comforts for your generals."

Sharpe hoped his own face mirrored the scorn on El Católico's. "And what were *you* going to do with it?"

443

The Spaniard shrugged. "Take it to Cádiz. By land."

Sharpe did not believe him; every instinct told him that El Católico had planned to steal the gold, keep it, but he had no proof. "Then we'll save you a journey. It will be our pleasure." He smiled at El Católico, who turned away and spoke rapidly to his men, and the seated fighters by the wall muttered angrily. Sharpe's men hefted their rifles and stepped one pace forward.

Patrick Harper stopped beside Sharpe and stretched his back muscles. "They're not happy, sir."

Sharpe grinned. "They think we're stealing the gold. I don't think they want to help us take it to Cádiz."

Teresa was staring at Sharpe as a cat might look at a bird. Harper saw her expression. "Do you think they'll try to stop us, sir?"

Sharpe lifted innocent eyebrows. "We're allies!" He raised his voice and spoke slowly so that any of the Spaniards with a smattering of English would understand. "We take the gold to Cádiz, to the Junta."

Teresa spat on the ground. Sharpe wondered if they had all known that the gold was hidden in the manure, but doubted it. If too many of the partisans had known then there was always a danger that someone would talk and the secret would be gone.

But there was something wrong. He had forgotten Captain Hardy in the excitement of finding the gold. He looked at El Católico. "Captain Hardy is missing."

"I know."

"What else do you know?"

El Católico licked his lips. "We think he was captured by the French."

Harper growled, stepped forward. "Let me ask the questions, sir. I'll break him apart."

"No." It was the girl who spoke. "Hardy tried to escape the French. We don't know where he is."

And against his better judgment Sharpe believed her.

"Sir!" Hagman was calling from the bell tower. "Mr. Knowles in sight, sir!"

Knowles had evidently strayed in the dark and lost his way, and

444

the young lieutenant looked exasperated and tired as the red-jack-eted men straggled into the village. His expression changed when he saw the gold. "I don't believe it."

Sharpe picked up a coin and tossed it to him. "Spanish gold."

"Good God!" The newcomers pressed round the lieutenant, fing-ering the coins.

"You found it!"

Sharpe smiled. "Harper did."

Knowles looked up. "Harper! How the devil did you do it?"

"Easy, sir, easy!" Harper launched himself on the re-telling of his exploit. He had been in the bushes, as Sharpe had told him, and listening to the sound of his captain scrabbling at the grave. "Noisy! I thought he'd waken the dead, so I did." Then there had been footsteps from the village. Harper nodded at Sharpe. "I knew he hadn't heard a thing, still scratching away in the graveyard, so I thought, I'm not going to move. The bastards might know about the captain, but I was hidden away." He pointed at El Católico who stared back, expressionless. "Then your man there comes round here, all on his own, and draws out his fancy sword, and pokes the manure! So I knew then what he was up to, sure enough, and when the bastard has gone off I poked in there myself." He grinned broadly, seemed to wait for applause, and Knowles laughed.

"But *how* did you know?"

Harper grinned. "Jostle a man in the street, sir, and he im-mediately puts a hand on his pocket to see if you have lifted his money." He jerked a thumb at the partisan leader. "Silly bas-tard hears that the captain's disturbing the worms so he can't resist sneaking round to make sure that the stuff is still safe! And here it is!"

Sharpe walked over to the strewed manure. "How many more bags?"

Harper brushed his hands together. "That's it, sir. I can't see any more."

Sharpe looked at his ebullient sergeant, whose clothes were slimy with dung. "Go and wash, Patrick. And well done."

Harper clapped his hands. "Right, lads! Clean-up time!"

Sharpe walked back to the gold and picked up another coin from the bag he had opened. It was a thick coin, he guessed weighing near to an ounce. On one side were the arms of Spain, surmounted by a crown, with a legend chased round its perimeter. He read it aloud. " 'Initium sapientiae timor domini.' Does anyone know what that means?"

Rifleman Tongue, the educated one, chimed in with a translation. "The beginning of wisdom, sir, is the fear of the Lord."

Sharpe grinned. "Quite right." He turned the coin over. On the other side was the profile of a man, his head covered in a wig of profuse curls, and at the foot of the profile was a date: 1729. Sharpe looked at Knowles. "Know what it is?"

"Doubloon, sir. Eight-escudo piece."

"What's it worth?"

Knowles thought about it, hefted the coin in his hand, tossed it into the air. "About three pounds ten shillings, sir."

Sharpe looked disbelieving. Sixteen thousand coins, each worth three pounds and ten shillings. He worked it out in his head: fifty-six thousand pounds. He started to laugh, almost hysterical in his reaction. This money would pay a day's wages to more than a million men. If he should live for a hundred years he would never earn the amount that was sagging in the leather bags at his feet; his salary was ten shillings and sixpence a day, less two shillings and eightpence for the mess charge, and then more deductions for washing and the hospital levy. As for the men, they were lucky if, in a year, they earned as much as just two of these coins. A shilling a day, less all the deductions, brought them down to the three sevens: seven pounds, seven shillings, and sevenpence a year; but there were few men who made even that much. They were charged for lost equipment, broken equipment, replacement equipment.

Knowles was looking serious. "I would guess it weighs a thousand pounds, sir. Probably more."

Nearly half a ton of gold, to be carried through the enemy hills, and the clouds were overhead now, heavy with rain. Sharpe pointed at the bags. "Fill thirty packs, Lieutenant, throw away everything

446

except ammunition, and we'll just have to take it in turns to carry them."

El Católico walked slowly towards Sharpe, keeping an eye on the riflemen who still covered the Spaniards with their guns. "The gold belongs to Spain. It will be used to kill Frenchmen. It should stay here."

Sharpe shook his head. "It belongs to the Supreme Junta in Cádiz. I am merely delivering it. If you don't believe me, why don't you come, too? We could do with some more backs to pile it on."

El Católico spoke quietly. "I will be coming with you, Captain."

Sharpe knew what he meant. The journey home would be a nightmare of fear, fear of ambush, but Wellington's "must" was the imperative in Sharpe's head. He turned away and, as he did, felt one solitary raindrop splash on his cheek. He knew that soon, within the hour, the clouds would burst and the streams and rivers rise with unimaginable speed.

Harper came back, scrubbed clean, his clothes soaking wet. He nodded at the partisans. "What do we do with them, sir?"

"Lock them up when we go." It would gain a little time, not much, but every minute was valuable. He turned to Knowles. "Are we ready?"

"Nearly, sir." Knowles was splitting open the bags while two men poured the coins into packs. Sharpe was grateful that so many of his men had looted French cowhide packs at Talavera; the British canvas and wood packs would have split open under the weight. The men hated the British packs, made by the firm of Trotters, with their terrible chest straps which, at the end of a long march, made the lungs feel as if they were filled with acid; Trotter's Pains, it was called, and all but a couple of the men had captured French equipment on their backs.

Another drop of rain, and then another, and now the rain was beating on the dry ground, big, warm drops. Sharpe turned to the company. "Wrap your locks! Stop muzzles!" Rain was the enemy of gunpowder and the most they could do was try to keep the rifles and muskets dry. Sharpe saw the ground soaking up the water. They had to leave soon, before the dust turned to mud.

"Sir!" Hagman was calling again from the tower. "Dago horsemen, sir. Couple of miles south."

Now time was everything. They must march fast, try to build a lead over the partisans' pursuit, but Sharpe knew it was impossible. The gold was heavy and they could not travel fast enough, and now rain was falling even harder, bounding up from the ground so that the earth seemed to have a sparkling mist an inch or two above its surface.

El Católico smiled, gesturing at the rain. "You won't get far, Captain. We'll chase you. Kill you."

Now it was Sharpe's turn to smile as he pushed past the Spaniard. "You won't." He took hold of Teresa's collar and pulled her out of the group of partisans. "She dies if even one of us gets hurt."

El Católico lunged for him; the girl twisted away, but Harper brought his fist into the Spaniard's stomach and Sharpe grabbed Teresa with a choking hold on her neck.

"Do you understand? If that gold does not reach the British army, she dies!"

El Católico straightened up, his eyes furious. "*You* will die, Sharpe, I promise you, and not an easy death."

Sharpe ignored him, "Sergeant?"

"Sir?"

"Rope."

The Spaniard watched, silent, as Harper found a rope and, at Sharpe's directions, looped and tightened it round Teresa's neck. Sharpe turned to El Católico.

"Remember her like that. If you come near me, she's dead. If I get back safely, then I'll release her to marry you." He gestured and the company pushed the Spaniards away. Sharpe watched them go, knowing that soon they would be on his tracks. But he had his hostage now. He looked at her, seeing the hatred in her face, and knew he could never kill her. He hoped El Católico did not know that or else, in the seething rain, the Light Company were all dead men.

They started out, silent and wet, on the long journey home.

14

For the first two miles, back along the same track they had come, the going was easy enough. The men climbed the slope, the rain hissed in their ears and there was the elation of being on the road home, but it could not last. The direct route westwards was not the most sensible route: it led straight towards Almeida and the burgeoning French army that was concentrating on the town. They were heading instead for the ford at San Anton, that Major Kearsey had told them of.

Teresa seemed unafraid, as if she knew Sharpe would not kill her, and she refused the offer of a greatcoat with a disdainful shake of her head. She was cold, soaked through, humiliated by the rope round her neck, but Sharpe left it on because it would have been simple for her to run away, unencumbered, into the slippery rocks. Harper held the other end looped round his wrist.

As the day went on, they found themselves walking a nightmare landscape on a plateau criss-crossed with ravines, and through merciless weather. Teresa watched, her mouth curved in an ironic smile, as her captors slipped, crashed painfully into the rocks, and blundered onwards in the storm. Sharpe prayed that the wind would stay in the north; he had lost all bearings and his only guide was the rain on his face. He stopped occasionally, let the men rest, and searched the wind-scoured plateau for pursuing horsemen. There was nothing; just the rain sweeping in slow curtains and the grey horizon where air and stone became indistinguishable.

449

Suddenly Knowles, leading the company, waved ahead. "Look!"

Even in the rain, in the crushing weather, it was a beautiful sight. The plateau suddenly ended, dropped to a wide valley through which meandered a stream and a track. The Agueda. It had to be the River Agueda, off to the left, and the stream at the bottom of the valley joined the river where the track led to the ford. Sharpe's heart leaped. They had made it, the ford of San Anton, and beside the track, on this side of the river, was an ancient fort on a rock bluff that once must have guarded the crossing. At this distance, he guessed a mile and a half, the walls looked broken, but the fortress had to mark the site of the ford. "Five minutes' rest!"

The company sat down, relieved. Sharpe perched on a rock, took out his telescope, and searched the valley. It was empty. No horsemen, no partisans, nothing but the stream and the track going to the river. A second road, running north and south, ran this side of the river, but it, too, was empty. By God! They had done it!

"Come on!" He clapped his hands. "To the river! We cross tonight! Well done!"

The rain still fell, blinding the men as they stumbled down the slope, but they could see their goal. There were British patrols on the far bank, to be sure not as many as there were French, but the River Agueda marked some kind of limit. They almost ran the last part of the slope, splashed through the stream, boots crunching on the gravel bed, then stamped onto the wet track as if it were a paved highway in the centre of London. The ford was a mile ahead, trees on both banks, and the company knew that, once they crossed, they could rest.

"Sir." Harper spoke quietly with a desperate resignation. "Sir. Behind."

Horsemen. Partisans who had ridden, not over the plateau, but up the direct road from Casatejada, now appeared on the track behind them. Teresa smiled, gave Sharpe a look of victory, and he ignored it. He called wearily to the company to halt. He could see no more than twenty or thirty horsemen, standing in the rain just three hundred yards behind. Perhaps El Católico could be threat-

450

ened, a bayonet at Teresa's throat, but Sharpe could only envisage failure, defeat. He took a deep breath. "They can't hurt us, lads. Bayonets. They won't charge bayonets!"

There was something strangely comforting about the sound of the blades scraping from the scabbards, to see the men crouching with bent knees as they fixed on the long blades. The band of horsemen came forward, spurred into a trot, and Sharpe stood with his men in the front rank. "We'll teach them to respect the bayonet! Wait for it!"

But the partisans had no intention of charging the small company. They split into two groups and galloped either side of the bedraggled soldiers, almost ignoring them. El Católico was there, a smile of triumph on his face, and he swept his hat off in an ironic gesture as he went past thirty yards away. Teresa jerked towards him, but Harper had her firm as the horsemen went on towards the fortress and the river. Sharpe knew what they were doing. The company would be blocked in, trapped in the valley, and El Católico would wait until the rest of the partisans, summoned from the south, could reach them.

He wiped rain from his face. "Come on." There was nowhere to go, so the best thing was to go on. He looked round at the far, shrouded hills across the river, the small fort, and then further north, at the spur of the hills that almost reached the river. And there he saw, on its blurred horizon, the shape of a horseman who had a strange, square hat.

"Down! Down! Down!" Something, an instinct, told him the French patrol had only just arrived on the skyline. He forced the men down, into cover in the stream bed, scrambling behind the shallow turf bank.

El Católico was much slower. Sharpe, lying next to Harper and the girl, watched the partisans ride on towards the ford and it was not until the French lancers were moving, trotting almost sedately down the slope, that the grey figure wheeled, waved his arm, and the partisans urged their tired mounts into a gallop. The Spaniards rode back into the valley, scattering as they picked their own course, and the lancers, a different regiment from the Poles', chose their targets and went for them with levelled blades. Sharpe, peering between tufts of grass, could see twenty lancers, but looking back to the northern skyline he saw more appear, then a group at the place where the hills almost met the river. He realized that a full French regiment was there, coming south, and as he tried to find a reason for their presence he saw the girl jerk the rope free, scrabble backwards, and she was up, white dress brilliant in the murk, running southwards towards the hills to where El Católico and his men were desperately fleeing. He pushed Harper down. "Stay there!"

They must see her! Sharpe shouted at her to get down, but the wind snatched away the words, and he forced himself on, getting closer. The girl stumbled on the far bank of the stream, and Sharpe crashed into her, his weight driving her into the gravel beside the water.

She fought at him, but he bore her down, took her wrists and forced them apart, using all his strength to keep them still. She kicked at him and he hooked his legs over hers, not caring if he hurt her, thinking only of the lance that could pin them both like wriggling insects. There were hooves near and he thrust his head down, cracking her forehead, as three lancers splashed by them in the stream, their mouths open in the gaping, silent shriek of a cavalry charge.

Teresa took a breath, twisted violently, and Sharpe knew she was about to scream. She had not seen the lancers, knew only that El Católico was near, and there was only one thing for Sharpe to do.

His legs were across hers, his hands were on her wrists, so he jammed his mouth on top of hers and forced her head down. One eye glared at·him, she jerked beneath him, twisted, but his weight smothered her and, very suddenly, she lay still.

A voice was close, it seemed almost on top of them, and they could hear the crunch of hooves in the gravel.

"Ici! Jean!"

There was a shout from further away, and the girl lay utterly still. Sharpe could see the sudden fear in her eye, and he raised his mouth from hers, turned his head, infinitely slowly, so that he could see all her face. "Lie still. Still," he whispered.

She nodded, almost imperceptibly, and Sharpe let go of her wrists though his hands stayed on top of them. The rain seethed down, dripped from his hair and shako onto her face. The voice came again, still shouting, and Sharpe heard, through the hissing rain, the creak of saddlery and the snorting of a horse. Her eyes stayed on his.

He dared not look up—the Frenchman could not be far. But he was searching for horsemen who had scattered into the rainstorm, not for a couple lying in a stream. Her hand gripped at his, and then, telling himself that a raised head increased the chance of discovery, he lowered his mouth towards her again. The Frenchman laughed, shouted something at his friends, and Teresa kept her huge, dark eyes open as Sharpe kissed her. She could have moved, but she did not.

The lancer shouted again, much closer, and then there was a reply, mocking and imperative: he was being called back. Sharpe could hear the horse's hooves crashing in the stream bed and then the sound receded, the voices faded, and Teresa shut her eyes, kissed him fiercely and, almost in the same movement, thrust his head away. She began to move, but he shook his head at her. "Wait."

He had seen what was at the end of the valley: a convoy, with rows of ox-carts whose ungreased axles screamed piercingly through the foul weather, and either side of the plodding carts the shapes of more horsemen, escorting the carts southwards towards the Almeida road. It could take an hour for the convoy to pass, but at least it had driven El Católico and his men away, and Sharpe realized with a sudden burst of elation that as long as the Light Company was not discovered then they should safely reach the ford when the French had gone. He looked at the girl. "Will you be still?"

She nodded. He slowly eased himself off her and lay down beside her. She turned over onto her stomach and the wet dress clung to the slim beauty of her body and he reached out and took the rope from her neck, fumbling at the knot with wet fingers. When it was off, he dropped it to the gravel. "I'm sorry."

She shrugged as if it was no matter. There was a chain round her neck and Sharpe, his hand already close, pulled it to find a square locket, made of silver. She watched, her dark eyes utterly expressionless, as he put a thumbnail under the catch and it sprang open. There was no picture but the inside of the lid was engraved: "My love to you. J." It took him a few seconds to realize it was in English, that El Católico would never have inscribed a piece of silver with English and he knew, with a sick certainty, that it had belonged to Hardy. J for Josefina.

"He's dead, isn't he?"

For a moment she did not move, but then she nodded.

"How did he die?"

"El Católico." She gave the answer readily enough and Sharpe knew that her loyalty was changing. "The gold—you keep it?" she asked.

Sharpe watched her eyes. "I think so. But to fight the French, not to take home. I promise."

She nodded and turned to watch the French convoy. Guns, coming from the French army of the north, and going to Almeida. Not field guns or siege artillery, but Bonaparte's favourite eight-inch howitzers, with obscene little muzzles which could throw explosive shells high into the air to fall in the packed houses of a besieged town. There were carts, too, presumably loaded with ammunition and powder.

Sharpe could feel the rain beating on his back, and he knew that the river would be rising, and that with every passing moment his chance of crossing the ford was receding. He turned to the girl again. "Why does El Católico want the gold?"

She shrugged as though it were a stupid question: "To buy power."

For a moment Sharpe wondered if she meant soldiers, and then saw she had spoken the truth. The Spanish armies were gone; the government, if it could be called a government, was in faraway Cádiz. For a ruthless man the whole country of Spain was one big opportunity: from the hills of old Castile, El Católico could fashion a kingdom that would rival those of the ancient barons who had built the fortresses dotting the border area.

Sharpe was still staring at the girl. "And you?"

"I want the French dead." The words were spoken with a terrible vehemence. "All of them."

"You need our help."

She looked at him very steadily, not liking the truth, but finally nodded. "I know."

He leaned forward and kissed her again, as the rain lashed at them and the stream soaked them and the carts of the French convoy screeched in their ears. She put a hand behind his head, held him, and he knew it was not a dream.

She pulled away, smiled at him for the first time. "You know the river rises?"

He nodded. "Can we cross?"

She glanced at the stream, shook her head. "If the rain stops tonight? Yes."

Sharpe had seen the extraordinary speed with which rivers, in these dry hills, rose and fell. She nodded at the fort. "You can spend the night there."

"And you?"

She smiled again. "Can I leave?"

"Yes."

"I'll stay. What's your name?"

"Richard."

She nodded, looked again at the fortress. "You will be safe. We use it. Ten men can stop the entrance."

"And El Católico?"

She shook her head. "He's frightened of you. He'll wait until tomorrow, when his men come."

Rain lashed across the valley, ran from rock and grass and swelled the stream as the wind tore at the landscape. Half in the water, half out, they waited for the convoy to pass, and for what the next day would bring.

The war would have to wait.

15

"Sir, sir!" Sharpe opened his eyes to see grey daylight on grey walls, and Lieutenant Knowles in the tower doorway.

"All right!" The girl was waking as well, blinking in sunrise as she remembered where she was. He smiled at her. "Stay here."

He scrambled to his feet, and strapped on the huge sword as he followed Knowles into the courtyard.

"Lieutenant?"

"Visitors, sir. Coming down the valley."

He followed Knowles to the raised rampart that formed the southeastern corner of San Anton's courtyard. Dawn was like a grey mist on the countryside, blurring the trees and the grassland across the river, but he could see rocks foaming the water's surface where there had been none the evening before. The river level was sinking fast and they would be able to cross today. He lifted his eyes to stare into the eastern hills. "We're popular this morning."

Horsemen were riding on the track from Casatejada, partisans in force, aiming for the oak groves where El Católico and his men had spent the night, and among them was Kearsey's blue coat. Sharpe spat over the rampart into the stream far below. "Keep them out, Robert. Don't let anyone, even the major, inside the walls."

His uniform was damp and uncomfortable. He looked up at the sky, saw the ragged clouds and knew that the storm had passed. Soon it would be hot, under a shadowless blue, and he wondered how much water the company had.

"Sergeant McGovern!" he called. "Take six men down to the river with all the canteens. Fill them up."

McGovern glanced at Lieutenant Knowles. "We've already done it, sir. No one interfered with us."

"It's as I said. El Católico's guarding the ford, not the castle. Any food?"

Knowles sighed. He had half hoped that Sharpe's morning temper would have been moderated by Teresa. "Just hard tack, sir. And not much of that."

Sharpe swore. "Right! All weapons cleaned!"

He ignored the grumbles, turned and leaned against the rampart. The night had gone quietly. Sometime after midnight the rain had stopped, and Harper had got a small fire going in the shelter of the broken tower. Teresa had been right. The fortress was approached by a single precipitous track, easy to defend, and El Católico had left them in peace.

Sharpe leaned over the rampart. He saw Kearsey leave the oak grove and head his borrowed horse towards the path which led to the castle.

Sharpe pulled on his damp boots and nodded towards the tower. "Keep the girl inside, Robert." Knowles nodded. "I'll meet the major outside. Inspect the weapons and get ready to move."

"Already?" Knowles seemed surprised.

"Can't stay here for ever." Sharpe buttoned his jacket and picked up his sword. "I'll go and give Major Kearsey the good news."

Sharpe walked briskly down the slope and waved cheerfully at Kearsey. "Morning, sir! A nice one!"

Kearsey reined his horse, stared down at Sharpe with unfriendly eyes. "What have you done, Sharpe?" The words were spat out with suppressed rage.

Sharpe stared up at the small major who was silhouetted against the sun. "I've brought the gold, sir. As I was ordered."

Kearsey nodded impatiently as if it were the answer he expected. "You kidnapped the girl, locked up our allies, disobeyed my orders, you have turned men who fought for us into men who simply want to kill you." He paused for breath, but Sharpe interrupted.

"And the men who killed Captain Hardy?"

Kearsey stared at Sharpe. "What?"

"El Católico killed him, stabbed him in the back. He's buried beneath a manure heap in the village." Teresa had told him the story during the night. "He found El Católico moving the gold. It seems he made a protest. So they killed him."

Kearsey shook his head. "How do you know?"

"I was . . . told, sir."

Kearsey was not prepared to give up. He shook his head, as if trying to clear a bad dream. "But you stole the gold!"

"I obeyed orders, sir."

"Whose orders? I am the ranking officer!"

Sharpe suddenly felt sorry for the major. Kearsey had found the gold, told Wellington, and had never been informed of the general's plans. Sharpe felt in his pocket, found his orders and hoped that the rain had not soaked through the folds of the paper. It had, but the writing was still legible. He handed it up to Kearsey.

Kearsey read it, his anger growing. "It says nothing!"

"It orders all officers to assist me, sir. All."

But Kearsey was not listening. For a few seconds he sat motionless, his eyes screwed shut, and then in a violent gesture he tore the paper into shreds. "I have worked, Sharpe, God knows I have worked to help the Spanish and the British get on together. And I am rewarded by this!" He held the scraps of paper up and then, with a sudden jerk, scattered them into the wind. "Are we to *steal* the gold, Sharpe?"

"Yes, sir. That's about the long and short of it."

"We can't." Kearsey's words were low and measured. "We have honour, Sharpe. That is our private strength, our honour. We're soldiers, you and I. We cannot expect riches, or dignity, or continual victory. We will die, probably in battle, or in a fever ward, and no one will remember us, so all that is left is honour. Do you understand?"

It was strange, standing in the growing warmth of the sun, and listening to the words that were wrenched from Kearsey's soul. Sharpe spoke gently. "The general spoke to me, sir. He wants the

458

gold. Without it the war is lost. If that's stealing, then we're stealing it. I assume that you will help us?"

Kearsey jerked himself upright. "We will take the gold to Wellington, Captain. But under my orders. You must release the girl, do you understand? I will not be a party to this underhand procedure. I presume she has not been harmed?"

"No, sir, she has not. Not yet." Sharpe's patience was at an end. If El Católico thought that the girl was safe, then his men would fall on the Light Company and Sharpe would face a death more painful than any sane imagination could invent. He looked up at Kearsey. "In ten minutes, Major, I am going to cut off one of her ears. Only halfway, so it will mend, but if any of those murderous bastards with El Católico tries to interfere with our crossing of the ford, then the whole ear will be sliced off. And the other ear, and her tongue. Do you understand me, sir? We are leaving, with the gold, and the girl is our passport and I'm not giving her up. Tell her father that, tell El Católico that! Understand?"

Sharpe's anger drove the major two steps down the slope. "I am ordering you, Sharpe . . ."

"You're ordering nothing, sir. You tore up my orders! We are going. So tell them, Major! You'll hear the scream in ten minutes!"

He turned away, his anger deafening him to Kearsey's words, and climbed into the stockade of the fort. His men saw his face and said nothing, but turned away and watched as the small, blue-uniformed major rode his horse back to the partisans.

Ten minutes later a sound came from the ruined tower of the Castillo. The scream rose to an unbearable pitch and then wavered down to a thin, sobbing desperation. Then the scream came again; higher. And afterwards the noise of boots on stone, shouted orders, and the company marched out with fixed bayonets on shouldered guns, and in the lead was Sharpe who held a rifle sling looped round Teresa's neck, and a gleaming saw-backed bayonet at her head. Teresa was crying, a white bandage round her head, torn from the bottom of her dress, and stained with bright blood. The men's faces looked shocked, as if their captain had dragged them to new depths of horror.

Sharpe shielded himself from El Católico's guns with the girl's body, and as the company, in a silence that seemed as if it could explode at any instant into dreadful violence, marched past the partisans, Cesar Moreno gazed at the blood-soaked bandage, at the spots of blood on his daughter's dress. "I will kill him," he said. "For every blade laid to my daughter, Sharpe will suffer a hundred!"

Kearsey touched his arm. "I'm sorry."

Moreno looked at him. "It was not your doing, Major." He nodded at where the Light Company were beginning their crossing, the lightly loaded men forming a human dam to help the gold-carriers to cross. "Go in peace."

Sharpe crossed last, holding the girl. The water level was low, but the current still strong, and it was awkward with one arm round Teresa's neck, but they made it and were pulled onto the far bank by Patrick Harper who nodded back over the river. "Felt sorry for her father, sir."

"He'll find out she wasn't touched."

"Aye, that's true. The major's coming."

"Let him."

They set off across the grassland, with the partisans never far behind. Harper walked with Sharpe and Teresa and he looked over the girl's head at his captain. "How's the arm, sir?"

"It's fine." Sharpe had cut open his left forearm to find blood to soak Teresa's bandage. "I'll survive. You'd better tell the lads that the girl's not harmed. Quietly."

"I'll do that." Harper went ahead.

Sharpe looked at the partisans, and then at Teresa. "You must keep pretending."

She nodded. "You keep your promise?"

"I promise. We have a bargain." It was a good one, too, and he admired Teresa for its terms. At least, now, he knew why she was on his side and there was only one regret; they would not be together long. The bargain called for them to be far apart, but who knew, perhaps he would meet her again.

At midday Kearsey had caught up with them, and launched into a rehearsed condemnation of Sharpe that had petered out when Teresa had spoken to him in Spanish, driving down his objections, until the major, confused by events he could not control, had fallen into an unhappy silence. Later, the company reached a steep ridge that ran directly west, towards their goal, and Sharpe led the way up its steep, razor-stoned flank with a sense of relief. The partisans could not take their horses up the slope, and their figures grew smaller and smaller as the company laboured upwards along the spine of the ridge. The sun beat down searingly and the men carrying the gold needed frequent rests, but each hour took them nearer the River Coa and Sharpe dared to hope that they had shaken off El Católico and his men. Ahead he could see the hills that led to the river, to safety, and he forced the company on.

Patrick Harper, carrying two packs of gold, nodded at the western hills to their front. "Are the French there, sir?"

Sharpe shrugged. "Probably." If the French were patrolling the hills, and they must be, then the company would be visible for miles. He made his own gold-filled pack more comfortable on his shoulder. "We'll keep going west in the night." He looked at his tired men. "Just this one effort, Sergeant, just this one."

16

The water in the canteens was brackish, the food down to the last mildewed crumbs, and in the hour before dawn the ground was slippery with dew. It was cold. The company, foul mouthed and evil tempered, slithered and fell as they went down the dark hillside into a black valley. Kearsey, his steel scabbard crashing against rocks, tried to keep up with Sharpe. "Almeida, Sharpe. It's the only way!"

Sharpe stopped, towered over the major. "Damn Almeida, sir."

"There's no need for cursing, Sharpe." Kearsey sounded peevish. "You don't understand. The French will be blocking the Coa. You must go south."

Sharpe turned away, slipped, and cursed as he sat down painfully on a stone. He would not go to Almeida. The French were about to start the siege and would be concentrating in force. He would go west, towards the Coa, and take the gold to Wellington.

The turf on the valley floor was springy, easy to walk on but Sharpe crouched and hissed at his men to be quiet. In the creeping dawn he could see that on the far side of the valley the hills rose again. It was a perfect place for a French ambush. Sharpe listened. He could hear nothing, see nothing, but his instinct told him the enemy was near. Ahead was foraging country, and Kearsey had claimed that the French would hold the countryside in force so that they could strip it of food. He knew the company was nervous, and he stood up. "Rifles! Skirmish line. Lieutenant! Follow with the company. Forward!"

This, at least, was a trade they knew and the riflemen split into skirmishing pairs and spread out into the thin, elastic screen that sheltered the main battle line in a fight. One man moved as his partner covered him, just as in battle one man reloaded while the other watched to see if any enemy was aiming at his comrade during the vulnerable and clumsy wielding of ramrod and cartridge. Fifty yards behind the greenjackets, the redcoats climbed the hill. Teresa stayed with Knowles, wearing Sharpe's greatcoat over the white dress. She could sense the apprehension among the men. The world seemed empty, the dawn rising on grey rocks and limitless grass, but Teresa knew, better even than Sharpe, that somewhere, watching them, were the French.

The sun rose, lancing its light across the ridge behind them, and Sharpe, ahead of the riflemen, saw it touch gold on the hillcrest seventy yards ahead. The rock was covered in light and at its base, half hidden by shadowed grass, was a dull red colour. He turned, casually, and waved his men flat as if he wanted to give them a rest. He yawned, massively, stretched his arms, and sauntered across the line to Harper. He looked down the slope and waved at Knowles, laconically indicating for the heavily laden group to lie down, and then he nodded amicably at the sergeant. "Bloody voltigeurs on the crest."

Voltigeurs, the French skirmishers, the light infantry who fought against the British light companies. Sharpe squatted on the ground, his back to the enemy, and talked softly. "Saw the red epaulette."

Harper looked over Sharpe's shoulder, flicking his eyes along the crest, and swore quietly. Sharpe plucked a blade of grass and pushed it between his teeth. Another twenty yards and they would have been in range of the French muskets. "There'll be infantry, . . . and cavalry as well."

Harper jerked his head sideways, down the slope, to the still-shadowed valley. "There?"

Sharpe nodded. "They must have seen us yesterday, walking along that ridge."

Harper yawned for the benefit of the watching enemy. "Time we had a proper fight, sir." He spoke mildly.

Sharpe scowled. "If we could choose where." He stood up. "We go left." The hillside to the left, to the south, offered more cover, but he knew, with a terrible certainty, that the Light Company was outnumbered and almost certainly outflanked as well. He blew his big whistle, waved to the south, and the company moved along the side of the hill while Sharpe quietly warned the riflemen of the enemy above.

Kearsey climbed up from the redcoats. "What are we doing, Sharpe?"

Sharpe told him about the skirmishers. Kearsey looked triumphant, as if he had been proved right. "So what do you do now?"

"I have no idea, Major, no idea."

"Told you, Sharpe! Capturing Eagles is all very well, but out here in enemy country we're sitting ducks."

"Yes, sir." There was no point in arguing. As Sharpe worked his way round the hill he knew that at any moment the journey could end, his men caught between voltigeurs and cavalry, and in a month's time someone at the army headquarters would wonder idly whatever happened to Captain Sharpe and the Light Company that was sent on the impossible job of bringing back Spanish gold.

Rifleman Tongue suddenly spun round. "Sir!" The shout was muffled by the bang of a musket, the smoke hanging in front of a rock just twenty yards away. Tongue was spinning and falling, and Sharpe raced past Harper and knelt by the rifleman, lifting up his head. "Isaiah!"

The head was heavy, the eyes sightless: the musket ball had gone cleanly between two ribs and killed him even as he shouted the warning. Sharpe could hear the ramrod rattle as the skirmisher pushed his next round into the barrel, and then the unseen enemy's partner fired, the ball missing Sharpe by inches. In the same instant Harper's rifle bullet lifted the Frenchman up, off the ground; he opened his mouth to scream, but only blood came out and he dropped back. Sharpe could hear his unseen partner scraping his iron ramrod; he ran forward. The second voltigeur saw him coming, panicked, and scrambled backwards, and Sharpe shot him in the base of the spine. He knew that the enemy skirmish line had bent down the hill, cutting their southward advance, and he waved his men back. They went down the hill, the musket balls over their heads, and found cover in the rocks. Tongue's body would have to stay there, another rifleman lost in Spain.

"Sir!" Knowles was pointing behind and Sharpe rolled over and looked back the way they had come. French skirmishers in faded blue jackets were angling down the hill behind them.

He stayed on his back, facing his men. "Rifles! Bayonets!" The French would understand that all right, and feel the fear. They had put a skirmish line on the hillside in front, thinking it would be enough to drive the British back downhill to where, still unseen, the cavalry must wait. "Lieutenant!"

"Sir?"

"You'll follow us."

We might get outside their cordon, he thought, and find a place to defend; anything was better than being driven like sheep. He tugged his sword out, felt its edge, and was on his feet. "Forward!"

He heard the Bakers cracking the morning apart as the Frenchmen put up their heads to fire at the small, spread band of men in green who screamed at them and had twenty-three inches of steel fixed to their rifles. But muskets were terrible instruments for precision work, and he let the enemy fire and knew the odds were in the company's favour. One man went down, but he was dragged up and they were through the gap and there were just a few panicked French fugitives ahead. Harper spitted one neatly between the ribs, kicked the blade free, and went on. Sharpe cut at a man with the sword, felt the bone-hammering jar as the Frenchman parried with his musket, and then he ran on and wondered what kind of a dent he had put in the heavy steel edge. "Come on! Uphill!"

That was not what the French expected, so it was the only way to go. The company had smashed the cordon, lost only one man, and now they forced their tired legs up the slope towards the eastern crest, while behind them the blue-coated officers re-aligned their men. Sharpe made the crest and kept running. The damned French were there, not expecting the British, but there all the same and lined up in companies, waiting for orders. They watched, astonished, as the British ran past their front, only a hundred paces away, and not a musket was fired.

Sharpe turned, waved the riflemen down and pushed Knowles and the red-jacketed men past. "Form up a hundred paces down!"

Knowles acknowledged, leaped over a boulder, and the company was gone.

"Rifles! Hold them up!"

This was a better way of fighting, letting the enemy come to them, and killing them when they were too far away to reply to the rifle fire. Sharpe fought as a private, ramming the balls down the rifling, picking his targets and waiting for the victim to rush forward.

He aimed low, never waiting to see if the man fell before dragging out another cartridge and starting to reload. He could hear the rifles around him, firing as fast as they could, which was not fast enough, and he saw Teresa with Tongue's weapon, her face already blackened with powder smoke, kneeling up to fire at a Frenchman. But still they came and he knew they were outnumbered horribly. There were a hundred skirmishers in front of them, pressing forward, lapping them, and the riflemen went back, firing at their enemies and always losing ground, getting closer and closer to the open ground of the valley.

"Back!" This was no place to die, not while the cavalry had still not appeared and there was a chance, however slim, that the company could fall back to the far side of the valley. He hurried the company down the hill, stopping and firing, running, reloading, and finding new cover. They were doing little damage to the enemy, but the French, terrified of rifles, kept their distance.

Pausing to watch the men go back, Sharpe glanced up the hill and saw the crest lined with the French companies, their uniforms bright, unfaded by the sun, and he knew this was one of the new regiments that had been sent by Bonaparte to finish the Spanish business once and for all. He was trying to find an officer to aim for among the voltigeurs when a ball smacked into the rock beside him and glanced up to hit his left armpit. It hurt like a dog chewing his flesh and, throwing up the rifle for a quick shot, he realized that the ricochet had done damage. He could hardly hold the rifle, but he squeezed the trigger, and went backwards, keeping pace with his men.

He turned to the riflemen, then, red eyes peering from blackened faces. "Form up, lads! Cross the valley!"

The girl fell in like another rifleman and he grinned at her, loving her for fighting like a man, for her eyes that sparkled with the hell of it. He waved his right arm. "March!"

They went away from the rocks, from the voltigeurs, out into the unnatural calmness of the grass. The French infantry did not follow, but stopped at the foot of the slope for all the world as if the Light Company were on a boat and they could not follow.

Major Kearsey saw Sharpe. "You're hit!"

"It's nothing, sir. A ricochet. I've had worse, sir. It'll mend."

Kearsey looked at the French infantry. "They're not following!"

"I know, sir. And their cavalry's waiting for us to get into the centre of the valley."

"What do we do?" Kearsey seemed to see nothing odd in asking Sharpe the question.

"I don't know, sir. You pray."

Kearsey took offence. "I have prayed, Sharpe! Precious little else for the last few days."

It had only been a few days, Sharpe thought, and was it all to end like this? He spoke gently. "Keep praying, sir."

It was thin pasture land, close-cropped and tough. The sun had reached the valley floor and insects were busy in the grass stems, oblivious of the battle overhead. Sharpe looked up and thought the valley was beautiful. It climbed between steep hills, and ahead was a stream bed which in spring would make the place a small paradise. He looked behind. Somewhere in the valley, he knew, the cavalry would be waiting. Pipe smoke went up from the sitting French infantry, front seats for the slaughter.

Patrick Harper fell in beside him, grabbed his elbow and, ignoring Sharpe's protest, pulled the arm up, his hands squeezing. "Does it hurt?"

"Yes, damn you!"

Harper let go. "No bone broken, sir. The ball's trapped. Ricochet?" Sharpe nodded. A full hit would have broken shoulder and upper arm. It hurt. Harper looked at the girl and back to Sharpe. "It'll impress the wee girl."

"Go to hell."

"Yes, sir." Harper was worried, trying not to show it.

Trumpets sounded and Sharpe saw the first horses appear to the north. His heart sank. Lancers again, two hundred of them, their lances tipped with red and white pennants. They trotted into formation in the valley and stared at the small group of British infantry.

Sharpe spat into the grass, looked left and right. "That way." He pointed to the eastern side of the valley, away from the French infantry. "On the double!"

They ran. Until suddenly a deep fold of dead ground to the south was revealed as horsemen filed from it, men in foreign uniforms,

467

sabres drawn. They did not wait like the lancers — instead they trotted forward, knee to knee, and Sharpe knew it was all over.

"Halt! Company square!" He put the girl in the centre, with Kearsey. "Bayonets!" They did it calmly, and he was proud of them. His shoulder hurt like the devil and something was wrong, everything blurred, and he shook his head to clear his vision and gave the rifle to Kearsey. "I'm sorry, sir. I can't hold it."

His sword was still drawn, a dent in the foreblade, and he pushed his way through to the front of the tiny square, an almost useless gesture of defiance. The sabres were nearer, the men riding like veterans, without excitement or haste, and Sharpe tried to place the French regiment with blue uniforms, a yellow stripe on the overalls, and tall brown busbies. Suddenly he realized his men were grinning. He tried to order the men to take aim, but nothing happened. His voice faded, his eyes seemed not to see. Harper caught him. "Hold on, sir, for God's sake, hold on."

Captain Lossow, resplendent in blue and yellow, saw Sharpe fall, cursed that his squadron had been delayed, and then, like a good professional of the King's German Legion, forgot about Sharpe. There was work to be done.

Lossow had two minutes, no more, and he used them well. He saw the company disappear behind his left shoulder; then the lancers were all that was ahead of him while far off to the left a battalion of French infantry scrambled untidily down the hill to add their firepower to the valley. He would not wait for them. He spoke to his trumpeter, listened to the charge, loved every note, and then he put his sabre in the air and let Thor have his head.

A good name for a horse, Thor, especially a horse like this one that could bite a man's face off or beat an enemy down with its hooves. It was good ground, comfortable, with no damned rabbits, and Lossow would pray at night for an opportunity like this. Lancers, idiots with long spikes who never knew how to parry, and all you had to do was get inside the point and the life was yours. He could hear his men galloping behind; he twisted in the saddle to see the fine sight, the horses neck and neck, as they should be, clods of turf flung up behind, blades and teeth shining, and was it not good of the German King who sat on the English throne to give him this chance?

The French were slow and he guessed they were new troops. A lancer should always meet the enemy at full speed or he was done. He steered Thor to the right as the trumpeter gave the call again, ragged this time because of the motion of the horse but enough to make a man's blood run cold, and he touched Thor with his left heel, never a spur in his life, and the huge horse turned like a dancer. The sabre was dropped so it pointed down like a spike from Lossow's outstretched hand, and he galloped, laughing, along the face of the enemy, and simply knocked the lances away. It would never last, someone would be bright enough to face him, but by then the chaos he had created in half a dozen Frenchmen had let his first troop into the gap, and Lossow knew the job was done and he let Thor rear up and deal with the brave fellow who challenged him.

"Left!" Lossow ordered, and at once the Germans turned, chewing up the French line, the sabres wicked in their work, and Lossow was satisfied.

He had a minute left so Lossow touched Thor with his heels and the horse went forward, and the sabre turned a galloping lance so neatly that Lossow thought he would remember that moment till the day he died, and the Kligenthal steel of the curved blade opened the Frenchman's throat as far as his spine, and he wished

that every moment was this good, with a fine horse, a good turf, a blade made by the dwarves themselves, and an enemy for breakfast.

He watched his men work, proud of them. They were disciplined, protecting one another, their sword drill immaculate and thorough.

"Recall."

The trumpet sounded, the men pulled back in perfect order and Lossow waved the sabre. The French lancers were done for, utterly

beaten, but he had expected no less. Poor devils. They were not
to know that Lossow's men had tracked this valley for three days,
waiting for a sight of Sharpe.

He looked up the valley. The rescued infantry were moving fast
now, each man gratefully holding onto a cavalryman's stirrup, and
Lossow brought the other hundred and fifty sabres back slowly,
screening the retreat, enjoying the warm sun, and saluting the
French infantry who were forming up, too late, their show spoiled.

471

AN HOUR LATER Sharpe opened his eyes, saw Harper leaning over him, pinning him to the ground, and Teresa was holding one hand, and then a German soldier came to him with a piece of iron, glowing hot.

"Still, Captain." Harper spoke gently, gripped hard.

The cauterizing iron hit him like the devils of hell, and it took all Harper's strength to hold him down. The shout was cut off as he fainted, as the flesh burned and stank, but it was done and Lossow's horse doctor nodded his satisfaction. They splashed water on his face, trickled brandy into his throat, and Sharpe opened his eyes, grimaced as the pain shot through him, and looked up to see a German officer. He had met the man before. Where? He remembered. In the village where Batten had been caught by the provosts. He stuck out his good hand. "Captain . . . ?"

"Lossow, sir. At your service!"

Sharpe smiled, a bit wanly. "You have our thanks, sir."

The German waved the formality away. "On the contrary. You have ours. A lovely fight! A fine horse, a good turf, and an enemy for breakfast!"

"Did you lose anyone?"

"Lose anyone? They were lancers, Captain! An angry toad would be more dangerous! Now, if they put sabres in the front rank, and lancers behind, they might be dangerous. But just lancers? No problem to us! We screened your retreat, and the French infantry formed up too late."

Sharpe nodded, grateful. "But thank you."

Lossow took a mug from Harper and put it on Sharpe's lap. "You got the gold."

"You know about it?"

"Why do you think I am here? A patrol to the south, me here, and all for you, Captain. The Lord Wellington wants the gold badly!"

Sharpe sipped at the stew in the mug. It tasted miraculous after the hard tack of the last week. "He can have it."

"*Ja*, but there are problems. French patrols." Lossow's hand described an arc to the west.

Sharpe forced his left hand round to hold the hot mug and it worked. He spooned the tough beef into his mouth. "We must get to the army."

"I know."

"We must." He looked to his right and saw one of Lossow's men sharpening his sword, using a stone and oil to smooth down the dent he had made in it, only that morning. He lifted Lossow's brandy bottle, and the spirit flowed like cream into his throat. He coughed. "Have you seen partisans?"

Lossow spoke quickly to one of his officers and then turned back to Sharpe. "Two miles away, Captain, keeping in touch with us. They want the gold?"

Sharpe nodded. "And me." He looked at the girl and back to the German.

"Don't worry, Captain. You're in good hands."

Teresa smiled at Sharpe, and came to him. Her dress was another four inches shorter and Sharpe realized he had been bandaged after the cauterizing iron had driven him back to unconsciousness. She still had the rifle, slung proprietorially on a shoulder. Lossow moved to one side to let her sit down.

Sharpe leaned back, sipped at the brandy, and dozed in the sun. The girl sat beside him, watching the Light Company rest, while beyond the tethered horses Lossow's picquets watched the French patrols comb the western valleys. The Light Company would move soon, cutting westward, but for now they could sleep and forget the one more river they had to cross.

THE SIEGE of Almeida had not yet begun. Sharpe, with a hurting shoulder and a seething sense of frustration, rode into the town's intricate defences. There had been no choice. Damned Frenchmen seemed to be everywhere out in the country. Much as Sharpe hated to admit it, he knew there was no sense in being chased ragged round the east bank of the River Coa.

Straw torches, soaked in resin, flamed and smoked in the tunnelled gateway as the Portuguese infantry watched the tired men ride and walk into the town. The insides of Sharpe's legs were sore, he hated riding horses, but Lossow had insisted. The gold was all on horseback, carried by the Germans, and there was still hope. The French had not even surrounded Almeida; they had ridden the last few miles unmolested, and Sharpe guessed that the cavalry patrols were concentrated to the north.

In the southern sky, beyond the bulk of the castle, he could see the glow of French fires but to the west, beyond the river, there were no fires, except in the distance, and they were British. Success was so close. They would feed the horses, and leave at dawn. One last effort, and it was done.

Kearsey, on another borrowed horse, led the procession into the Plaza, which seemed to be the only inhabited place in the town. Sharpe turned to Knowles. "Lieutenant—go to the lower town, find billets. Knock a house open." There were dozens of empty houses. "Meet me back here. Sergeant?"

Harper came alongside the horse and Sharpe gestured at Teresa. "She'll need a room. I'll join the company when I'm finished here."

Brigadier Cox's headquarters were dark inside and Kearsey, Sharpe and Lossow waited in an echoing hallway.

"Major!" Cox was at the top of the stairs, pulling on shirt and trousers. "You're back! Come into the drawing room. Candles!"

There was a bustle as Portuguese servants brought in candles, wine and food. Sharpe sat, exhausted, in a deep, comfortable chair, and helped himself to the wine.

Cox nodded at him amicably. "Captain. Captain Lossow. What can I do for you?"

Sharpe sat up, surprised. Did Cox not know? "We have the gold, sir. We must take it to Celorico. We wanted to feed the horses, rest, and leave at dawn. With your permission, sir, we'd like the western gate opened an hour before first light."

Cox nodded, leaned over and poured himself a small glass of wine. "Whose gold is it?"

Sharpe felt an immense burden come back. "I am under orders from Lord Wellington, sir. Orders to take the gold to him."

Cox's eyebrows shot up. "Good! Let me see the orders then!"

Sharpe glanced at Kearsey, who reddened. The major cleared

his throat. "The orders were accidentally destroyed, sir. No blame to Captain Sharpe."

Cox peered at Kearsey. "You saw them? What did they say?"

"That all officers should render assistance to Captain Sharpe." Kearsey spoke in a neutral voice.

Cox nodded. "Did the orders specifically mention the gold?"

"For God's sake, sir!" Sharpe exploded, but Cox banged on the table.

"I have a problem, gentlemen." He pulled papers towards him, and held out a thick piece of parchment in the candlelight. "A request from the Spanish government, our allies, that the gold does not pass through British hands. Damned strange, really."

Lossow coughed. "Strange, sir?"

Cox nodded again. "Fellow arrives today, full fig, and tells me about the gold. It was the first I knew about it. He's got an escort for it. Spanish colonel. He's called Jovellanos."

Sharpe looked at Kearsey. "Jovellanos?"

"El Católico." Kearsey stretched for the piece of paper and held the seal up to the candle. "It's in order, sir. Genuine."

"How the hell can it be in order?" Sharpe's right hand was gripped tight into a fist. "He's a bloody bandit! He wrote the damned thing himself! We have orders, sir, from Lord Wellington. That gold goes to Celorico!"

Cox, who had been friendly, scowled at Sharpe. "I see no need for anger, Captain. Colonel Jovellanos is here, my guest."

"But, sir," Lossow broke in, "Captain Sharpe speaks the truth. The gold is important. It has to go to the Lord Wellington."

Cox took a deep breath. "Damn it, gentlemen, I am facing a siege which will begin any day now. The enemy's guns are in sight, the placements are being dug, and now you bring me this!"

Sharpe repeated doggedly, "We have orders, sir."

"So you say." Cox picked up the paper. "Does Joaquím Jovellanos have authority from the Junta for Castile?" Kearsey nodded. "And the gold is theirs?" The nod again. The paper dropped onto the table. "The general gave me no orders!"

Sharpe sighed. He guessed what had been in Wellington's mind.

The fewer people who knew of the gold, the better. But now an English brigadier in the Portuguese army was faced with a Spanish colonel, an English captain, a German cavalryman, Spanish gold, and no orders. He had an idea. "Sir, is the telegraph working?"

Cox frowned. "Yes, Captain. There's a relay station over the river, towards Pinhel."

"When can the first messages be sent?"

"Usually an hour after dawn."

Sharpe nodded impatiently. "Would you, sir, consider a message to the general requesting orders concerning the gold?"

Cox looked at him. "Of course. First thing tomorrow?"

"Please, sir."

Cox stood up. "Good! Problem solved. I'll tell Colonel Jovellanos tomorrow and you can get a night's sleep. I must say you look as if you need it. Good God." He was peering at Sharpe's shoulder. "You're hurt!"

"It will mend, sir." Sharpe finished his wine, damned if politeness would stop him. And damn Wellington, too, who had held the cards too close to his chest so that Cox, a decent man, was put in this position. "Sir? How many men in Colonel Jovellanos's escort?"

"Two hundred, Sharpe. God save me, I wouldn't want to meet them in a dark street."

Nor I, thought Sharpe, nor I. He stood up, waited for the commander of the garrison to leave. Where was El Católico? He wondered.

Lossow, at least, understood. "My men will guard tonight," he insisted, and Sharpe smiled his thanks.

Cox wished them a goodnight at the front door as if he were a host bidding a genial farewell to valued dinner guests. "And sleep well! The message goes first thing!"

Knowles and Harper waited outside. Knowles had done well, unbarring a huge house that stabled the Germans' horses, housed everyone. On the second floor, behind a huge, polished door, was a bedroom with a feather mattress, a canopied bed, rugs, and the smell of old wood and fresh sheets.

Sharpe closed the door, cutting off the sounds of his men who

476

were sharing wine with the Germans, and looked at the girl. "El Católico's here."

She nodded. "What did you expect?"

He unbuckled his belt and untied the faded, red sash, wincing with the pain from his shoulder. Teresa helped him undress and propped herself beside him on the huge, soft bed.

"What does he want?"

"Later," Sharpe said. "Later." His right arm was still good and he pulled the girl close to him. Her hair fell onto his face, her mouth was beside his ear.

"Can I keep the rifle?"

"It's all yours," he said. "All yours."

18

It was not yet dawn, but the sky had the grey luminance that came before first light, and Sharpe wanted to be at the telegraph early. He was reluctant to move, to lose the warm body, but others were stirring in the house and a cockerel, exploding into sound in the courtyard, jerked him upright. He lay back again, taking five more minutes, and pulled Teresa close. "Did Hardy want you?"

She smiled. "Yes. He wanted me. But Joaquím was too close." She pushed hair away from her eyes. "He wants everything. My father's men, land, money, me. He's strong."

Somewhere a door scraped on old hinges, boots crossed a yard, and Sharpe knew it was time to be up. "And you?"

"I want to kill Frenchmen."

"You will."

"I know."

Now, looking at the sudden smile, he wished that he was not going. He could, he decided, be happy with this woman. He swung his legs out of bed, and put on his crumpled clothes.

Teresa helped him with the jacket buttons. "You'll come back?"

"I'll be back. The soldiers are here; you're safe."

He left her in the bedroom and went down to where the kitchen fire was blazing. Harper pushed a mug of tea over the table. A dozen men of the company were in the kitchen, sawing at new bread. Sharpe scraped his boots and his men looked up. "The girl." He wondered if he sounded embarrassed, but the men seemed not to mind. "Look after her till I get back."

They nodded, grinning at him, and he was suddenly immensely proud of them. She would be safe with them, scoundrels though they were, just as a king's ransom in gold was safe with them. It occurred to him that most officers would never have trusted their men with the gold. They would have feared desertion with the temptation of so much money, but it had never crossed Sharpe's mind. These were his men, and he trusted his life with their skills, so why not gold, or a girl?

Robert Knowles cleared his throat. "When will you be back, sir?"

"Three hours?" An hour till the message could be sent, an hour for the reply to come, and then another hour unpicking the details with Cox. "Keep an eye out for El Católico. He's here. Keep a guard, Robert, all the time, and let no one in."

It was cold in the street, the sky still dark grey, but as Sharpe, Lossow, and Harper mounted the final steps to the rampart of the castle they could see the eastern sky blazing with the coming sun. The telegraph was unmanned, the sheep bladders tied to the mast, the wind slapping the ropes in a forlorn tattoo.

The sun shattered the remnants of night, dazzled over the eastern hills, and streaked its bleak, early light into the countryside round Almeida. As if in salute there was a blare of bugles, shouts from the walls, and Lossow clapped Sharpe's shoulder and pointed south.

"Look!"

478

The bugles had responded to the first formal move of the siege. The waiting was over. In the dawn light the Portuguese gunners had seen the fresh earthworks that had been thrown up a thousand yards from the fortifications. It was the first French battery, and, even as Sharpe watched, there was the flat crack of a Portuguese cannon. Through his glass, Sharpe saw an eruption of earth where the round shot struck the ground just in front of the French battery. The ball must have bounced right over the top and he knew the Portuguese gunners would be satisfied. After another two firings their gun barrel would be hot and the shot would carry further and he listened for the next shot, saw it fall a little beyond the first, and watched as the French soldiers hurried to take cover. "Next one."

He straightened up. Over the roofs of the town he could see the smoke of the cannon drifting in the breeze, saw another smudge as the Portuguese fired again, and then, a second later, heard the crash and watched the earthworks blow apart.

"Bravo!" Lossow pounded his fist on the ramparts. "That's held them up for five minutes!"

Sharpe panned the telescope westward, to the road that led to the Coa. He could see that, apart from one earthen barricade, there had been no real attempt by the French to seal it off. He handed the glass to Lossow. "We can do it."

The German looked at the road, smiled. "It will be a pleasure."

There were footsteps on the circular stone stairway and the young midshipman, holding a thick sandwich, emerged onto the ramparts and looked startled to see the waiting men. He put his sandwich in his mouth, saluted, rescued his sandwich.

"Morning, sir." He put down the pile of books he was carrying in his other hand.

"Morning." Sharpe guessed the boy was no older than fifteen. "When do you start sending?"

"When the messages get here, sir."

Sharpe pointed to the books. "What's all this?"

"Lessons, sir. Principles of Navigation. I've got to pass the exam soon, sir, even though I'm not at sea."

"You should join the Rifles, lad." Harper picked up one of the books. "We don't stuff your head with mathematics."

Sharpe looked westward. "Where's the relay station?"

The boy pointed northwest. "Between the two hills, sir. It's over the river, on a church." He unlocked a trunk that was part of the mast's foundation and dragged out an iron tripod carrying a telescope twice the size of Sharpe's.

In the plaza, in front of the cathedral, Sharpe saw the foreshortened shape of a naval officer walking towards the castle. "Are those your messages?"

The midshipman leaned over. "Yes, sir. Captain Charles usually brings them."

As Sharpe watched he saw three men rolling a keg of powder from the cathedral. He guessed that the guns on the wall kept very little ready powder, fearing a spark and an explosion that would save the French weeks of work. He was glad he would not be here for the siege, for the helpless feeling of watching the earthworks creep closer as the siege guns fired slowly, but with massive force.

"Good morning! You must be Sharpe!" Captain Charles, gold lace at his cuffs, sounded cheerful. He looked at the midshipman. "Morning, Jeremy. Here you are." He handed the first message sheet over and the boy leaped to the ropes, tugged and dropped them, sometimes looking at the sheet Captain Charles had given him, but mostly doing it from memory.

Sharpe looked over his shoulder at the sheet of paper. 48726, 91858, 38197, it said.

"Code," Captain Charles boomed at him. "Jolly clever, yes?"

"Is that the gold message?"

"Gold? Don't know about that. Only three messages this morning. That one tells the general that the 68th Regiment of the Line are outside since yesterday. This one's the daily report on available shot, and the last one's about the French battery."

"God Almighty!" Sharpe started towards the stairs, but Lossow touched his arm.

"I'll go." The German was serious. "You stay."

He ran down the stairs and Sharpe turned back to Captain Charles. "What the hell's happening at headquarters?"

Charles sniffed, handed a second piece of paper to the midshipman. "Affairs of state. I don't know. Your major, the Spanish colonel, and it's all arm-waving and table-thumping. Not my style, dear boy. Oh, I say! That *is* clever!" He was staring to the south.

Sharpe turned, picked up the telescope, and trained it on the French battery. Nothing was happening; the earthworks still lay split open, and men were not even attempting to repair the damage. "What is it!" he asked.

"Over there." The elegant captain was pointing further to the right. "A second battery, hidden. We bang away at a heap of earth and the clever devils sneak the real battery into place. Jolly clever."

It was clever. Sharpe saw French soldiers dragging away branches that had cloaked the excavation of a battery that, judging from the activity around it, was ready to open fire. The siege gun, hidden by shadows, could harass the defenders' guns as the French built their breaching batteries forward.

Charles rubbed his hands. "Things will hot up soon. They've been slow."

Sharpe saw a cloud of smoke grow at an incredible speed just in front of the new battery earthwork, hardly visible, more of an impression than something he really saw. Then there was a pencil trace in the sky. He knew what it was, the sight of the shot racing directly towards them. The castle shook, and the stones of the huge keep seemed to waver and crack. And mixed with the reverberating crash of falling masonry came the thunder of the siege gun.

"Damn good shooting." Harper growled.

The sound of the replying batteries was thinner than the giant gun, but more frequent. It took a long time to reload a siege gun. Sharpe, through the telescope, watched as the smoke of the discharge cleared and the Portuguese balls crashed into the redoubt, but to no apparent damage. The hard-packed earth soaked up the cannonade and the aperture was just wide enough for its purpose. Behind it the artillerymen sponged out and rammed home the next huge missile. He kept watching. "Here it comes."

The tower shook again. Charles brushed at his immaculate uniform. "Distinctly unfriendly."

"Has it occurred to you that they're after the telegraph?" Sharpe asked.

"Good Lord. You could be right." He turned to the midshipman. "Hurry along, sailor!"

A shout came from the stairway and Lossow appeared, covered in dust, grinning and holding a piece of paper. "The message."

Sharpe grabbed the boy. "Stop everything. Send that! Hurry!"

Captain Charles looked annoyed, but was reluctant to interfere, and watched as the boy clattered the ropes up and down. "I'm just cancelling the last message, sir. Then I'll send yours."

Another shot boomed overhead leaving a wind behind it, hot and violent, and Harper glanced at Sharpe and raised his eyebrows. Lossow pursed his lips. "They've got the range."

"The boy's doing his best," Sharpe said irritably. "What was the delay?"

"Damned politics." Lossow spread his hands. "The Spanish insisted on the message saying that they did not want British help. Cox is mad, Kearsey's saying his prayers, and your Spanish friends are sharpening their swords."

The black, tarred sheep bladders leaped up on the ropes, quivered for a second, and fell as the boy danced between the halyards, hauling away number by number.

"Sir?" Harper was watching the battery. "Sir!"

"Down!"

The ball, twenty-four pounds of iron, struck a glancing blow on one of the crosstrees. As it spun off into the unknown, the telegraph ripped itself completely from its base like a tree torn bodily by a hurricane. The boy, holding onto a rope, was lifted into the air, screaming until another halyard whiplashed round his neck and tore his head horribly from his shoulders. His blood sprayed the four men and then the mast pounded back onto the ramparts, killing Charles instantly.

"Sweet Jesus." Harper stood up. "Are you all right, sir?"

"Yes." Sharpe's shoulder hurt like the devil. "Where's the boy?"

482

"He went over the wall, sir. Poor wee thing."

Lossow swore in German, stood up, flinched as he put his weight on his left leg. "Just a bruise."

Harper looked at the drifting smoke. "Just four shots. That's good shooting." There was a reluctant respect in his voice. He kicked the fallen beam. "Perhaps they can rig another telegraph, sir?"

Sharpe shrugged. He turned to Lossow. "Come on. We must persuade Cox to let us out of here."

"*Ja*. Not easy, my friend."

Sharpe's face was grim. "We'll get out. With or without him, we'll get out."

19

Light, like carved silver, slashed the cathedral's gloom, slanted across the crouching, grey pillars, and inched its way over the worn flagstones as the sun moved higher. Sharpe waited while a priest mumbled, lost in the depths of the choir.

"What day is it?" he asked, seeing Harper cross himself.

"Sunday, sir."

"Is that Mass?"

"Yes, sir."

"You want to go?"

"It'll wait."

Lossow's heels clicked in the side aisle; he came from behind a pillar, blinking in the sunlight. "Where's Cox?" He disappeared again.

483

Damn the French, thought Sharpe, he might as well have stayed in the warm bed with his arms round the girl. Cox had not been at his headquarters, he was said to be visiting the magazine, and so they waited for him. Sharpe slammed his scabbard on the floor, hurting his shoulder and swore again. I'm in love with her, he thought, God damn and blast it.

"Amen to that, sir." Harper had infinitely more patience.

Sharpe felt ashamed. This was a church. "I'm sorry."

The Irishman grinned. "Wouldn't worry, sir. It doesn't offend me and if it offends Him then He's plenty of opportunity to punish you."

Sharpe lifted his eyes to the huge roodscreen that hung in the grey shadows. Just one more night—is that so much to ask? Just one more night, and we can leave at dawn tomorrow. At last there was the creak of the cathedral door, the rattle of heels, and Cox came in with a crowd of officers. Sharpe stood straighter. "Sir!"

Cox appeared not to hear him and headed straight over the floor towards the crypt steps.

"Lossow!" Sharpe called. "Come on!"

Portuguese soldiers stopped them at the top of the steps and stood silently as they pulled felt slippers over their boots. Then the three men, their heels protected against sparking on stone, went down into the crypt. The light was dim, coming from only a handful of lanterns, their horn panes dulling the candle flames. There was no sign of Cox or his officers, but at the far end a leather curtain swayed in a doorway. "Come on." Sharpe led them to the curtain, forced its stiff weight aside, paused at the head of a short flight of steps which dropped into a dark cavern, and gasped.

The lower crypt was jammed with barrels, piled to the low, arched ceiling, row after row of them, reaching back into a gloom that was relieved only by an occasional horn lantern. To right and left were further aisles, stacked with more barrels. Sharpe tried to imagine a French shell smashing through the stonework and sparking the barrels. It could not happen: the buttressed floors were too thick.

Cox was at the very end of the vault, listening to an officer, and the conversation was urgent. It was partly in Portuguese, partly in English, and Sharpe could hear enough to understand the problem. Water was seeping into the crypt, not much, but enough to have soaked two bales of musket ammunition that were stored there.

Cox swung round. "Who put it here? We must move it!" He saw Sharpe. "Captain! Wait for me in my headquarters!"

"Sir . . ."

Cox whirled angrily. "I have enough problems, Sharpe!"

Harper touched Sharpe's elbow. "Come on, sir."

Sharpe turned, but Cox called him again. "Captain! Where is the gold?" The faces of the Portuguese officers looked accusing.

"In our quarters, sir."

"Wrong place, Sharpe, wrong place. I'll send men and it will be put in my headquarters."

"Sir!" But Lossow restrained him, and Cox turned back to the damp walls and the problem of moving thousands of rounds of musket cartridges up to the cathedral floor.

Sharpe resisted the German's pull. "I will not give up the gold."

"I know, I know. Listen, my friend. You go to the headquarters and I will go back to the gold. I promise you, no one will touch it."

Lossow's face was deep in shadow, but by the tone of his voice Sharpe knew the gold was safe. He turned to Harper. "Go with him. On my orders no one, but no one, is to go near that gold."

The cathedral bells reverberated with noon, the sun was almost directly overhead, and Sharpe walked slowly across the main plaza behind two men pushing a barrel of gunpowder. Out beyond the ramparts the French would be digging their trenches, making new batteries, and the oxen would be hauling the giant siege guns. Almeida was about to become the whole war, the point of effort, and when it fell there would be nothing between Masséna and the sea. Except the gold.

Suddenly Sharpe stopped, utterly still. The gold, Hogan had said, was more important than men or horses. He looked at the castle, and then at the cathedral, and despite the sun, he felt cold. Was it more important than this? Than a town and its defenders? He shivered. He was not afraid of decisions, they were his job and he despised men who feared to make them, but in the sudden moment, in the middle of the great plaza, he felt fear.

He waited in headquarters through the long afternoon, and still Cox did not come. Once he heard a Portuguese battery open fire, but there was no reply, and the town slumbered again. Then the door opened and Sharpe, half asleep in the big chair, started to his feet. Teresa's father closed the door silently.

"She was never harmed?"

"No."

The man laughed. "You are clever."

"She was clever."

Cesar Moreno nodded. "Why did she side with you?"

Sharpe shook his head. "She didn't. She's against the French."

"Ah, the passion of youth." He came nearer, walking slowly. "I hear your men won't release the gold?" Sharpe shrugged and the Spaniard followed the gesture with a smile. "Do you despise me?"

"No."

"I'm an old man. I just want peace."

It occurred to Sharpe that Cesar Moreno was making sure he had supporters on both sides. The old man looked at him. "Walk carefully, Captain Sharpe. He's better with the sword than you."

"I will walk carefully."

The Spaniard turned, looked at the varnished pictures on the wall that told of happier times, plumper days. "Cox won't let you take the gold," he said quietly. "You know that?"

"I didn't know."

"Cox is an honourable man, like Kearsey, and they know the gold is ours. How will you beat that, friend?"

"Watch me." Sharpe smiled.

"I will. And my daughter?"

"She'll not come to any harm. And she'll come back to you very soon."

Teresa's father nodded. "I hope so. But she is headstrong. I watched her, from the day I betrothed her to El Católico, and knew one day she would spit in my face, and his. She waited her moment, just like you."

486

"And now he waits his?"

"Yes. Go carefully." He went to the door, waved a hand. "We will meet again."

Sharpe sat down and poured a glass of wine. He was tired to the bone, and his shoulder ached. The shadows lengthened on the carpet till he slept, not hearing the evening gun, or the door opening.

"Sharpe!"

He jerked upright. "Sir?"

Brigadier Cox strode over the floor, trailing staff officers. "What the devil's happening, Sharpe? Your men won't release the gold!"

Kearsey came through the door and with him was a Spanish colonel, magnificently uniformed in gold lace and looping silver. It took Sharpe a few seconds to recognize El Católico. The face had not changed: the powerful eyes, the glint of humour. It was the face of an enemy.

"Are you deaf, Sharpe?" Cox shouted. "The gold! Where is it?"

"Don't know, sir. Waited here, sir. As ordered, sir."

Cox grunted. "I've made a decision. I'm sorry, Sharpe, but the gold is obviously Spanish, and Colonel Jovellanos is an accredited representative of the government of Spain." He gestured at El Católico who smiled and bowed.

Accredited representative? The bastard must be handy with a pen, Sharpe thought, and suddenly it occurred to him that one of the fat gold coins would make a superb seal, pressed into the red wax with the ornate coat of arms downwards. El Católico must have obliterated the writing with a file.

The brigadier sat down wearily, pulled a sheet of fresh paper towards him, uncapped his ink, and took a fresh goose quill. "At ten o'clock tomorrow morning, Captain, August 27th, 1810. . . . " He was writing quickly, paraphrasing the formal order as the quill scratched on the paper. "A detachment of my troops will take charge of the bullion. . . . They will deliver the gold to Colonel Jovellanos who will be ready to leave at the north gate." Cox looked up. "Colonel?"

El Católico nodded and clicked his heels. His voice was at its

silkiest, he shot a look of triumph at Sharpe. "Could the transfer be tonight?"

Sharpe held his breath. Cox was frowning, looking at the paper. "Ten o'clock will do, Colonel." Sharpe suspected he did not want to cross out the top lines of the closely written order. Cox smiled at El Católico, gestured at Sharpe. "After all, Captain Sharpe can hardly leave!"

El Católico smiled politely. "As you say, sir."

The brigadier pulled another sheet of paper forward. "At ten o'clock tomorrow morning, Captain Sharpe, your company will join my defences on the south wall. Captain Lossow leaves. I don't need cavalry, but you must stay. Understand?"

488

God in heaven! "Yes, sir."

The cathedral clock began chiming. Kearsey put a hand on Sharpe's elbow. "I'm sorry, Sharpe."

Sharpe nodded, listening to the bell. He was oblivious to Kearsey's concern, to El Católico's triumph, or Cox's preoccupation. Ten o'clock, and all not well. The decision had been forced on him.

SERGEANT HARPER was waiting for Sharpe outside Cox's headquarters. "Home, sir?"

"No. Over there." He pointed at the cathedral.

They walked across the plaza, lit by the moon. Sharpe thought of the girl, knew that El Católico had another score to settle more

489

personal than the gold, and was glad to have Harper as his escort. "What happened at the house today?"

Harper laughed. "Not a lot, sir. They turned up for the gold, so they did, and first we couldn't speak the Portuguese and then Mr. Lossow couldn't understand their English, and then the lads put on their spikes, and the Portuguese went home."

"Where's the girl now?"

"Still there, sir." Harper grinned at him, reassuringly. "Down in the kitchen with the lads, having her weapons training. She'd make a good recruit. Learned how to use a sabre." Sharpe laughed. It sounded like Teresa.

"And Mr. Knowles?"

"Enjoying himself, sir. All-round defence, sir, and keep your eyes open, and Mr. Knowles doing the rounds every ten minutes. They won't get in. What's happening to us, sir?"

Sharpe shrugged, looked up at the dark windows of the houses. "We're supposed to hand the gold over tomorrow. To El Católico."

"And are we, sir?"

"What do you think?"

Harper grinned, said nothing, and then crouched, sabre held up. One of the few Portuguese civilians left in the town, hurrying from an alleyway, shrank against the wall and babbled incoherently. "All right." Sharpe said. "On we go."

By the cathedral doors Sharpe could see the dark shapes of sentries. He crossed to them, and the Portuguese guards snapped to attention, saluted. He and Harper went inside.

Votive candles threw small wavering pools of yellow light on patches of the great stone vault. The tiny red glow of the Eternal Presence flickered at the far end and Sharpe waited while Harper dipped a finger and crossed himself.

The Irishman stepped alongside Sharpe. "What are we doing, sir?"

"I don't know." Sharpe chewed his bottom lip, then walked towards the steps to the vault. More sentries stiffened as they approached and Sharpe waved them down. "Slippers, Sergeant."

There was a small pile of ammunition by the head of the steps, saving the soldiers who came to fetch it for the ramparts the bother of pulling on the felt slippers. And against the door that flanked the great processional gates there were a dozen bales of paper cartridges.

They went down the stairs to the crypt, past planks laid two feet apart, so that the barrels could be rolled up easily. By the intermittent light of the horn lanterns Sharpe saw that the rest of the garrison's supply of small-arms ammunition was now stacked either side of the vault. He padded down the corridor between and knelt by the leather curtain. There were two thicknesses of stiff leather, weighted at the bottom, a precaution in case there was a small explosion in the first vault. The stiff leather could soak up a minor blast, protect the massive dump of gunpowder beneath, and Harper watched, astonished, as Sharpe drew his sword and cut off the weights, clenching his teeth as he sawed through the leather.

"What the hell, sir. . ."

Sharpe looked up at him. "Don't ask. Where are the sentries?"

"Upstairs." The sergeant knelt beside him. "Sir?"

Sharpe looked at the broad, friendly face. "Don't you trust me?"

Harper was offended. "Of course I trust you. Just tell me." The Irishman's anger was real.

Sharpe shook his head. "I will. Later. Come on."

Upstairs, taking off the slippers, Sharpe nodded at the candles. "Funny keeping them alight."

Harper shook his head. "They're a long way from the vault, sir." His voice showed that he was slightly mollified. "Anyway, it s insurance; a few prayers never did any army any harm." He stood up. "Where now, sir?"

Harper was mystified as Sharpe led the way to a building not far from the north gate. It was a bakery. Sharpe tried the door, but it was locked. Harper gestured him to one side, moved at the barrier, grunted as he hit it and then turned with a smile as the wood splintered away in front of him.

It was pitch black inside but Sharpe felt his way over the floor, past a table that must once have been the counter for the shop, and found huge brick ovens, cold now, hunched at the back of the bakery. He went back to the street. "Come on." They climbed the shallow ramp to the battlements. Sentries lined the ramparts, bunched near the gleaming batteries that had been dug into the wall's heart, and in front of them, were the outer defences: gently sloping, deceptive, filled with Portuguese troops whose fires cast strange glows on the deep ditches. Further out, French fires were visible, and from the far darkness came the occasional ring of a pickaxe, the thump of earth being pried loose.

Sharpe followed the ramparts' top to the north gate and Harper watched his captain stare moodily down at the sentries, the vast gate, the companies of infantry who lived between the granite traps to guard the entrance of the town. He could guess what was in Sharpe's mind. "No way out, sir."

"No." The last small chance gone. "No. Back to the house."

They went down steps and found a street that went towards the lower town, and Sharpe stayed away from the dark houses with their blind windows and shut-up doors. Their boots rang cold on the cobbles, they peered into the alleyways. Almeida was quiet, eerie, and Sharpe drew his sword.

"Sir?" Harper's voice was worried. "You wouldn't be planning, would you, to . . ."

Suddenly there was a shout from down the street, the flare of torches, and a Portuguese patrol, muskets ready, pounded towards them and Sharpe saw the officer leading with a drawn sword. The officer stopped, suspicion on his face, and then grinned, spread his arms, and laughed. "Richard Sharpe. Of all the devils! What are you doing?"

Sharpe laughed, and pushed his blade into the scabbard. He turned to Harper. "Sergeant, meet Tom Garrard. Once a sergeant in the 33rd, now a lieutenant in the Portuguese army." He took Garrard's hand, shook it. "You devil. How are you?"

Garrard beamed at him, turned to Harper. "We were sergeants together. God, Dick, it must be years. It's good to see you. A bloody captain! What's the world coming to?" He gave Sharpe a salute and laughed.

"It's years since anyone called me 'Dick'. You well?"

"Couldn't be better." He jerked a thumb at his men. "Good lads, these. Fight like us. Well, well, well."

Harper looked at Garrard curiously. It was a year since the Portuguese government had asked the British to reorganize their army and one of the changes was to offer commissions to experienced British sergeants so that the raw untrained Portuguese troops were given officers who knew how to fight.

Garrard sheathed his sword. "Anything I can do?"

"Open a gate for us. Tonight."

Garrard looked at him shrewdly. "How many of you?"

"Two hundred and fifty. Cavalry and us."

"That's impossible. I thought you meant just you two." He stopped, grinned. "You with this gold?"

"That's us. You know about it?"

"God Almighty! Orders from everyone to stop the gold leaving. We didn't even know there was any gold here." He shook his head. "I'm sorry, Dick. Can't help."

Sharpe smiled. "Doesn't matter. We'll manage."

"You will." He grinned again. "I heard about Talavera. That was well done. It really was."

Sharpe pointed at Harper. "He was with me."

Garrard nodded to the Irishman. "Proud of you." He looked at his men. "We'll do it next time, won't we, lads?" The Portuguese smiled back, nodding shyly at Sharpe.

The farewells were said, promises to look each other up, and Sharpe glanced at Harper. There was work to do. "Still no sign of El Católico?" He looked up at the rooftops. "Do we have sentries on the roof?"

"The roof?" Alarm showed on the sergeant's face.

"Come on!"

He began running, the sword in his hand. They reached the house and the sentries, startled, pushed open the courtyard gate. There was the smell of horses, torchlight, and he leaped up the steps, banged open the kitchen door, and there was the company, eating, the firelight, candles, and Teresa, unharmed, at the end of the table.

20

Lossow shook his head. "He's not here."

"He's close."

The German shrugged. "We've searched." They had looked in every room, every cupboard, even up chimneys and on the thick-tiled roof, but there was no sign of El Católico.

The cavalryman took Sharpe's elbow. "Come and eat."

The gold was locked in a store room off the kitchen and Sharpe glanced anxiously at the door as he spooned down the meat and vegetables. Lossow watched him. "You think he'll come tonight?"

Sharpe nodded. He glanced at Teresa. "Yes, he'll come."

She looked at him, almost with a challenge. "What will you do?"

The men of the company, some of the Germans, were listening to the conversation. Sharpe jerked his head at the door. "Come into the small room. We'll talk."

Harper took a jug of wine, Lossow and Knowles their curiosity, the girl followed them. She paused outside the small sitting-room door and put cool fingers on his hand. "Are you going to win, Richard?"

He smiled. "Yes." If he did not, then she was dead. El Católico would want revenge on her.

Inside the sitting room they pulled off dustcovers and sat in comfortable chairs. Sharpe was bone-tired, and his shoulder ached with a deep, throbbing pain. He trimmed a candle wick, waited for the flame to grow, and talked softly. "We're ordered to surrender

494

the gold tomorrow. Captain Lossow is ordered to leave, we are ordered to stay."

Lossow stirred in his chair frowning. "So it's all over?"

"No. Whether Cox likes it or not, we go."

"And the gold?" Teresa's voice was steady.

"Goes with us."

By some strange instinct they all relaxed, as if the statement was enough.

Sharpe took a deep breath. "I can't tell you why, I don't know how, but the difference between victory and failure depends on that gold. On Wellington's instructions, we have to take it out. There are no explicit orders; I can only tell you what I was told. The gold is more important than men, horses, regiments or guns. If we lose it, the war is over."

"And if you take it?" Teresa was shivering now.

"Then the British will stay in Portugal." He shrugged. "I can't explain that, but it's true. And if we stay in Portugal then next year we'll be back in Spain. The gold must go with us. The question is," he went on, "How?"

There was silence in the room. Harper looked asleep, his eyes closed, but Sharpe guessed that the Irishman was way ahead of the others. Knowles pummelled his chair arm in frustration. "If only we could get a message to the general!"

"We're too late. Time's run out." Sharpe did not expect them to provide an answer, but he wanted them to think through the argument, so that when he provided the solution, they would agree.

Lossow leaned forward into the candlelight. "Cox won't let you go. He thinks we're stealing the gold."

Knowles was frowning. "Do we make a run for it, sir?"

Sharpe thought of the granite-faced ditches, the rows of cannons, the bent tunnels in the gateways. "No, Robert."

"So . . ." Knowles was about to ask "how?" He shrugged instead. Teresa stood up. "Is your coat upstairs?"

Sharpe nodded. "Cold?" She still had only the thin white dress. He stood up as well, thinking of his fear of El Católico. "I'll come with you."

Harper and Lossow stood, but Sharpe waved them down. "We'll be all right, a minute, no more. Think about it, gentlemen."

He led the way up the stairs, peering into the darkness, and Teresa put a hand out to him. "You think he's here?"

"I know he is." It seemed ridiculous; the house had been searched and re-searched, yet all Sharpe's instincts said that El Católico would come for his revenge this night. He drew his sword as they went into the candlelit room with its canopied bed.

Teresa found Sharpe's coat, put it round her shoulders. "See? It's safe."

"Go downstairs. Tell them I'll be two minutes."

She looked puzzled, but he pushed her through the door. He could feel the hairs rise on his neck, the prickling of the blood beneath the skin, the old signs that the enemy was near, and he sat on the bed and pulled off his heavy boots so that he could move silently. He wanted El Católico to be near, to get this thing over, so that he could concentrate on what must be done tomorrow. He thought of the Spaniard's flickering rapier, but it must be faced, and beaten, or else in the morning he would be constantly looking behind him. He padded across the boards and blew out the candles.

He opened the curtains and stood on the balcony. Nothing stirred in the street, the houses and church across the road were dark and shuttered; only the French campfires lit the southern sky, silhouetting the tower of the church in their red glow. And something was wrong. There was a smell of tobacco where there should have been none.

Sharpe swung his leg over the balcony, and dropped into the street.

The group in the small room would wonder where he was, but it need not take long. Forewarned was forearmed, and he sneaked silently, on his bootless feet, into the alley that angled behind the church, holding the huge sword in front of him. He listened for any noise. There was nothing, except the sound of the wind. He felt excitement inside, the imminence of danger, but still there was no sound, no movement, and he peered up at the church roof innocent in the moonlight. Was it too fantastic, that all El Católico had to do was pour musket fire from the church roof into the bedroom? There was a small door in the wall, barred and locked. But beside it the masonry was rough and crudely repaired, and he knew he would not be satisfied until he had seen over the church roof's edge, so he stuck the huge sword behind his back, jammed into his belt with the handle over his shoulder, and reached up with his right hand for a grip on the masonry blocks.

He moved slowly, climbing as silently as a lizard, feeling with his toes for each foothold and reaching up with his hands for the gaps between the stones. His left shoulder hurt, made him wince with pain, but he moved up because he could see the top, and it was not far, and he could not rest until this private business was done. Near the top a cornice went round the roof, and the hand-holds ran out. He needed one more handhold and he saw it, off to his left, where a metal stanchion jutted downwards to support a lamp-holder over the doorway. He reached for it, found the rusting metal, tugged, and it held. He transferred his weight to his left shoulder, and then the stanchion moved. It was a tiny movement, a grating of metal on stone, but it threw him off balance. His left arm saved him, and it was as if someone had plunged a hook into his armpit, and fresh blood sprang from the opened wound and soaked his chest. He clenched eyes and teeth, gasped with the pain, and, throwing caution aside, threw up his right arm, found the very top of the cornice and slowly, with exquisite relief, took the weight from the left arm.

He froze, waiting for a blow on his exposed right hand, but nothing moved. Perhaps the roof was deserted? He pushed with his right foot, and slowly, inch by inch, his eyes went past the stonework and there, suddenly, was the sky.

The roof was empty. He took the sword from its place behind his back and crouched just within the cornice. By now Harper and Lossow would be looking for him. But he could smell tobacco smoke more strongly now and he felt a fierce confirmation of his suspicions. He crept forward, into a flat space at the foot of the bell tower, a large square area hidden from the house behind him by the loom of the transept roof, and now he could hear voices calling him, Lossow shouting at sentries. He was about to call back when he heard a creak, and jumped to one side.

At his feet a trapdoor opened, an inch or two at first, sending out a plume of cigar smoke. Then it was pushed back until held by a chain. "Who is that?" It was El Católico's voice, deep and silken.

"Sharpe." He was standing behind the trapdoor, invisible from below, unassailable. El Católico chuckled. "May I come up?"

"Just you?"

"Just me." The voice was amused, tolerant. Sharpe saw a light coming, and then a hand put an unmasked lantern on the roof and there was El Católico's dark head, and his other hand brought up his rapier which he tossed, ringing, onto the far side of the roof. "There. Now you can kill me. You won't, though, because you are a man of honour." He smiled. "May I come up? I'm alone."

Sharpe nodded. He waited till the Spaniard was on the roof and then kicked the trapdoor shut. It was heavy, thick enough to stop a bullet. El Católico watched. "You are nervous. They won't come up." He cocked a friendly eye at Sharpe. "Why are you here?"

Above the church roof Sharpe could see the sudden flare of torches. There were shouts across the street. He ignored them. "To kill you. Why are *you* here?"

"To pray with you." El Católico laughed, jerked his head at the street. "They're making so much noise they won't hear us." He opened the cloak. "You see? No pistol. I have only the sword. You can kill me, of course, before I reach it, but I don't think you will." He had talked as he moved and then he stopped, picked it up, and turned round. "I was right. You see? You are a man of honour!"

Sharpe could feel the new blood wet on his chest. There was sweat on the palm of his sword hand, but he would not give the Spaniard the satisfaction of seeing him wipe it off, and he rested his sword as El Católico, with studied ease, dropped his cloak and flexed the blade.

"A fine blade, Captain. From Toledo. But then, I forget, we have already tried each other." He moved into the swordsman's crouch, right leg bent, left leg extended behind. "On guard."

The rapier flickered towards Sharpe, but the rifleman did not

498

move. El Católico straightened up. "Do you not want to fight?"

Sharpe had so little time. He had to unsettle the Spaniard. El Católico knew he would win, could afford to be magnanimous, was anticipating the inevitable display of his superior swordsmanship. Sharpe still kept his blade low.

"Captain! Are you frightened?" El Católico smiled gently. "You're afraid I'm the better man."

"Teresa says not." It was not much, but enough. Sharpe saw fury in El Católico's face, a sudden loss of control, and he brought up the huge blade, rammed it forward and knew that El Católico would not parry, but simply kill him for the insult. The rapier flickered, lightning fast, but Sharpe turned his whole body, saw the blade go past, and brought his elbow hard into El Católico's ribs, turned back and hammered down with the brass-guarded hilt of the sword onto the Spaniard's head. El Católico was fast. He twisted away, the blow glanced off his skull, but Sharpe heard the grunt and he followed it with a sweeping killer of a blow, but the Spaniard leaped backwards, and again Sharpe had failed.

There was a hammering from downstairs, the blast of a musket, and El Católico smiled. "Time to die, Sharpe. *Requiem aeternam dona eis, Domine.*" He came forward like quicksilver, past Sharpe's clumsy parry, and the blade drew blood at Sharpe's waist. *"Et lux perpetua luceat eis."* The blade went to the other side of Sharpe's waist, razored his skin, and was gone. Sharpe knew he was being toyed with while the prayer lasted, and he could do nothing. He went for El Católico's eyes, stabbing the empty air, and the Spaniard laughed. "Go slow, Sharpe! *Te decet hymnus, Deus, in Sion.*"

Sharpe lunged desperately, but El Católico just swayed to one side and the rapier came low, aiming at the thigh for another flesh wound, and Sharpe had only one desperate insane idea left. He kicked his thigh forward and kept going, pushing the blade painfully into his flesh so that El Católico could not use it. The Spaniard tried to drag it free, and Sharpe felt a tearing in his leg, but he was still driving forward and he hit the Spaniard in the face with the heavy guard of his sword, and El Católico abandoned the rapier and went backwards. Sharpe followed, the rapier stuck clean through his thigh and El Católico grabbed at it, missed, and fell. Sharpe swung his blade down, stabbed down till the point hit the roof. There would be no fiefdom in the mountains, no private kingdom for El Católico.

There were shouts below. "Captain!"

Sharpe looked down. He could hear footsteps pounding in the alleyway, and he suspected the partisans were abandoning the unequal conflict.

"Up here! On the church roof!" He took hold of El Católico's rapier. The wound hurt, but he had been lucky and the blade had gone through the outer muscles and the blood and pain were worse than the damage. He pulled at the sword and it slid free.

There was a thumping on the trapdoor. "Who's that?"

"Sergeant Harper!"

The trapdoor was pushed up and Harper appeared, a smoking torch in one hand. He looked first at Sharpe, then at the body. "God save Ireland. What were you doing, sir? A competition to see who could bleed the most?"

Teresa came up, followed by Lossow and Knowles, and Sharpe felt the tension flow out of him. He watched Teresa kneel by the body, search quickly beneath the blood-stained clothes and find, round the dead man's waist, a money belt, thick with coins. She opened one of the pockets. "Gold."

"Keep it." Sharpe was feeling his leg, tracing the wound, and he knew he had been lucky and that the blade had torn a smaller wound than his stupidity deserved. Teresa took his sash as a temporary dressing, and bound it tight.

Lossow looked at the body. "What now?"

"Now?" Sharpe wanted a glass of wine, another plate of stew. "Nothing. They have leaders. We still have to hand the gold over."

Teresa spoke in Spanish, angry and vehement, and Sharpe smiled, flexing his left arm. "On the other hand, if El Católico's lieutenants don't produce the gold, then they may not be leaders much longer."

"Then who will be?" Knowles sat down on the parapet.

"La Aguja." Sharpe had trouble pronouncing the Spanish "J". "La

500

Aguja. The needle." He had made up the name, and saw that it pleased her. "Teresa. We have a bargain."

Knowles looked astonished. "Miss Moreno?"

"Why not? She fights better than most of them. But to make that happen we must keep the gold from the Spanish, get it out of the city, and finish this job."

Lossow sighed, scraped his unused sabre back into its scabbard. "Which brings us back to the old question, my friend. How?"

Sharpe had dreaded this moment, wanted to lead them gently towards it. "Who's stopping us?"

Lossow shrugged. "Cox."

Sharpe nodded. He spoke patiently. "And Cox has his authority as commander of this garrison. If there were no garrison, there would be no authority, no way to stop us."

"So?" Knowles was frowning.

"So, at dawn tomorrow we destroy the garrison."

There was a moment's silence, broken by Knowles. "We can't!"

"God in his heaven!" Lossow's face was appalled, fascinated.

Teresa did not seem surprised. "How?"

So Sharpe told them.

Almeida stirred early, well before first light, as men stamped their boots on cobbled streets and made the small talk that is the talisman against great events. In far-off cities, St. Petersburg and Vienna, Stockholm and Berlin, men looked at maps. If Almeida could hold, then perhaps Portugal could be saved. But eight weeks at the most, they said, and probably just six, and then Masséna's troops would have Lisbon at their mercy. The British had had their run and now it was over. A pity of course, but what did anyone expect?

Brigadier Cox was on the southern ramparts waiting for the first light to show him the new French batteries. He hoped for a great defence that would make history and block the French until the rains of late Autumn would save Portugal; but he also imagined the siege guns blasting through the great walls, and then the screaming, steel-tipped battalions that would come forward. Cox knew that the town was the last obstacle to French victory and, in his heart, he did not believe that it could hold out until the roads were swamped and the rivers made impassable by rain.

High above the southern ramparts, by the castle and cathedral that topped the hill, Sharpe pushed open the bakery door. The ovens were curved shapes in the blackness, cold to the touch, and Teresa shivered beside him despite being swathed in his long, green rifleman's greatcoat. He ached. His leg, shoulder, the sliced cuts either side of his waist, and a head that throbbed after talking too deep into the early morning.

Knowles had pleaded, "There must be another way!"

"Tell me," he had replied, and now, in the cold silence, Sharpe still tried to find another way. To talk to Cox? Or Kearsey? But only Sharpe knew how desperately Wellington needed the gold; to Cox and Kearsey it was unimaginable that a few thousand gold coins could save Portugal, and Sharpe could not tell them how because he had not been told. He damned Wellington's secrecy. It would mean death for hundreds; but if the gold did not get through it would mean a lost war.

Teresa would be gone away. According to their bargain they would part in a few hours, he to the army, she back to the hills and her own fight. He held her close, but then they stepped apart as footsteps sounded outside and Patrick Harper pushed open the door and peered into the gloom.

"Sir?"

"We're here. Did you get it?"

"No problem." Harper sounded happy enough. "One barrel of powder, sir, compliments of Tom Garrard."

"Did he ask what it was for?"

Harper shook his head. "He said if it was for you, it was all right." He brought the great keg through the door. "Bloody heavy, sir."

"Will you need help?"

Harper straightened up with a scoffing look. "An officer carrying a barrel, sir? This is the army."

"You know what to do."

Sharpe looked through the dirty window, across the plaza, and in the thin light saw the cathedral doors were still shut. Perhaps the pile of cartridges had been moved? Had Wellington sent a messenger on a fast horse with orders for Cox on the half chance that Sharpe was in Almeida? He forced his mind away from the nagging questions. "Let's get on with it."

Harper took his bayonet and chipped at the centre of the barrel, making a hole, widening it till it was the size of a musket muzzle. He grunted his satisfaction. "I'll be on my way."

"Go slowly." Sharpe wanted to tell the sergeant that he did not have to do it, it was Sharpe's dirty work, but he knew what the Irishman would have said. Instead he watched as Harper picked up the barrel by its ends, jiggled it until powder was flowing from the hole, and then started an awkward progress out of the door and across the plaza. He kept to the gutter, and Sharpe, through the window, watched as the powder trickled into the stone trough and went, inexorably, towards the cathedral. He could not believe what he was doing, driven by the general's "must" and then, in a heart-stopping moment, the cathedral doors opened and two sentries came out, adjusting their shakos, and Sharpe knew they must see what was happening. He clenched his fists and Teresa, beside him at the dirty glass pane, was moving her lips in what seemed to be a silent and inappropriate prayer.

"Sharpe?"

He turned, startled, and saw Lossow. The German gestured down the hill, away from the cathedral. "We have the cellar open."

"I'll see you there." The company's house had a deep cellar that

503

opened onto the street. Lossow wished him luck and slipped away.

The sentries were watching the sergeant, seeing nothing unusual in a man carrying a barrel, not even stirring as he put it down, on one end, hard by the smaller cathedral door, and squatted beside it. Unobtrusively Harper began to work a strake loose so that the fuse could reach the remaining powder in the keg. Then he rose and strolled the twenty yards to the sentries, chatted with them. Sharpe thought they would surely see the splintered wood! But no, they laughed with Harper, and suddenly he was walking back, yawning.

Sharpe took out a tinder box, a cigar, and with shaking hands struck flint on steel and blew the charred linen in the box into a flame. He lit the cigar, puffed it, hated the taste, until the tip glowed red. Teresa watched him. "You're sure?"

"I'm sure."

The girl held his arm as he went into the street. The sky was pearl grey over the cathedral with a wisp of cloud that would soon turn white. It promised to be a beautiful day. He drew on the cigar again and through his mind went jumbled images of the men who had built the cathedral, knelt on its wide flagstones, been married there, seen their children baptized in its granite font, and been carried on their last journey up its pillared chancel. He thought of the dry voice saying *must*. Of the priest white-washing the rood-screen, of the battalion with its wives and children, the bodies in the cellar, and he leaned down and touched the cigar tip to the powder, and it sparked and fizzed, the flame beginning its journey.

The first French shell, fired from an ugly little howitzer in a deep pit, landed in the plaza, bounced, just yards from the cathedral, and the sentries dived for shelter. Sharpe plucked at Teresa and Harper. "The ovens!"

They ran, through the door and over the counter, and he picked up the girl and thrust her headfirst into the great brick cave of the bread oven and climbed in behind her. Harper was clambering into the second and then Sharpe heard an explosion. It was small, scarcely audible over the crash of French shells, and he knew that the barrel had exploded and he wondered if the cathedral door had held the blast, or had the cartridges been moved; and then there

504

was a second explosion, louder and more ominous, which seemed to go on, like a muffled volley from a battle in deep fog, and he knew that the cartridges, down in their stacks, behind the door, were setting each other off in an unstoppable chain of explosions.

He wondered, crouched foetus-like in the oven, what was happening in the cathedral. He saw, in his mind's eye, the lurid flames, gouting shafts of light, and then there was a bigger explosion and he knew that the chain had reached the powder stacked at the top of the steps, until even this was drowned by a seething roar, growing and terrifying, as in the first crypt, crate by crate, cartridge by cartridge, the ammunition of Almeida was exploding.

He had thought that the sound could only grow, till it was the last sound on earth, but it seemed to die into a silence that was merely the crackling of flames. Sharpe uncurled his head and looked through the gap between the oven and its iron door, and he could not believe that the leather curtain to the deeper crypt had held. Then the hill moved. The sound came, not through the air, but through the ground itself like the groaning of rock.

The French gunners jumped to the top of their pits and looked past the low, grey ramparts and crossed themselves. The centre of the town had gone, turned into one giant flame that rolled up and up in a boiling cloud. Men could see great stones in the flame, timbers, carried upwards as if they were feathers, and then the shock hit like a giant, hot wind, and with it came the sound. It was like all the thunder of all the world poured into one town.

The cathedral disappeared in flame and the castle was scythed clean from the ground. The blast took the north of the town and unroofed half the southern slope, and the bakery collapsed onto the ovens. Sharpe was deafened, gasping in the thick dust and heated air, and the girl prayed for her soul, as the blast went past like the breath of the pit.

On the ramparts the Portuguese died as the wind plucked them outwards and the great defences nearest the cathedral were smashed down. New boilings of flame and smoke writhed over Almeida, shudder after shudder, until finally the monstrous explosions died, leaving only fire and darkness.

A French gunner, old in his trade, who had once taught a young Corsican lieutenant how to lay a gun, spat on his hand and touched it to a hot muzzle of the barrel that had fired the last shot. The French were silent, unbelieving, and, in the killing ground before them, stones, tiles, and burned flesh dropped like the devil's rain.

Twenty-five miles away, in Celorico, they heard the sound and the general put down his fork and went to the window and knew, with terrible certainty, what it was. The smoke came later; a huge, grey curtain that smeared the eastern sky, turned morning sunlight into dusk. Almeida had been destroyed.

KEARSEY WAS DEAD, killed as he said his prayers on the town rampart, and five hundred other men had been snatched into eternity by the flame, but Sharpe did not know that yet. He knew he was dying of suffocation and heat, and he braced his back against the smooth, curved interior of the massive oven and pushed with his legs at a charred length of timber that blocked the door. It collapsed and he pushed himself out, and turned to pull Teresa clear. She spoke to him, but he could hear nothing, Harper crawled out of the other oven, his face ashen.

The ovens had saved their lives. They were built like small fortresses, with walls more than three feet thick, and a curved roof that had sent the blast harmlessly overhead. Down the street Sharpe had to look a hundred yards before he saw a house that had survived the blast, and it was ablaze. He took Teresa's arm. "Come on!"

They ran towards their own house, at the bottom of the hill, away from the horror, through the Portuguese soldiers who stared, open mouthed, at the inferno that had once been a cathedral.

Sharpe broke open the cellar door and the men scrambled out. He hit his ears, shook his head, willing the sound to come back. Damn it, the decision had been made, and he put his head down and thought of the general, and of the blazing pit, and he hated himself. He was a man too proud to fail, and that was why the general had picked him.

"You had no choice, sir." Knowles was speaking, the voice sounded far away, but he could hear. "The war, sir. You said it had to be won."

Then celebrate it tomorrow, Sharpe thought, or the next day. He turned to Lossow. "We'd better find Cox."

The smell of roast flesh hung in the air. A dead battalion, thought Sharpe, killed for the gold, and he wondered if Wellington himself would have put the cigar onto the powder, and then he thrust the thought away as Lossow led the way up a sloping rampart to where Cox and his staff officers surveyed the damage.

It was all over, anyone could see that, the town indefensible. Cox tried to stiffen the will to go on fighting, but they all knew it was done. There was no ammunition left, nothing to fight with. There would be no unpleasantness; the surrender would be discussed in a civilized way. Cox pushed his way out through the group and saw Sharpe and Lossow waiting. "Sharpe. Lossow. Thank God you're alive. So many gone."

"Yes, sir."

Cox was biting back tears. "A shell must have set off the small ammunition. We should have had a magazine!" Then he noticed the blood on the rifleman's uniform. "You're wounded?"

"No, sir. I'm all right. Permission to leave, sir?"

Cox nodded, an automatic reaction. The gold was forgotten in the horror of the lost war. Sharpe plucked Lossow's sleeve. "Come on."

At the bottom of the ramp, Cesar Moreno waited for them. He put a hand out to stop Sharpe. "Teresa?"

Sharpe smiled, the first smile since the explosion. "She's safe. We're leaving now."

"And Joaquím is dead?"

There was nothing Sharpe could say. Lossow went ahead and Moreno checked Sharpe with his hand.

"She'll take over, I suppose?"

The rifleman nodded. "Probably. She can fight."

Moreno gave a rueful smile. "She knows whose side to be on."

Sharpe looked at the smoke, at the flames on the hilltop, smelled the burning. "Don't we all?" He shook himself free, turned again to the grey-haired man. "I'll be back for her, one day."

"I know."

The French had left their lines to gape at the smoking ruins at the northern wall. There was nothing to stop the company leaving and they took the gold and went east, under the smoke, and back to the army. The war was not lost.

Epilogue

"What happened, Richard?"

"Nothing, sir."

Hogan moved his horse forward to a patch of succulent grass on the hilltop. "I don't believe you."

Sharpe stirred in his saddle. "There was a girl."

"Is that all?"

Sharpe stared a challenge at the gentle Irish major. "We were sent to get the gold, we got it, and we brought it back."

"The general's pleased," Hogan said in a neutral tone.

"He'd damn better be pleased! For God's sake!"

"He thought you were lost." Hogan's horse moved again, cropping the grass, and the major took off his cocked hat and fanned his face. "Pity about Almeida."

"Which would you rather have had, sir?" Sharpe's voice was very cold. "The gold, or Almeida?"

Hogan pulled his horse up. "The gold, Richard. You know that." He waved his arm at the landscape.

It was perhaps one of the greatest feats of military engineering ever, and it had taken up the gold. Without the gold the ten

508

thousand labourers, some of whom Sharpe could see, would have packed up their shovels and picks and simply waited for the French. Sharpe watched the giant scrapers, hauled by lines of men and oxen, shaping the hills. "What do you call it?"

"The Lines of Torres Vedras."

Three lines barred the Lisbon peninsula, three giant fortifications made with the hills themselves. The first line, on which they rode, was twenty-six miles long, stretching from the Atlantic to the Tagus, and there were two others behind it. The hills had been steepened, crowned with gun batteries, and the lowland flooded. Behind the hillcrests sunken roads meant that the twenty-five thousand garrison troops could move unseen from the French, and the deep valleys were blocked with thousands of thorn trees.

Sharpe stared eastwards, at the unending line, and he found it hard to believe. So much work, so many escarpments made by hand, crowned with hundreds of guns encased in stone forts, their embrasures looking to the north, to the plain where Masséna would be checked. Hogan rode alongside him. "We can't stop him, Richard, not till he gets here. But here he stays. He'll never break the lines, never, they're too strong. And he can't go round, the navy's there. So here he stops, and the rains start, and in a couple of months he'll be starving and we come out again from Lisbon to reconquer Portugal."

"And on into Spain?" Sharpe asked.

"On into Spain." Hogan sighed, waved again at the huge scar of the unbelievable fortress. "And we ran out of money. We had to get money. Gold."

"And you got it. Sharpe's gold."

Hogan bowed to him. "Thank you. Tell me about the girl."

Sharpe told him as they rode towards Lisbon. He remembered the parting after they had left the river fortress, unchallenged. They had stopped beside the Coa and Sharpe had handed Teresa the one thousand gold coins he had promised. She had smiled at him.

"This will be enough for our needs. We go on fighting."

Sharpe had looked at her dark beauty. "You can stay with us."

"No. But you can come back. One day."

He had nodded at the rifle slung on her shoulder. "Give that one to Ramon. I promised him." He unslung his own rifle and handed it across. "This is yours, with my love. We'll meet again."

"I know." She turned her horse and waved.

"Kill a lot of French!" he had shouted.

"All there are!" And she was gone, galloping with her father and her men, and he missed her, missed her.

Author Bernard Cornwell has spent years meticulously researching Wellington's military campaigns. Here he describes how far Sharpe's Gold *was based on actual historical events.*

The explosion at Almeida happened on the morning of August 27th, 1810. The event was much as described in *Sharpe's Gold*. The magazine in the cathedral blew up and destroyed, besides the cathedral itself, the castle, five hundred houses, and part of the fortifications. It was estimated that more than five hundred of the garrison died. Brigadier Cox wanted to continue the defence, but bowed to the inevitable and surrendered the next day.

It must have been one of the biggest explosions of the pre-nuclear world. A year later the French added to the destruction. They, in turn were besieged in Almeida and abandoned its defence after blowing up part of the walls; their garrison of fourteen hundred men successfully escaped the British besieging force.

Despite its misfortunes the town's defences are still impressive. They are repaired and intact, surrounding what is now a shrunken village, and it is easy to see where the explosion occurred. Nothing was rebuilt. A graveyard marks the site of the cathedral, the castle moat is a square, stone-faced ditch, and granite blocks still litter the area where they fell.

No one, conveniently for a writer of fiction, knows the precise cause of the catastrophe, but the accepted version is that a leaking keg of gunpowder was rolled from the cathedral and a French shell

510

ignited the accidental powder train which fired back to musket ammunition stored by the main door. This, in turn, flashed down to the main magazine and so the greatest obstacle between Masséna and his invasion of Portugal was gone. One Portuguese soldier, very close to the cathedral, saved his life by diving into a bread oven and now his presence of mind has been borrowed by Richard Sharpe. The most unlikely stories often turn out to be the truth.

The Lines of Torres Vedras existed and truly were one of the great military achievements of all time. They can still be seen, decrepit for the most part, grassed over, but with a little imagination Masséna's shock can be realized. He had pursued the British army to within a day's march of Lisbon, had survived Wellington's crushing victory at Bussaco on the way, and surely he must have thought his job done. Then he saw the lines. They were the furthest point of retreat for the British in the Peninsula; they were never to be used again, and four years later Wellington's superb army marched over the Pyrenees into France itself.

Bernard Cornwell

Sharpe's Gold is, sadly, unfair to the Spanish. Some partisans were as self-seeking as El Católico, but the large majority were brave men who tied up more French troops than Wellington's army. The Richard Sharpe books are the chronicles of British soldiers and, with that perspective, the men who fought the *guerrilla*, the "little war", have suffered an unfair distortion. But at least, by the autumn of 1810, the British army is safe behind its gigantic lines and the stage is set for the next four years; the advance into Spain, the victories, and the ultimate conquest of France itself.

Richard Sharpe and Patrick Harper will march again.